Creation of Adam, a fresco by Michelangelo in the Sistine Chapel. This may be
interpreted as a symbolic representation of Creation by evolution.

THEODOSIUS DOBZHANSKY ————————

PROFESSOR OF ZOOLOGY AND MEMBER OF THE
INSTITUTE FOR THE STUDY OF HUMAN VARIATION
COLUMBIA UNIVERSITY

Evolution, Genetics, and Man

JOHN WILEY & SONS, INC. — NEW YORK

LONDON

575
D65e

FIFTH PRINTING, MARCH, 1961

42,851
april, 1962

Copyright © 1955
by
John Wiley & Sons, Inc.

Library of Congress Catalog Card Number: 55–10868

Printed in the United States of America

Preface

For almost a century the influence of the theory of evolution has been felt far beyond the limits of biology. In fact, this influence has been growing apace, and in our day the idea of evolution has become an integral part of the intellectual equipment of Western Civilization. In biology this idea is pivotal. To a beginning student no less than to a teacher and to a specialist, the idea of evolution makes sense of what would otherwise be wearisome descriptions of arid facts to be memorized, only to be forgotten as soon as the course is over. In the light of evolution the same facts and descriptions of creatures which we have seldom or never seen become fascinating. Learning them turns out to be an intellectual adventure.

Biological evolution is a part of the evolution of the cosmos. The rise and the development of mankind are a part of the story of biological evolution. Man cannot reach a valid understanding of his own nature without a knowledge of his own biological background. It may, then, be that the study of evolutionary biology is the most important practical endeavor open to the human mind. Accordingly, an effort is being made in this book to show to the student that biology is not only a craft which is interesting to technicians and devotees but also a part of the fabric of modern humanistic thought. I am quite conscious that this goal is too ambitious and that it has not been fully attained.

I hope that this book may be useful not only as a guide in courses devoted to the study of biological evolution but also as collateral reading in courses of general biology, general zoology, general botany, and anthropology. A sizable proportion of the space in this book is devoted to presentation of material which is usually given in elementary courses of genetics. Chapters 2, 3, 4, parts of 5 and 11, and smaller parts of other chapters deal with genetics. This emphasis is unavoidable, since modern evolutionism is incomprehensible except on the basis of familiarity with fundamentals of genetics. Therefore, although it has not been my intention to turn this book into a brief textbook of genetics, a student who uses it will acquire an elementary knowledge of the subject. The book will probably fit the requirements of courses given in some institutions of higher learning, courses entitled "Genetics and Evolution" or "Evolution and Genetics."

An effort has been made to use, wherever possible, examples dealing with man and to point out the bearing of the topics discussed on human problems. The opinion once held fairly widely, that man is most unfavorable as material for biological and especially for genetic studies, is becoming less and less prevalent. Even though we cannot arrange many genetical experiments with man, there is an abundance of kinds of information bearing on the genetics and evolution of man which are not available for any other organism. And after all is said and done, the species *Homo sapiens* happens to be more interesting to most students than any other species, no matter how unserviceable it may be for some experiments. Being men, we understand many biological phenomena in man more easily and more clearly than we do the biology of much "simpler" organisms.

Although this book is meant to be comprehensible to a student with no more than an elementary previous knowledge of biology (at about high school level), some more "advanced" material and discussion of a number of unsettled and controversial problems have been included. As a result, the book contains more material than can be adequately covered in an average one-term course; but this superabundance of material is deliberate. The subdivision of the chapters into short sections with descriptive subheadings should make deletion of the unwanted material easy. On the other hand, what can be more challenging and inspiring to a student of average and above-average intelligence than to learn that science is not something all completed and finished, merely to be memorized from books, but a growing body of knowledge, in the development of which this same student may have a hand if he so chooses? Is finding this out not equally, or even more, valuable to a student than learning more "facts"?

In place of a conventional chapter on the history of evolutionary theories, the history of various ideas and concepts is discussed in this book in the same chapters which present the modern status of those ideas and concepts. This arrangement of material does not in any sense mean an underestimate of the importance of the history of science or of its interest to an intelligent student. But modern evolutionary thought is a result of confluence and integration of the work of many biological disciplines, which even in a recent past were developing more independently than they are now. The history of the evolutionary doctrine as a whole, from a modern standpoint, has never been written, and for the time being it seems more convenient to present the historical information piecemeal.

The "Suggestions for Further Reading" given at the end of most chapters are meant to assist the student who may wish to go beyond the limits of this book in exploring problems of evolutionary biology. These "Suggestions" are certainly not meant to serve as bibliographies in which a reference to an authority for every fact and name mentioned in the text may be located.

I am deeply indebted to several colleagues and friends who have read chapters of this book and suggested corrections and improvements. The greatest thanks go to Professors Ernst Mayr, of Harvard University, Charles Birch, of the University of Sydney, Australia, and A. B. da Cunha, of the University of São Paulo, Brazil, who have read the manuscript in its entirety. Chapters 1, 2, and 3 were read also by Drs. Alfred Mirsky and Stanley Gartler; Chapters 4 and 5 by Dr. M. Demerec; Chapters 6 and 7 by Dr. Phillip M. Sheppard; Chapters 6, 7, 8, and 10 by Professor H. L. Carson; Chapters 8, 10, and 12 by Professor John A. Moore; Chapter 9 by Professor P. C. Mangelsdorf; Chapter 11 by Professor Aubrey Gorbman; and Chapters 13 and 14 by Professor L. C. Dunn, Mr. Stephen Dunn, and Mr. M. D. Coe. Quite obviously, I remain solely responsible for all errors of commission and omission which doubtless will be found in the book. Mr. Stephen R. Peck has drawn many of the excellent illustrations which adorn the text. Several colleagues have contributed other illustrations and photographs, as acknowledged in the legends to these figures. Finally, thanks are due Miss Adelaide Richardson, who prepared the typescript.

Th. Dobzhansky

São Paulo, Brazil
October, 1955

Contents

1 ⸻

Nature and Origin
of Life

The purpose of science is twofold. Science strives, in the first place, to understand man and the universe of which he is a part. In the second place, science endeavors to provide man with the means to control his environment. The quest for understanding is a function of theoretical, fundamental, or pure science. Knowledge and understanding are sources of satisfaction even when they do not yield any immediate material benefits. Control of the environment is a function of applied science or technology.

Understanding things, however, is the surest approach to controlling them; and the distinction between pure and applied science is, therefore, not always sharp. This distinction often describes the attitudes of mind of investigators and students rather than the subject matter of their investigations and studies. Some discoveries of greatest practical utility have been made by scientists engaged in exploration of the laws of nature without regard for their possible utilization. For instance, the germ theory of disease and much of the modern food technology are outgrowths of the studies of the great French biologist Pasteur (1822–1895) on the nature of life.

Cosmic Evolution. Discoveries made in various branches of science during the nineteenth and twentieth centuries have converged to establish an evolutionary approach to the understanding of nature. The universe has not always been as it is now. Nature as we observe it today is the outcome of a historical process of development, evolution. The human race with its social, intellectual, and artistic achievements, the world of living creatures, and inanimate nature, all evolved gradually and by stages from very different antecedents.

The classical atomist view of nature, which dominated physical sci-

1

ences up to the beginning of the current century, held that the basic physical and chemical properties of matter were always as they are today. Matter consists of atoms of several scores of chemical elements, and the atoms combine with each other according to certain rules which the chemists describe. All material objects in the universe consist of different combinations of atoms, but the atoms themselves were believed to be unchangeable and indivisible. The very word "atom" means indivisible in Greek.

Classical atomism was right as far as it went, but it oversimplified the actual situation. Physicists have shown that atoms consist of still smaller units—electrons, neutrons, protons. Atoms of chemical elements have been transformed in laboratory experiments into other elements. Moreover, modern cosmology, the study of the universe, assumes that the atoms which exist today have had a history. One of the theories is that the atoms were formed from a primordial substance, called the "ylem," and the inference is that they were formed in a tremendous explosion, which occurred supposedly more than 5 billion years ago. This stupendous event is, then, the first discernible date in the history of the universe and the beginning of *cosmic evolution*. After the formation of the atoms, cosmic evolution led to the concentration of the original cloud of atoms into galaxies. This process took a relatively "short" time, some 30 million years. The stars and planets were formed within the galaxies. Our earth came into existence presumably as one of these planets; it is, therefore, only a little "younger" than the universe itself.

The work of geologists has shown that the earth underwent many transformations during its long history. Again and again mountain ranges rose above the plains, and were leveled back by erosion; portions of land sank beneath the seas, and sea bottoms rose to become land; the climates of many parts of the world changed from warm to cold, and vice versa.

Biological Evolution. Our earth is an insignificantly small particle of the universe, yet we cannot be sure that life exists anywhere except on this small particle. The evolution of life, biological evolution, has, to our knowledge, been enacted on earth alone. How long ago life appeared on earth, however, is a problem fraught with uncertainties. The most ancient indisputable and abundant fossil remains are estimated to be some 500 million years old. These ancient (Cambrian, see Chapter 12) fossils are remains of creatures which inhabited the seas. Because the principal types, or phyla, of the now-existing marine organisms are represented among Cambrian fossils we can suppose that much evolution took place before these organisms could have appeared, and, therefore, that the origin of life took place long before then.

The extreme scarcity of the fossil record of the beginning stages of biological evolution is probably due to two causes. First, the most primitive organisms now living are too small and too delicate to be preserved as fossils, and this was most likely true in the early stages of organic evolution. Second, the geological strata older than 500 million years (and many of those younger than that) were altered by heat and by great pressures in such ways that whatever fossils had been present in them were destroyed. For all these reasons it is conjectured that life appeared on earth much earlier than 500 million years ago. Unaltered pre-Cambrian rocks are rare, and they contain a few doubtful fossils, which some authorities interpret as seaweeds and algae but others regard as possibly formed without participation of life. Perhaps more hopeful are very ancient deposits of carbon apparently of organic origin. Holmes claimed in 1954 that one such deposit in Africa is between 2.6 and 2.7 billion years old. If confirmed, this claim will mean that organic evolution became superimposed on cosmic evolution very long ago (Table 1.1).

The first land-growing plants appeared, as shown by the fossil record, at least 400 million years ago. Land animals were added later—some 300 million years ago. The first known land-inhabiting vertebrate animals are still more recent—200 to 250 million years. Mammals, the class of animals to which man belongs, were evolved some 125 million years ago and became diversified and widespread at most 75 million years ago. Mankind is a newcomer even among mammals. The first traces of man's presence are less than one million years old, which is less than one per cent of the time span during which mammals are known to have lived.

Human Evolution and Evolution of Culture. With the appearance of man a third kind of evolution, that of the human spirit, became superimposed on the background of the biological and cosmic evolution. Of course the entry of man on the evolutionary stage did not mean that biological evolution had come to an end, no more than the origin of life meant the termination of cosmic evolution. The three kinds of evolution proceeded at the same time.

The Greek Anaximander (611–547 B.C.), the first evolutionist to leave a trace in the history of human thought, taught that life arose from mud warmed up by sun rays. Plants came first, then animals, and finally man. But, reasoned Anaximander, man could not have

TABLE 1.1

SOME APPROXIMATE DATES OF COSMIC, BIOLOGICAL, AND HUMAN EVOLUTION

Years Ago (Approximate)	Events
100	Publication of Darwin's *Origin of Species*
100–200	Industrial Revolution
300–400	Life of Galileo and birth of modern science
1955	Birth of Christ
3000	Beginning of Greek civilization
3500	Beginning of Chinese civilization
5400	Beginning of civilization in Mesopotamia
5400	Beginning of First Dynasty in Egypt
6200	Introduction of Calendar in Egypt
15–25 thousand	Man in America
20–50 thousand	Cro-Magnon man in Europe
20–75 thousand	Old Stone Age in Europe
500–800 thousand	First man-made tools
75 million	Beginning of the Age of Mammals
125 million	The first mammals appear
500 million	Beginning of the fossil record
2.5 billion	Appearance of life on earth
5 billion	Appearance of atoms of the chemical elements, followed by the formation of the galaxies, stars, and planets

arisen directly from mud, since as a child he is unable to feed or to take care of himself. Hence he must have arisen from another animal. This, then, is the first statement of the view that man is *biologically unique* (see Chapter 13). At present we are confident that man is a product of biological evolution; his evolution was brought about by the same fundamental causes as the evolution of all other organisms. But in man the biological evolution has transcended itself. Man is able to use language symbols, to arrive at decisions by a process of abstraction and reasoning, and to distinguish between good and evil. Children inherit their biological heredity from their parents through the sex cells, but they inherit their *culture* by learning from other human beings, not necessarily related to them by descent. Biological heredity is set at fertilization, and it remains more or less constant thereafter (Chapter 6). Cultural heredity is acquired throughout life, but principally during childhood and youth (Chapters 13 and 14).

To develop culture, the human species had to evolve a human biological organization. No animal, not even the anthropoid apes, can acquire the rudiments of human culture. The important thing, however, is that the biological organization which enabled man to acquire and develop culture has conferred on him, for that reason, an immense biological advantage (Chapter 13). Man adapts himself to his environment chiefly by using his technical skills, his knowledge of things, his science, art, religion, in brief his culture. Now, as indicated above, the process of transmission of culture is vastly more efficient than biological heredity, which comes only from our parents and other direct ancestors, and can be transmitted only to our offspring. By contrast, learning, art, belief, or wisdom can be transmitted by precept, by speech, or by writing, to any number of human beings, regardless of their being related by descent or not. Every one of us has "inherited" the wisdom of people whom we never met in the flesh. In many instances these people died centuries before we were born (see Chapter 13).

The rise of man from the animal level to truly human estate was slow at first. A few bone fragments of a creature which combined some human-like and some ape-like features were discovered in South Africa, together with charcoal remains. This discovery led the discoverer, Dart, to surmise that the creature was a user of fire, and to name it *Australopithecus prometheus* (pithecus, ape; Prometheus, the discoverer of fire). The dating of this fossil is, most unfortunately, quite uncertain; the creature may have lived half a million to more than a million years ago. Dart's interpretation of his find is regarded as doubtful.

There is, however, no doubt that at least 20,000 years ago there appeared in Europe a race of people who, judging by their bones, might have looked pretty much like ourselves. The drawings of animals which they made on the walls of the caves which they inhabited on the territory of the present France show that they possessed an exquisite artistic feeling (Figure 1.1).

The first light of recorded history dawned in the valley of the Nile, in Egypt, some sixty-two centuries ago. Within a few centuries a cultural awakening took place in several countries—in Egypt, in Mesopotamia (Iraq), in India, and somewhat later in China. Despite the numerous, and often grievous, setbacks, the development of human cultures has proceeded since then with, seemingly, accelerating tempo.

To a philosopher the cosmic, biological, and cultural evolutions are integral parts of the grand drama of Creation. A scientist, though he recognizes the unity of the evolutionary process, must perforce confine his studies within narrower bounds because the methods of in-

vestigation used by physicists, chemists, astronomers, geologists, biologists, anthropologists, sociologists, artists, and theologians are so diverse that no one person is able, at present, to use them all with equal
competence. In this book our attention is focused on biological evolu-

Figure 1.1. Drawings of animals on walls of Lascaux caves in France, made by
man of the Old Stone Age.

tion. The relevance of the biological findings to human problems, as
well as the importance of the environment in the midst of which the
evolution of life is enacted, will, however, be pointed out whenever
possible.

Characteristics of Living Matter. As yet nobody has offered a
satisfactory formal definition of life, and we shall not attempt to produce one. For despite the lack of a definition there is usually no
difficulty in deciding whether a given object is or is not living. Living
beings usually possess the following combination of attributes:

A chemical composition including *proteins* and *nucleic acids.*
A definite *organization.*
Maintenance and growth through *assimilation.*
Reproduction and *heredity.*
Irritability and *adaptation.*

The living bodies consist very largely of oxygen, carbon, hydrogen, and nitrogen, that is, chemical elements which are quite common also in the inorganic nature. To those are added a number of other common elements, as shown in the following table, which indicates the percentages of the various elements in the human body:

Element	Per Cent	Element	Per Cent
Oxygen	65	Potassium	0.35
Carbon	18	Sulphur	0.25
Hydrogen	10	Sodium	0.15
Nitrogen	3	Chlorine	0.15
Calcium	2	Magnesium	0.05
Phosphorus	1	All others	0.05

Some organisms contain rather higher proportions of chemical elements which are present only as traces in the human frame. Thus the blood of many mollusks has a greenish color owing to the presence of copper, and the ascidians (a group of marine animals) contain some vanadium. But there is certainly no chemical element that would be confined to living protoplasm. Carbon comes nearest to deserving to be called "the stuff of life," because it is capable of forming innumerable complex compounds with other elements which occur in living matter. These "organic" compounds are far more characteristic of life than the elements which enter into the composition of living bodies. Proteins and nucleic acids are the two classes of such compounds which are important, because they are universally present in all life. But we cannot be entirely sure that some very different classes of chemical compounds could not produce life.

Proteins are large, and often huge, molecules, with molecular weights usually in tens or in hundreds of thousands, and often in millions. The proteins consist, in turn, of chemically linked building blocks known as amino acids. About twenty different amino acids are commonly found, all of them characterized by the presence of "amino groups" NH_2 and a carboxyl group, COOH, in their molecular makeup. Their molecular weights are in hundreds. An important property of amino acids is their ability to combine in a great variety of complex patterns such as are found in proteins. The specificity and constancy of the organization of living beings (see below) is presumed to rest on the specificity of the proteins. Enzymes, chemical substances which mediate many important chemical reactions taking place in living bodies, are among the proteins. The action of enzymes is as a rule highly specific since each enzyme mediates one and only one kind of reaction.

Nucleic acids are compounds of so-called nucleotides. A nucleotide, in turn, consists of a nitrogen-containing purine or pyrimidine base, a sugar, and a phosphoric acid. Depending on the kind of sugar involved, two types of nucleic acids can be distinguished, called, respectively, ribonucleic acids (RNA, for short) and desoxyribonucleic acids (or DNA). The DNA is invariably present in the chromosomes of the cell nucleus, whereas RNA is a characteristic constituent of the cell cytoplasm. The nucleotides are, in living cells, associated with each other to form compounds of, often, very high molecular weight. Furthermore, nucleic acids link up with proteins to form *nucleoproteins*. It appears that nucleoproteins are present in all existing living bodies, down to the simplest viruses.

Organization and Individuality. There is no question but that comprehension of the chemical processes which occur in living organisms is essential for an understanding of life, and that our knowledge of these processes is as yet insufficient. But we should not think of an organism as though it were simply a mixture of chemical substances. Life occurs always in discrete units, in individuals, which possess a fairly constant and usually highly complex structure or organization. From men, elephants, and whales to insects, polyps, and lowly amoebae, and from pine and oak trees to grasses, algae, and down to the simplest organisms, we can always discern the characteristic external structures (morphology), internal gross and microscopic anatomy, and the physiological properties of individuals of every species of organisms.

Inanimate objects do not usually possess definable individuality. Mountain ranges, rocks, rivers, or seas are not discrete individuals, since they do not have a cohesive structure that would be characteristic also of other individuals of a species. To be sure, crystals seem to foreshadow on the inorganic level the discreteness and the constant organization of living individuals. The shape of crystals is fixed by their chemical structure; the atoms inside a crystal are arranged in a definite pattern. Under proper conditions a crystal can grow and even restore missing parts, which makes us think of regeneration of missing parts in lower organisms. Most crystals, however, consist of a single chemical compound, whereas organisms contain enormous numbers of substances arranged into strictly defined patterns.

Living individuals very seldom occur singly. Representatives of a species usually live in communities, members of which are related by mating and parentage bonds. Sometimes members of communities form colonies, and become so completely interdependent that it is no

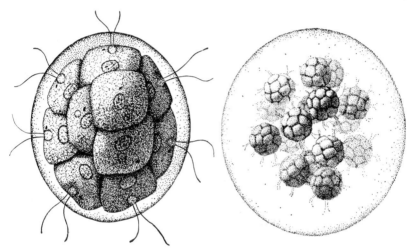

Figure 1.2. One individual or several? The microscopic alga Pandorina, several cells of which live together in a common gelatinous envelope. The drawing on the right shows each cell divided to form new groups which are about to become independent.

longer easy to delimit the constituent individuals. Thus some of the lower plants, algae, live in colonies composed of several or many cells (Figure 1.2). The whole colonies as well as the constituent cells may be referred to as "individuals." Cells are the fundamental building blocks of the bodies of all higher organisms, including man, but we have no doubt that it is the whole man, rather than each of his cells, that is the individual, since the cells of the body are incapable of independent existence (except in artificial tissue cultures). In some organisms, however, such as corals or the Portuguese man-o-war, multicellular individuals become again associated into colonies and lose their independence to such an extent that it becomes reasonable to regard the colonies as individual units (Figure 1.3). It is obvious that individuality is not an all-or-none affair but a matter of degree.

Self-reproduction. A human being begins his existence when a spermatozoon fertilizes an egg cell (Figure 1.4). A fertilized human egg cell is just large enough to be visible to a naked eye. Its weight is estimated as about one twenty-millionth of an ounce (slightly more

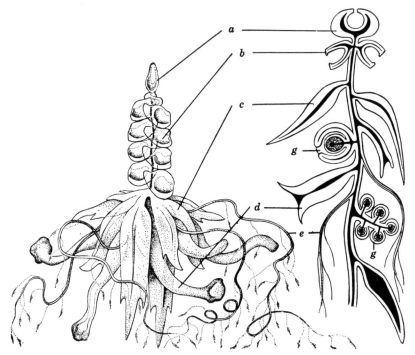

Figure 1.3. A siphonophore, a colonial marine animal consisting of several different kinds of individuals specialized to perform different functions. The appearance of the colony is shown on the left, and a scheme of its structure on the right. The individual which functions to make the colony float vertically in water is marked *a*; *b*, individuals which act as swimming bells; *c*, protective "leaves"; *d*, gasterozoids which ingest food; *e*, tentacle; *g*, gonophor or sexual individual.

than one millionth of a gram). Starting from this insignificant bit of matter, the body grows until it attains the adult size and weight of, say, 150 to 160 pounds. This is, then, an approximately fifty-billion-fold increase.

What is the source of material for this stupendous growth? Clearly, it is the food consumed—first by the mother in whose body the embryo coming from the fertilized egg develops, and then by the growing individual himself. Now food is derived ultimately from the environment in which the organism lives. For green plants this is water and certain mineral salts taken in from the soil, oxygen and carbon dioxide from the atmosphere, and the energy of a part of the sunlight spectrum. All animals, and most of the chlorophyll-less plants, require for food some of the organic substances found in the bodies of other animals or plants. All life is derived from the energy of sunlight bound by the chlorophyll of green plants.

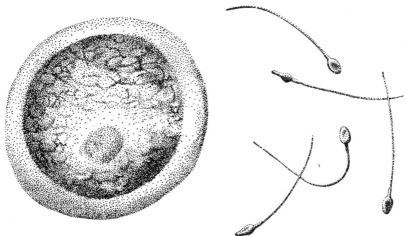

Figure 1.4. A human egg and a sperm. The sperm is magnified more strongly than the egg.

When a crystal grows in a supersaturated solution, the growth occurs by addition of the substance from the solution to the surface of the crystal. The growth of living bodies is a different story. The food undergoes a series of profound chemical changes before it is assimilated, that is, becomes a component part of the organism. Thus animals break down the proteins ingested as food into amino acids, and then build their own proteins from these constituents. Now it is surely a most significant fact that the body *reproduces itself* from the food which it consumes: in the process of assimilation and growth the food is transformed into a likeness of the assimilating body and of its ancestors. Indeed, the human body, whether an embryo or an adult, transforms food not merely into human flesh but into an individual who resembles his parents and relatives more or less closely. The outcome of growth and development depends very largely on the nature, the *heredity*, of the body and only secondarily on the food which it assimilates. The same kind of diet can maintain life not only of different men but also of other species of animals, for example, of dogs and cats kept as domestic pets. It is the heredity which causes the processes of assimilation to result in self-reproduction.

The production of a likeness of the assimilating body and of its ancestors is most strikingly apparent when the organism grows or gives rise to a progeny. An oak tree brings forth acorns, each able to grow into an oak. An oyster gives some hundred million eggs in a single spawning, each potentially a new oyster. Owing to heredity, to self-reproduction, every form of life tends to transform the materials in the environment capable of serving as food into copies of itself. Self-reproduction continues in adult bodies which no longer grow in size or in weight; it continues as long as life itself. Every organism not only assimilates foods but also breaks down the assimilated products and reconstructs them again. This continuous buildup and breakdown of living matter is the *metabolism*.

Studies on metabolism have disclosed that most of the components of the animal body are frequently renewed, as can be shown very clearly with the aid of "tracers," such as isotopes of the elements which compose the living bodies. For example, an animal can be fed a diet in which certain of the atoms of the usual carbon (C_{12}) have been replaced by those of a radioactive carbon isotope, C_{14}. The radioactive carbon presently appears as a component of various tissues of the body, in which it can be localized with the aid of both physical and chemical methods. The C_{14} thus enters the living protoplasm, but after a lapse of a certain time (variable for different tissues and substances), the structures containing C_{14} are broken down, and the isotope appears in the waste products of the organism. Similar experiments have been done with other isotopes—"heavy" water, radioactive sulphur, phosphorus, iodine, etc. The phenomenon of self-reproduction in living bodies is universal.

Adaptation. Every organism responds in definite ways to outside stimuli; the ability of making such responses is referred to as the property of *irritability*. Even the simplest unicellular animals and plants, such as amoebae and flagellate algae, move towards food and away from too intense heat or cold, and towards moderate light and away from darkness or too intense light. Seeds of the higher and spores of the lower plants respond by sprouting or germination to some conditions and by remaining dormant to others.

A striking and fascinating fact is that many, although not all, responses of living beings to outside influences are *adaptive*, that is, promote health, survival, and reproduction of the reacting organisms.

Consider, for example, the complex physiological processes which are set in motion by wounds, injuries, or bone fractures, and which result in healing and repair of these injuries. Invasion of the body by disease-producing bacteria, viruses, and other parasites calls forth remarkable defense reactions which tend to localize, combat, and finally extinguish the infections. Owing to the scarcity of oxygen at high elevations in the mountains, man experiences difficulties in living and working at high altitudes. The human body reacts, however, to the high-altitude conditions by altering the composition of the blood and by other physiological changes which facilitate securing enough oxygen for respiration.

Homeostasis. In all these and in countless other instances we observe a remarkable "wisdom of the body." Environmental stimuli evoke processes which maintain or restore the welfare of the body in changed environments. The organism normally stands to its environment in a relation of adaptedness. When the environment changes, this harmonious relation may be disturbed and must be restored by *homeostatic* reactions on the part of the organism. Adaptedness to the environment can, of course, be observed not only in man but in all organisms, animal and plant, primitive and complex. The ubiquity of homeostatic reactions in the living world has even led some biologists to view adaptation as some kind of mystical principle. Many vitalists (see page 19) regarded the ability of the organism to respond adaptively to external stimuli as an elemental property of life. The great Lamarck, one of the pioneers of evolutionism, built his theory on the assumption that organs are always strengthened by intensive use and weakened by prolonged disuse (Chapter 4). It will be shown below (Chapters 5 and 6) that the origin of adaptations can be understood better on the basis of Darwin's theory of natural selection, without invoking any alleged mystical properties of living matter. For the time being it is sufficient to point out that, although the widespread adaptedness of living beings to their environment justly excites our admiration, in some instances adaptive reactions are conspicuously lacking.

The sun-tanning reaction of the human skin protects the body from sunburns. There is, however, no protecting reaction to shield the body from harmful X-rays, radium rays, and similar radiations. In general, pain is a warning signal produced by injuries or by invasions of the body by poisons and parasites. Yet in the human species the biologically "normal" and essential function of childbirth is accompanied by intense pain. Most harmful substances are repellent, but some, such as narcotics, produce pleasant sensations instead of pain. Man must rely on food for his supply of numerous vitamins essential for health; but many other animals, even some mammals, can manufacture some of these vitamins for themselves.

There are some basic facts which point towards a solution of the problem of adaptation. In general, every living species reacts adaptively to the external stimuli which occur frequently in the environments in which this species has evolved. Thus the human species had for countless generations to deal with the danger of sunburn, but it did not encounter X-ray burns until very recently. The painfulness of childbirth is probably a disharmony resulting from the comparatively recent acquisition by our species of the erect posture and from the correlated changes in the pelvis bones. When the normal food supply of a species contains an abundance of a certain vitamin, there is no obvious advantage for this species to manufacture the vitamins in its own body. Homeostatic reactions are not to be taken for granted as gifts of nature; they must be understood and explained. The modern theory of evolution seems to provide a reasonable explanation.

Viruses—the Simplest Organisms. Invention of the microscope resulted during the eighteenth and nineteenth centuries in the discovery of a hitherto unknown world of tiny creatures. Some of them, particularly bacteria, appeared at first to be mere droplets of a viscous substance. Yet, despite their small size, bacteria possess an immensely complex organization, at any rate immeasurably more complex than anything in inorganic nature. Then, in 1892, Ivanovsky discovered still smaller organisms which are too small to be seen in ordinary light microscopes. They were later named filterable viruses, since they are small enough to pass through filters of unglazed porcelain and other materials which retain ordinary bacteria. In recent years many viruses have been made visible by means of electron microscopes. In 1935 Stanley isolated from tobacco plants infected with the so-called mosaic disease a protein which can form crystal-like structures (Figure 1.5). A minute amount of this protein injected into healthy plants causes them later to develop the mosaic disease. Most important of all, an amount of the virus protein about one million times greater than the amount injected can be obtained from the diseased plants several days after the injection.

Viruses known at present are a diversified collection of forms. Their common property, apart from their small size, is that all of them are parasites which develop only in living cells of animal or plant hosts. In other words, no free-living viruses are known. Some viruses cause diseases in their hosts, among them such scourges as smallpox, polio-myelitis, yellow fever, measles, influenza, and common cold.   Plant viruses are responsible for serious losses to agricultural crops.   Bac-teriophages reproduce in living bacterial cells and cause dissolution (lysis) of the cells (Figure 5.1).

Some of the viruses, despite their smallness, have proved to be quite complex organisms. This is true, for example, of bacteriophages. It

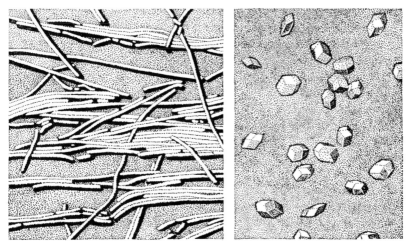

Figure 1.5.   Viruses as seen in electron microscopes.   Tobacco mosaic virus (left) and bushy stunt virus (right).   Very greatly magnified.

is a plausible hypothesis that many viruses are actually degenerate de-scendants of larger organisms such as bacteria.   But, especially among viruses which cause plant diseases, there are some forms interesting because of their apparent simplicity.   The crystalline tobacco mosaic virus was shown by Stanley to be chemically a nucleoprotein (ribose nucleoprotein).   Its molecular weight is estimated to be as high as 50 million.

Is tobacco mosaic virus and are other viruses living beings? Al-though a majority of biologists are now of the opinion that this ques-tion must definitely be answered in the positive, it is interesting that there existed and still exist some dissenting opinions.   The very pos-sibility of such a disagreement suggests that some viruses, such as the tobacco mosaic virus, may be not far removed from the boundary of the living and the non-living.

A conclusive evidence of the living nature of the tobacco virus, apart from its nucleoproteinaceous structure, is that the virus repro- duces itself at the expense of materials in the tobacco leaves. To be sure, the objection has been raised that the virus may somehow be synthesized by the cells of the tobacco plant or may be preformed in these cells. Indeed, the virus multiplies only in living, not in dead, cells of tobacco leaves. The objection is not valid; many a parasite, the living nature of which cannot be doubted, cannot be cultivated outside the body of a host. Tobacco cells assuredly contain sub- stances which are susceptible of being converted into the virus sub- stance; otherwise the virus could not infect the tobacco plants. But the conversion does not take place unless a particle of the virus is first introduced into the plant. Similarly, human intestine contains sub- stances from which intestinal parasites can be built, and grocery store shelves contain materials which can be converted into human bodies. Yet in all these cases the conversion occurs only in the self-reproducing, living, bodies of a given species.

The Continuity of Life. The idea that life is, in the last analysis, but self-reproduction of living matter is quite foreign to a mind un- tutored in biological science. Until a few centuries ago nobody doubted *abiogenesis* or *spontaneous generation,* that is, origin of living creatures from non-living matter. Aristotle (384–322 B.C.) thought that worms and snails were products of putrefaction and that plants could arise also without seed. This hypothesis was accepted by such pioneers of science as Bacon (1561–1626) and William Harvey (1579– 1657). Paracelsus (1493–1541) revealed the recipe, which, he said, had until then been kept in greatest secrecy, for producing a "homun- culus" or an artificial man. He might be produced, allegedly, through putrefaction of the human semen in a cucurbit placed for 40 weeks inside the belly of a horse. The power of heredity was taken equally lightly. Plutarch (A.D. 46–125) records that human beings were born of mares, asses, and goats. The notion that wheat and barley trans- form into wild oats and other weeds was discussed in ancient Rome by Virgil and Pliny, and was believed by some until about the seven- teenth century. It has quite recently been resurrected by Lysenko and his followers in Russia.

The continuity of life and heredity was revealed only gradually. Redi (1626–1698) showed that fly maggots did not arise from putrid meat. He placed decaying meat in a jar covered with fine gauze, so that the flies were unable to reach the meat. No maggots appeared. Spallanzani (1729–1799) found that meat or meat juice did not pu- trefy unless spores of putrefaction bacteria were introduced with dust from the air. He showed that when meat juice was boiled and then sealed airtight no bacteria developed. His experiment did not satisfy all the believers in spontaneous generation, who objected that boiling destroys "the life-giving powers" of air and of meat juice. It was Pas-

Figure 1.6. Louis Pasteur (1822–1895).

teur (Figure 1.6) who gave the definitive evidence that life arises only from pre-existing life. He, among others, did the experiment of boiling meat juice and other liquids suitable for the development of bacteria in a special flask which admitted the outside air through a curved tube. The dust with the bacterial spores settled in the curved tube, and the liquid in the flask remained free of bacteria. This work not only established a fundamental biological principle but led to numerous practical applications—pasteurization and sterilization so important in canning and dairy industry as well as in medicine.

Hypotheses Regarding Origin of Life on Earth. If life comes only from life, then every living creature which exists now is a direct descendant of the first bit of living protoplasm which appeared on earth (unless life arose from inanimate nature repeatedly). The origin of the first life of necessity is a highly speculative issue. Indeed, our inability to observe spontaneous generation in nature or to bring it about artificially in laboratory experiments shows that life must have arisen under some conditions which no longer obtain at present and about which we can make only the vaguest guesses.

Attempts have even been made to avoid the issue by supposing that life was introduced on our planet from other heavenly bodies. Spores or other germs of life may have arrived on earth in a meteor or with cosmic dust. But we are not certain that life exists or ever existed outside the earth, and, if it did, could stand the transport through the interplanetary space. In any case, we must face the problem of the origin of life in the universe.

All life that now exists, including the simplest viruses, has as its physical abode highly complex organic compounds, nucleoproteins. Not only nucleoproteins but even their constituent amino acids and nucleic acids are synthesized exclusively in living organisms and never spontaneously from inorganic substances (some of the amino acids can, however, be made synthetically in laboratories). Spontaneous formation of these energy-rich compounds is highly improbable on the basis of physicochemical considerations. Nevertheless, several scientists, Oparin in Russia, Dauvillier and Desguin in France, Bernal in England, Urey, Miller, and Blum in America, have tried to visualize conditions under which chemical substances now formed only in living organisms could have arisen without intervention of life.

In the early stages of the history of the earth the prevalent high temperatures permitted the existence of water only in the form of superheated steam. The atmosphere contained no free oxygen, but it may have contained some simple carbon compounds, such as methane (CH_4), which are now found in the atmospheres of some stars. Similarly nitrogenous compounds, such as ammonia (NH_3), were probably formed. With the cooling of the earth and the formation of liquid water some chemical reactions became possible which are not likely to occur now. This is particularly so because high-energy ultraviolet radiations were then presumably reaching the earth's surface. They are now absorbed in the upper atmosphere by oxygen and ozone.

Under such conditions simple aldehydes, such as formaldehyde (CH_2O), would be formed, and these might be slowly condensed into sugars. Organic acids also could be formed and, reacting with ammonia, could give other compounds, including simple amino acids, such as glycine (CH_2NH_2COOH). Proteins would arise by linking together several amino acids.

A possible reason why these chemical compounds do not now exist in non-living media is that they would be used up as food by living organisms soon after being produced. While life was absent, organic compounds could accumulate in the water of lakes and seas. Even so, spontaneous formation of complex proteins and nucleoproteins is a most improbable event, at least in terms of short time intervals. Given eons of time, a highly improbable event may, however, take place somewhere in the universe. Such a "lucky hit" happened to occur on a small planet, earth, a mere speck in the vast cosmic spaces. As soon as a particle appeared that was able to reproduce itself, that is, to engender synthesis of its copies from materials present in its environment, the evolution of life was launched. The primordial living particle may, for example, be visualized as a kind of simple virus. Of course this virus must have been able to multiply in the inorganic environment, or in environments containing only the organic compounds accumulated through processes of the kind outlined above.

There are several reasons why the self-reproduction of particles is stressed as the essential step with which life commenced. Self-reproduction of necessity implies growth through assimilation, maintenance of definite organization, and transmission of heredity. It will be shown in the following chapters that self-reproduction and heredity may lead, through action of natural selection, to adaptation to the environment and to progressive evolution. Formation of the first self-reproducing particle, whatever might have been its precise chemical makeup, was, at least potentially, the dawn of organic evolution. Although at present self-reproduction is not known to occur except in nucleoproteins, self-reproducing units of other composition might have occurred on earth or in other parts of the cosmos.

Vitalism and Mechanism. Our understanding of the fundamental life phenomena is admittedly sketchy, and the hypotheses about the origin of life are only conjectures set up to promote further thinking and experimentation. Science in general and biological science in particular have only begun to explore the design and the working of nature. Most biologists believe that the best working hypothesis is that life phenomena involve merely complex patterns of interaction of physical forces and of chemical reactions. This assumption is called *mechanism.* Its alternative, *vitalism,* is that, in addition to the forces similar in kind to those operating in inanimate nature, life involves powers which are restricted to the living world.

It is curious to think that vitalism was accepted by most biologists in the seventeenth and eighteenth centuries, together with the belief in the frequent occurrence of spontaneous generation (see page 16). At that time life was regarded as a manifestation of a special *vital force* (vis vitalis). Such a possibility could not be dismissed outright. Physics knows several forms of energy: mechanical energy, heat, light, electricity, and the energy of atomic nuclei. There may exist also a vital energy, it is argued. The development of biology in the nineteenth and twentieth centuries has failed, however, to reveal the operations of such an energy, although some of the physical and chemical processes involved in many biological phenomena, such as animal and plant metabolism, muscle contraction, nerve conduction, and other phenomena, have become partly known. This certainly does not mean that all biological processes are now understood in physical and chemical terms, but it is true that the realm of phenomena in which manifestations of the vital force may still be suspected has been shrinking steadily for at least two centuries. Few or no biologists now consider the assumption of vital force a profitable hypothesis, and this notwithstanding the downfall of the belief in spontaneous generation, which seemed to increase the gap between the living and the non-living.

Vitalism, however, continues to exist in a subtly changed form and as a minority opinion. It is admitted that life is basically a complex of physical and chemical processes. And yet Sinnott believes that living cells possess a "psyche," a drive akin to human volition, which presides upon the development of a fertilized egg into an embryo and into an adult. The so-called finalist school, particularly in France and in Germany, believes that the evolution of life has been governed by a perfectionist urge, or by striving to produce man (cf. Chapter 14).

It is hard to see what is gained by such speculation. Just what is the meaning of the assertion that the cell or the body is directed by a psyche or by a perfectionist urge? If these factors somehow direct the flow of physical and chemical processes, they must themselves be forms of physical energy, even though peculiar and as yet unknown ones. But this is a return to the old belief in a vital force, although under different names. If, on the other hand, the psyche or the supernatural guide is outside and above the physicochemical matrix of life processes, a biologist is still obliged to find mechanistic explanations of these processes. Consider, for example, the origin of life from inert matter. Was it the psyche which built the first nucleoprotein molecule from simpler compounds? If so, the psyche must be some enzyme or some energy-rich radiation. No matter how small is the push which you want the supernatural to deliver to a material process, the supernatural is inexorably debased to the level of a physical energy.

Acceptance of mechanism as a biological theory is not, however, inconsistent with esthetic and religious views of existence. Man is a complex of chemical compounds, but this fact alone is said to describe him adequately only to those who would use him for fertilizer. Regardless of what he is chemically, man yearns for sympathy and understanding. A primeval forest, a mountain meadow, or a coral reef have beauty which is appreciated the more we become familiar with the organisms which occur there. Religion leads us to appreciate the meaning and value of the world and of man.

Suggestions for Further Reading

Gamov, G. 1952. *The Creation of the Universe.* Viking Press, New York.

This is a very well-written account of cosmic evolution, understandable to non-physicists.

Bernal, J. D. 1951. *The Physical Basis of Life.* Routledge & Kegan Paul, London.
Blum, H. F. 1951. *Time's Arrow and Evolution.* Princeton University Press, Princeton.
Oparin, A. I. 1953. *Origin of Life.* 2nd Edition. Dover Publications, New York.

The books of Bernal, Blum, and Oparin contain, among other things, interesting speculations concerning the problem of the origin of life.

Plunkett, C. R. 1944. *The primary physicochemical basis of organic evolution.* In J. Alexander's *Colloid Chemistry,* Volume 5, pp. 1173–1197. Reinhold, New York.

An excellent discussion of the importance of self-reproduction as a basis of life and of evolution.

Russell, E. S. 1945. *The Directedness of Organic Activities.* Cambridge University Press, London.
Sinnott, E. W. 1950. *Cell and Psyche. The Biology of Purpose.* University of North Carolina Press, Chapel Hill.

The books of Russell and Sinnott outline modern variants of vitalistic theories of life.

Simpson, G. G. 1949. *The Meaning of Evolution.* Yale University Press, New Haven.

Also available in a paper-covered edition. A general discussion of evolution and its philosophical implications by an outstanding paleontologist.

Zirkle, C. 1936. *Animals impregnated by the wind.* *Isis,* Volume 25, pp. 95–130.
Zirkle, C. 1951. *The knowledge of heredity before 1900.* In L. C. Dunn's *Genetics in the Twentieth Century,* Macmillan, New York.

The two papers by Zirkle give a review of the amazing and amusing speculations concerning generation and heredity put forward from antiquity to relatively recent times.

2

The Gene as the Basis of Evolution

Every species of organism reproduces itself. The process of heredity converts the food derived from the environment into more or less faithful copies of the assimilating organism and of its parents and more remote ancestors. The reproductive potentials of many organisms are immense. With abundant food and at favorable temperature, the colon bacteria, *Escherichia coli,* double in number about every twenty minutes.

Heredity is a conservative force. If children and parents were completely identical, evolution could not occur. Heredity, however, is opposed by a process of change, variability. Self-reproduction occasionally results in an imperfect copy of the parental living unit, and the altered copy, called a mutant, then reproduces the altered structure until new mutations intervene. One of the major achievements of biology during the current century has been the demonstration that the units both of heredity and of mutation are bodies of molecular dimensions, called genes.

In the last analysis evolution is a sequence of changes in the genes. Darwin and other pioneers of evolutionary biology realized very clearly the basic importance of heredity for understanding evolution. However, it is only during the current century, and particularly during the last twenty to thirty years, that a theory of evolution based on the findings of the study of heredity, genetics, has become possible. A brief outline of the fundamentals of genetics is, therefore, essential in a book dealing with evolution. Such an outline is given in Chapters 2, 3, 4, and also elsewhere in this book in connection with the various problems of general evolutionary biology discussed.

Mendel's Experiments on Plant Hybrids. The basis of the modern theory of heredity was created by Gregor Mendel (1822–1884). Be-

Figure 2.1. Gregor Mendel (1822–1884).

fore Mendel (Figure 2.1) it was believed that heredity is transmitted from parents to offspring by "blood." The parental "bloods" were supposed to mix in the progeny so that the heredity of the child was a solution, or an alloy, of equal parts of parental heredities. The heredity of a person was thought to be an alloy in which the heredities of each of its four grandparents were represented by one-quarter, of each of the eight great-grandparents by one-eighth, etc. (This was called Galton's law of ancestral heredity.) Even so perspicacious a mind as Charles Darwin's accepted these beliefs of his time. People unfamiliar with biology accept the notion of "blood" heredity even now; indeed, this notion is a part of the everyday language.

Mendel's classical experiments consisted in crossing different varieties of garden peas and observing the distribution of the characteristics of the parental varieties among the hybrid offspring. He published the results of his work in 1865 in a single paper. Although he stated very clearly the laws of heredity now regarded of great importance, his work failed to attract the attention of contemporaries. In 1900 these laws were rediscovered independently by Correns in Germany, De Vries in Holland, and Tschermak in Austria. Their importance was recognized, and the development of a new science, genetics or the study of heredity, proceeded apace.

Mendel crossed varieties of peas differing in single contrasting traits, or characters, such as a variety with purple and one with white flowers, with yellow and with green seeds, with round and with wrinkled seeds, tall and dwarf varieties, etc. In the first generation of hybrids, called the F_1 generation, the trait of one of the parents was usually *dominant,* whereas the alternative trait of the other parent was suppressed, or *recessive.* Thus the cross purple $\times$ white flowers gave hybrids with purple flowers, yellow $\times$ green seeds gave dominance of yellow, round $\times$ wrinkled seeds resulted in recessivity of wrinkled, and tall $\times$ dwarf variety gave hybrids in which the tallness (dominant) masked the dwarf size (recessive).

The F_1 hybrids were allowed to produce offspring. The progenies of the F_1 hybrids are the second generation (F_2) hybrid progenies. In these F_2 progenies Mendel observed a fundamental fact: the dominant and the recessive grandparental traits reappeared in about three-quarters and one-quarter of the progeny respectively (a ratio 3 dominant : 1 recessive). Thus Mendel obtained F_2 offspring among which approximately 75 per cent of the plants had purple and 25 per cent white flowers (Figure 2.2).

Mendel's Law of Segregation. Segregation of the traits of the parental varieties in the F_2 generation of hybrids shows that these traits are not inherited through miscible "bloods." They are transmitted from parents to offspring by discrete bodies, which, many years after Mendel's death, Johanssen has named *genes.* In the hybrids the

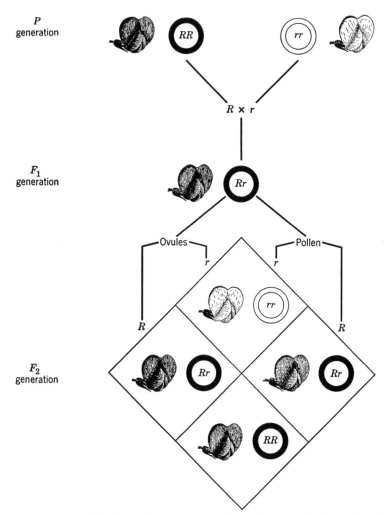

Figure 2.2. Mendel's law of segregation. Cross of a purple-flowered and a white-flowered strain of peas, showing dominance of the purple color and segregation of purple and white in the second generation of hybrids (F_2). R stands for the gene for purple, and r for the gene for white flower color. Black rings symbolize purple-flowered and white rings white-flowered plants.

genes neither mix nor contaminate each other. Thus the gene for purple flowers does not fuse with the alternative (*allelic*) gene for white flowers, even though the purple dominates the development of the color in the flowers of the F_1 hybrid plants. The white flowers in the F_2 generation are just as white as in the original white variety. They do not become pink or rose-colored, although the contrasting alleles for the purple and white colors are carried for a whole generation side by side in the bodies of the F_1 hybrids. When the hybrid, or *heterozygous,* plants form their sex cells the purple- and white-producing genes *segregate.* The sex cells are "pure": they carry either a purple or a white allele. This is the law of segregation, or Mendel's first law.

It is convenient to symbolize the dominant and the recessive gene alleles by capital and by small letters respectively (Figure 2.2). Thus the purple-flowering variety of peas can be written *RR*, and the white-flowering, *rr*. The sex cells carry either *R* or *r*. The F_1 hybrid plants are heterozygotes, *Rr*. In the process of formation of the sex cells by *Rr* heterozygotes the alleles segregate, and equal numbers of *R*-containing and *r*-bearing sex cells are produced. In the formation of the F_2 progenies these sex cells combine at random: *R* female cells or *r* ovules are fertilized by *R* or *r* male cells in proportion to their abundance

It can now be predicted that among the F_2 plants approximately one-quarter will be *homozygous* for *R*, that is, will carry two similar alleles, *RR* (Figure 2.2). About half of the plants will be heterozygous, *Rr*, and about one-quarter will be homozygous, *rr*. Because of the dominance of *R* and the recessiveness of *r*, the homozygotes, *RR*, and the heterozygotes, *Rr*, will be similar in having purple flowers, whereas the homozygotes, *rr*, will have white flowers (Figure 2.2). Although the *RR* and the *Rr* plants are not distinguishable in their flower color, Mendel saw a way to test the validity of the prediction based on his theory. He permitted the purple-flowered F_2 plants to produce further progenies (F_3). About a third of these progenies had only purple flowers; these were the progenies of *RR* plants. In about two-thirds of the progenies purple- and white-flowering plants appeared in ratios approaching 3 purple : 1 white; these were the progenies of *Rr* plants.

Mendel's Principle of Independent Assortment. In some of the crosses made by Mendel the varieties of peas differed in two or more conspicuous traits. For example, he crossed a variety with yellow and round seeds with one having green and wrinkled seeds (Figure 2.3). Mendel knew that the yellow color is dominant over green, and that

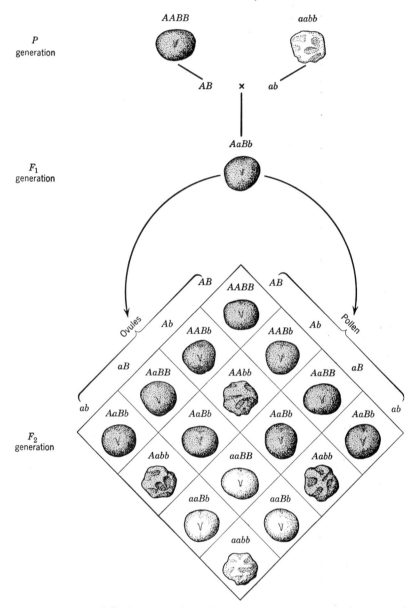

Figure 2.3.   Mendel's law of independent assortment.   Strains of peas with yellow and smooth seeds and with green and wrinkled seeds are crossed.   The letters *A* and *a* stand for the genes for the yellow and green colors, and *B* and *b* for the smooth and wrinkled seed surfaces, respectively.

the wrinkled seed surface is recessive to round. The F_1 generation hybrid seeds were, as expected, yellow and round. What, however, will the F_2 hybrids be like? The traits of the seed color give in F_2 a segregation in a ratio of 3 yellow (dominant) : 1 green (recessive) seeds. The seed surface segregates in a similar ratio, 3 round : 1 wrinkled F_2 hybrid seeds. However, will the yellow color be linked in segregation with the smooth surface, and the green color with the wrinkled surface? Or will the characteristics of color and surface segregate independently? Mendel showed that the latter possibility is realized. The proportions of yellow and green colors among the smooth seeds are the same as among the wrinkled ones. In other words, the F_2 generation consists of about nine-sixteenths ($\frac{3}{4} \times \frac{3}{4}$) of yellow smooth, three-sixteenths ($\frac{3}{4} \times \frac{1}{4}$) of yellow wrinkled, three-sixteenths ($\frac{3}{4} \times \frac{1}{4}$) of green smooth, and one-sixteenth ($\frac{1}{4} \times \frac{1}{4}$) of green wrinkled seeds. This, then, is a segregation in the ratio of 9 double dominants : 3 with one dominant and one recessive : 3 with the other dominant and the other recessive : 1 double recessive.

In terms of genes these facts are interpreted as shown in Figure 2.3. Let A stand for the dominant allele which produces the yellow color and a for its recessive green alternative; B for the dominant smooth surface, and b for the gene which gives rise to a wrinkled seed surface. The varieties crossed are *AABB* and *aabb*, respectively. The sex cells of these varieties are *AB* and *ab*, and the F_1 is a double heterozygote, *AaBb*. The essential point is that the allele pairs *A-a* and *B-b* assort independently when the genes segregate during the formation of the sex cells in the hybrids. The F_1 hybrid forms, then, four kinds of sex cells in equal numbers with the gene combinations *AB*, *Ab*, *aB*, and *ab*. Random union of these sex cells gives the sixteen combinations shown in Figure 2.3. Remembering that the gene A is dominant over a, and B dominant over b, we can easily deduce that the different combinations of seed color and seed surface will appear in the ratio 9 : 3 : 3 : 1 indicated above.

The principle of independent assortment, or recombination, is sometimes referred to as Mendel's second law. Although this "law" is not obeyed in some instances (see page 54), the facts which led to its formulation are important. They show that the heredity transmitted through sex cells is a mosaic of corpuscles, genes which are to some extent independent of each other. The different variants, alleles, of the same gene do not fuse but segregate in heterozygotes, and different genes undergo segregation independently of one another.

Mendelian Inheritance in Man. Mendel's laws apply to all living beings and thus represent perhaps the most fundamental biological laws yet discovered. Segregation and recombination of hereditary traits have been observed in most diverse animals and plants. It would be difficult to count the number of species of organisms in which gene heredity has been observed to occur.

Soon after 1900, examples of Mendelian inheritance were found in man. Of course, controlled hybridization experiments cannot be arranged in man, but this drawback is compensated for by the abundance of data on the distribution of various traits in human families and populations. Let us consider as an example the inheritance of the ability to taste the substance known as phenyl-thio-carbamide (PTC, for short). Solutions of this substance have an intensely bitter taste to about 70 per cent of Americans, but to about 30 per cent they are almost tasteless. The numbers of tasters (those able to taste PTC solutions) and non-tasters (those who find them without taste) in 800 families with 2043 children are summarized in Table 2.1. The

TABLE 2.1

INHERITANCE OF THE ABILITY TO TASTE PTC SOLUTIONS

(After Snyder.)

Number of Families	Parents	Children	
		Tasters	Non-tasters
86	Non-taster × Non-taster (*tt* × *tt*)	5 (?)	218 (*tt*)
289	Taster × Non-taster (*TT* or *Tt* × *tt*)	483 (*Tt*)	278 (*tt*)
425	Taster × Taster (*TT* or *Tt* × *TT* or *Tt*)	929 (*TT* or *Tt*)	130 (*tt*)

explanation which accounts best for the data is that the tasters carry a dominant gene *T*, and the non-tasters are homozygous for its recessive allele, *t*. Marriages between two non-tasters (*tt* × *tt*) should produce only non-taster children. Actually 218 non-tasters and 5 tasters have been recorded. These "exceptions" are due to the fact that some people who are actually "tasters" do not find weak solutions of PTC particularly bitter; in any large material on human heredity the occurrence of some illegitimate children must also be reckoned with. Some of the parents recorded as tasters were doubtless homozygous (*TT*), and others heterozygous (*Tt*), for the gene *T*. Some families in which one or both parents were tasters produced, accordingly, only tasters, whereas others produced both taster and non-taster children (Table 2.1).

Mendelian inheritance of dozens or even hundreds of human traits has been established with varying degrees of certainty. Many of these traits are perfectly "normal." For example, the blue eye color behaves in most families as a recessive to brown (but in other families

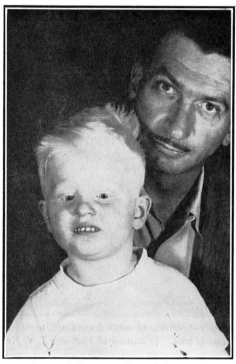

Figure 2.4. An albino boy with his non-albino father. Albinism is due to homozygosis for a recessive gene which prevents the development of pigmentation. (Courtesy of Professor J. V. Neel.)

the situation is more complex, because some people who have the dominant gene for the brown eye color have nevertheless eyes of an indefinite grayish or greenish color). Albinism (virtually pigmentless skin, straw-colored hair, usually pink iris of the eyes, Figure 2.4) is also caused by a recessive gene. Albinos are rare in most human populations; in England about one person in 20,000 is an albino. Albino children are usually born in families in which both parents have the dominant normal pigmentation but are heterozygous for the recessive gene for albinism. A few instances of marriages of two albinos are known, and as expected all the children produced by such marriages are albinos.

Inheritance of Diseases. Many diseases and malformations are caused by defective genes. A recessive gene, which is fortunately rare in most human populations, causes juvenile amaurotic idiocy when homozygous. This disease first manifests itself by failing eye-

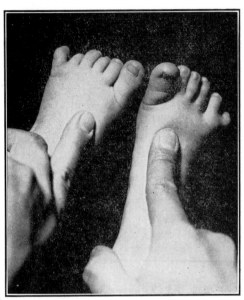

Figure 2.5. Polydactyly—presence of extra fingers and toes. This is inherited as a dominant trait. (Courtesy of Professor J. V. Neel.)

sight in children 4 to 7 years old and leads to blindness, mental deterioration, and finally to death before the age of adolescence. Another recessive gene causes a fatal anemia (Cooley's anemia) in homozygous infants; but the same gene has a slight dominant effect also in the heterozygote, where it causes some abnormality of the red blood cells and a mild anemia. A dominant gene, when heterozygous, causes polydactyly, or the presence of extra fingers (Figure 2.5). Another dominant is responsible for chondrodystrophic dwarfism—very short arms and legs, with a normal-sized head and trunk.

Number of Genes. The number of genes in a sex cell is not known either for man or for any other organism. It is difficult to determine the number of genes because of an important limitation of our methods of studying the genes. Indeed, we discover the existence of a gene by observing Mendelian segregation in progenies of crosses in which the parents differ in some traits. If all men were tasters, or all non-tasters of PTC, we would not so much as suspect that the genes *T-t* exist. As a matter of fact, the discovery that PTC tastes bitter to some but not to other people was made by accident, when one chemist working with this substance felt a discomfort which his non-taster colleague found hard to understand. If albinos were unknown, or if everybody in the world had brown eyes, or only blue eyes, the genes for albinism and for the eye color would remain unknown.

A gene must undergo a change and be represented by at least two alleles before its existence can be ascertained. Very rough estimates of the total number of genes have nevertheless been attempted. These estimates are of the order of 5000 to 15,000 genes in the sex cell of the vinegar fly, Drosophila, and 10,000 to 100,000 genes in a human sex cell.

Mendelian segregation and assortment are observed in the offspring of crosses. Now, crossing or hybridization presupposes that the organisms reproduce sexually. In some lower organisms, especially among bacteria, sexual reproduction was unknown until recently, and the existence of genes in such organisms was not rigorously established until Lederberg found that some strains of the colon bacteria can be crossed. Recombination of traits has recently been found even in bacteriophages, making it probable that these organisms, visible only in electron microscopes, contain several genes. Only the simple viruses such as the tobacco mosaic virus are perhaps comparable to single genes. For this reason they are sometimes referred to as "naked genes."

Some Applications of Mendel's Laws. As stated above, Mendel crossed a variety of peas that had yellow and smooth seeds with a variety that had green and wrinkled seeds. Owing to the recombination of genes he obtained in the F_2 generation of hybrids not two but four varieties: with (1) yellow smooth seeds; (2) yellow wrinkled seeds; (3) green smooth seeds; and (4) green wrinkled seeds.

Crossing, hybridization, evidently may lead to production of new varieties, which is important in the breeding of agricultural crops and animals. Suppose that a variety of wheat is valuable because it is genetically resistant to frost but has the drawback of being susceptible to rust fungi. Another variety has a satisfactory rust resistance but is not frost resistant. It is then expedient to cross these varieties, and to look among the F_2 hybrids for plants resistant both to frost and to rust. Of course plants devoid of either resistance are also likely to appear. Combinations of good as well as of bad genes are impartially produced by the Mendelian segregation. It is, then, the business of the breeder to pick out, to *select*, the valuable combinations of genes. Some of the most valuable crop varieties have been obtained by selection among hybrid progenies derived by crossing two or several less valuable varieties.

When the parents crossed differ in more than two genes the diversity of genetic constitution obtained by recombination may be very great. With three genes eight homozygous gene combinations can be formed among hybrids, with four genes sixteen, with five genes thirty-two, and, in general, with n genes 2^n gene combinations. In some F_2 progenies of parents differing in many genes no two individuals may appear alike.

Gene Differences among Siblings. Segregation and assortment of genes take place not only in the offspring of artificially made crosses. In sexually reproducing organisms the individuals that mate differ usually in many traits and in many genes. Every human being, technically speaking, is a hybrid, a heterozygote, for many pairs of alleles. With 10 heterozygous genes there may be produced 2^{10} (1024) kinds of sex cells with different combinations of genes; with 20 genes, 1,048,576 kinds of sex cells; and with 250 genes, about as many kinds as there are electrons and protons in the universe. Nothing can be more certain than that only a negligibly small fraction of the potentially possible gene combinations in any species are ever realized.

Nature is prodigal in the number of sex cells that are generated in many organisms. In man a single ejaculation contains about 200 million spermatozoa. Suppose that an individual who produces these spermatozoa is heterozygous for thirty or more genes. It becomes unlikely that any two spermatozoa will contain the same combination of genes. Since most people are heterozygous for probably more than thirty genes, it is most unlikely that any two spermatozoa, or any two eggs, have the same genes. In other words, siblings, brothers and sisters, rarely if ever receive the same complements of genes from their parents. Only identical twins, who arise through division of a single fertilized egg, carry the same genes. Unrelated persons would differ, on the average, in more genes than do brothers or sisters. It is, then, a reasonable guess that no two persons alive (identical twins excepted) carry the same genes. Every human being is a carrier of a unique, unprecedented, and probably unrepeatable gene complex. This is true as well for sexually reproducing and cross-fertilizing species other than man.

Genetic Endowments of Parents and Children Compared. According to the "blood" theory, a parent transmits his heredity as a whole to every one of his children. On this basis, if among your ancestors there was a passenger on the *Mayflower*, you would possess a particle of every one of his qualities. In contrast to this, the gene theory shows that every parent transmits to his child only half of the genes which he himself has. The father and the mother of a single child have transmitted to the future generations one-half of their genes, but the other half of the genes which they carry will be irretrievably lost. However, every child gets a somewhat different set of genes from each parent. A parent of two children has transmitted approximately three-quarters of his genes, and failed to transmit one-quarter; a parent of three children has handed down to posterity about seven-eighths, and a parent of n children a fraction $1 - (\frac{1}{2})^n$ of his genes.

Looked at from the progeny point of view, siblings are likely to have approximately half of their genes in common, whereas the other half will be different. The "blood" theory regarded the heredity of a child a fusion product of parental heredities. If this were so, the heredities of brothers and sisters would be similar or even identical. The outcome of hybridization, of sexual union of dissimilar parents, had to be a leveling-off, a neutralization, dissolution, of the differences between the heredities of the varieties crossed. The gene theory leads to precisely opposite conclusions. Sexual reproduction continuously generates new combinations of genes. The diversity of hereditary constitutions is thus maintained and increased by sexual unions, a fact that is of immense importance for evolution. In later chapters it will be shown that sex may be regarded as an adaptation of living matter which permits living matter to secure the evolutionary advantages of gene combination.

Manifold, or Pleiotropic, Effects of Genes. In the examples of Mendelian inheritance discussed above, a gene carried in the sex cells was always spoken of as representing a discrete trait of the adult organism. A gene in peas caused a yellow seed color or a wrinkled seed surface, and in man we found genes "for" tasting PTC, for eye color, for amaurotic idiocy, etc. This way of describing and naming genes is convenient because it is concise; but it is also misleading because it seems to imply that every gene has an exclusive influence on one and only one character. In reality, the gene theory does not assume that the genes are rudiments or representatives of particular body parts or of particular traits. The development of the organism is due to all the genes acting together in concert. All the genes which the organism has interact with the environment, and in so doing they make the fertilized egg develop by stages into a fetus, an infant, a child, an adolescent, an adult, an old man or an old woman, and finally a cadaver. It should always be kept in mind that, despite the shorthand designations which geneticists use in naming genes, many, and probably all, genes influence several or many traits of the organism which carries them. Genes have *manifold* or *pleiotropic* effects.

Some early geneticists liked to speak of genes determining "unit characters"; yet pleiotropism of genes was known already to Mendel. He crossed a variety of peas with purple flowers, brown seeds, and a dark spot on the axils of the leaves to a variety with white flowers, light seeds, and no axillary spot on the leaves. In the segregation observed in the hybrids, the just-mentioned traits of the flowers, seeds, and leaves always stayed together as a unit. Their inheritance can be accounted for by a single gene which visibly influences several traits.

The work of Morgan (1866–1945) has made the vinegar fly (*Drosophila melanogaster*) and its relatives classical materials for genetic studies. One of the variants (mutants) differs from normal (wild-type) flies of this species by having vestigial wings (Figure 4.5). The cross vestigial $\times$ normal gives an F_1 progeny with normal wings and a segregation in a ratio 3 normal : 1 vestigial in the F_2 generation. The gene for vestigial (vg) is, accordingly, recessive to that for normal wings (Vg). Careful comparison of vestigial and normal flies discloses, however, that the wing size is by no means the only difference between them. Vestigial flies have also the third joint of the halteres (balancers) rudimentary, a certain pair of bristles on the body erect instead of flat, and some of the reproductive organs changed in shape. Moreover, vestigial flies deposit fewer eggs than normal, their life is on the average shorter, and their larvae are the losers if they are made to compete with normal larvae in crowded cultures. To a human observer, the wing size is certainly the most striking difference between vestigial and normal flies. To the flies, the differences in fecundity, longevity, and viability may be more important.

Examples of manifold effects of genes could be multiplied at will. Studies on hereditary diseases in man and in higher animals have shown that the genes produce not single traits but more or less complex systems, or *syndromes,* of characters. These syndromes often include changes in many body parts, organ systems, and physiological functions of the organism.

The origin of pleiotropism is easy to understand. The genes bring about the development of the organism through physiological, and ultimately biochemical, processes in the cells, tissues, organs, and the whole body. The genes produce, or influence the production of, enzymes which are so important in cell metabolism. It may be that every gene is responsible for the production of one and only one enzyme; on the other hand, it is possible that the same gene, at any rate in higher organisms, makes different enzymes in different tissues and at different stages of development in the same tissue. However that may be, a change or a removal of an enzyme may alter profoundly the metabolism of cells and of the body. An alteration of this sort may result in a group, a syndrome, of changes.

"Characters" Are Abstractions. To think that genes determine characters is misleading because a "character" or a "trait" is an abstraction which an observer makes to facilitate the description of his observations. For example, a manual of anatomy contains thousands of names for parts, ridges, holes, and other structural details of bones, muscles, and other organs. We may say that each name corresponds to a "character," but the number of the structures named is limited only by the convenience of those who have to talk and write about these structures. Yet a critic of genetics argued that if we must assume one or more genes for each structure, the number of genes will be infinite, hence the genes do not exist!

The solution of this imaginary difficulty is simple enough. The organism with all its "characters" is an outcome of a process of development, which is a system of physiological, and ultimately physicochemical events. In the last analysis, these events are by-products of the self-reproduction of the genes. Characters or traits which we observe are the outward signs of the occurrence of the development process. How many characters we observe depends on how we look at the organism, on how careful and detailed our studies are, and above all on how we choose to describe our observations. But the genes are there, independent of how we talk or write about them.

Interaction of Genes in Development. Every gene may affect many visible traits; most traits are influenced by several or by many genes. Interaction of gene effects in development may lead to some extremely complex situations which are at first sight quite different from simple Mendelian inheritance. Analysis of situations of this sort in terms of the gene theory was one of the outstanding problems of genetics during the first decades of its existence (roughly, from 1900 till 1920).

Breeds of domestic and laboratory animals show quite a variety of coat colors. In horses, cattle, sheep, cats, dogs, rabbits, guinea pigs, mice, rats, poultry, pigeons, canary birds, and other species the coat and plumage colors are determined by interaction of numerous genes. We choose the inheritance of the coat colors in horses as an example, although there is no agreement among the investigators about the interpretation of some parts of this complex subject.

Coat Color in Horses. The entire coat of some horses, including the mane, tail, muzzle, and lower parts of the legs, is chestnut (sorrel) in color. Mating of chestnut stallions and mares gives only chestnut foals. Chestnut is due to homozygosis for a recessive gene, *b*. The dominant allele, *B*, of the gene turns chestnut into black. Black horses are either homozygous, *BB*, or heterozygous, *Bb*, for this gene. Another dominant gene, *I*, turns black into bay—a brownish coat with black mane, tail, muzzle, and lower parts of legs. A black horse, then, is always homozygous for the recessive allele, *ii*, in addition to having at least one dominant *B* (Figure 2.6). But neither *I* nor *i* has any visible effects in the absence of *B*; accordingly, chestnut horses may or may not carry *I*. As a result, horses of these colors may have the following genetic constitutions:

Chestnut	Black	Bay
bb ii	*BB ii*	*BB II*
bb Ii	*Bb ii*	*Bb II*
bb II		*BB Ii*
		Bb Ii

The matings black × black produce, then, either only black or black and chestnut foals. Black × chestnut may give black, chestnut, and bay. All three colors may also appear in the matings bay × bay, bay × black, and bay × chestnut. Addition of a further dominant, *D*, transforms the coat into dun (dilute yellow), sand-colored ("buckskin"), or bluish ("mouse") coat, with black or chestnut mane, tail, muzzle, lower parts of legs, and a stripe on the middle of the back. Chestnut, black, and bay horses are, then, homozygous, *dd*, for the recessive allele, *d* (= non-dun). The dun color (*BBIIDD*) is characteristic of the wild horse of Mongolia (*Equus przewalskii*), which is one of the progenitors of the domestic horse. A race of the same species, known as tarpan, lived in the steppes of Eastern Europe until it was finally destroyed a century ago (see Chapter 9). This race was mouse colored and probably had the genes *BBiiDD*.

Two further genes, *G* and *R*, make the horse respectively gray and roan. A foal homozygous or heterozygous for *G* (*GG* or *Gg*) is born

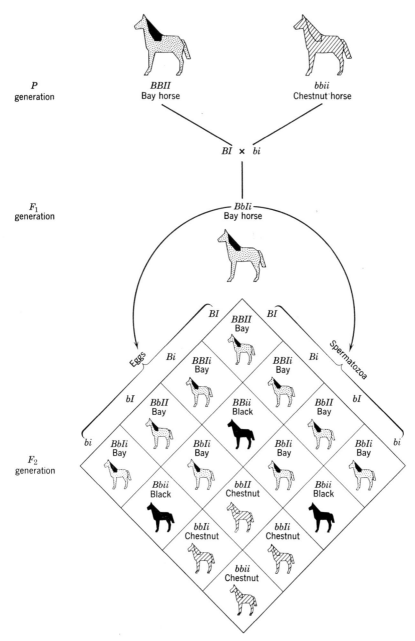

Figure 2.6. Inheritance of some of the pelage colors in horses. Cross of a bay and a chestnut (sorrel) horse gives bay in F_1, and bay, black, and chestnut in the F_2 generation. The bay color is produced by simultaneous presence of the genes I and B; B without I gives black, whereas homozygosis for b yields chestnut regardless of whether I is or is not present.

with only a few white hairs scattered in an otherwise chestnut, black, bay, or dun coat (depending on the other genes). The proportion of white hairs rapidly increases, however, with age, making the horse first dappled gray and eventually white (with black skin). The gene for roan (R) acts in a different way: it causes the appearance of rather numerous white hairs interspersed with hairs of other colors, the amount of white not greatly increasing with age.

There are several further genes the effects of which on the coat color are not completely understood. A dominant gene causes the horse to be pied with large white areas on the trunk (pied, piebald, or pinto horses). The presence of white markings on the face and on the lower parts of the legs seems, however, due to a quite different gene, which is recessive to its "normal" allele, causing absence of white markings on these parts. A "white" horse, having a light skin (that is, not an old gray), may be due to extreme development of the "pinto" markings. There is another gene, however, which gives a white coat when homozygous and a characteristic pale ("palomino") coat in heterozygous condition.

Polygenic Inheritance. Analysis of such traits as the coat color in horses is facilitated by the fact that most of the genes which influence the trait produce discrete and easily perceptible effects. Very often, however, the trait is caused by interaction of several or many genes, each of which taken separately produces only a small effect. Such genes are referred to as *multiple genes* or *polygenes*.

Inheritance of the Skin Color in Man. Davenport has suggested (1913) that the difference in skin color between Negroes and whites may be due to the cooperation of two pairs of genes without dominance. This view undoubtedly oversimplifies the situation. Considerably more than two pairs of genes influence the skin color in man. To explain the principle of polygenic inheritance, let us assume three pairs of pigment genes, such that a Negro has the genetic structure $P_1P_1P_2P_2P_3P_3$, and a white, $p_1p_1p_2p_2p_3p_3$. Each gene denoted by a capital letter causes production in the skin of a certain amount of dark pigment. The effects of different genes are additive; that is, each gene adds a certain amount of pigment regardless of presence or absence of other pigment genes. A Negro, then, would carry six pigment genes, and a white no pigment genes (this is admittedly inexact, since whites who are not albinos always have some skin pigment).

A Negro $\times$ white marriage produces F_1 hybrids (mulattoes), who should be $P_1p_1P_2p_2P_3p_3$. With three pigment genes the mulattoes have, on the assumptions made, half as much skin pigment as the

Negro parent. A mulatto produces, then, eight kinds of sex cells, with the genes $P_1P_2P_3$, $P_1P_2p_3$, $P_1p_2P_3$, $p_1P_2P_3$, $P_1p_2p_3$, $p_1P_2p_3$, $p_1p_2P_3$, and $p_1p_2p_3$. Accordingly, marriages of mulattoes will give progenies of the genetic constitution shown in Figure 2.7. It can be seen that almost a third—20 out of 64 mulattoes—of the F_2 generation will carry three pigment genes and will accordingly have about the same skin color as the mulattoes of the F_1 generation. Almost a half—30 out of

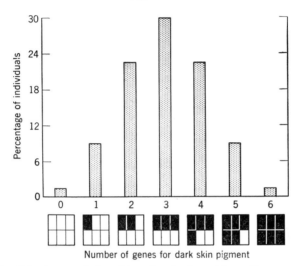

Figure 2.7. Inheritance of the skin color in the white × Negro cross, on the assumption that the color difference is due to three pairs of pigment genes which exhibit no dominance. The heights of the bars in the diagram show the percentages among the second generation hybrids of individuals with no, with one, two, three, four, five, and six color-producing genes.

64—will have two or four pigment genes and will have somewhat lighter or somewhat darker skins than the average F_1 mulatto. About six in 64 will have five pigment genes and will be intermediate between Negro and mulatto, and about the same number will have one pigment gene and a skin intermediate between mulatto and white. And only a minority—one out of 64—will have six pigment genes and full Negro skin color or no pigment genes and a white skin color.

Marriages of mulattoes and Negroes or of mulattoes and whites produce children most of whom have skin colors intermediate between those in the parents. Indeed, with three pairs of pigment genes at play, three-eighths of the sex cells of the mulattoes would have two pigment genes, three-eighths, one pigment gene, one-eighth, three pigment genes, and one-eighth, no pigment genes (Figure 2.7). The mulatto × Negro cross would, then, give three-eighths of the children with five pigment genes, three-eighths with four, and one-eighth each with six and with three pigment genes. The mulatto × white cross would give three-eighths of the progeny with two pigment genes, three-eighths with one, and one-eighth each with three and with no pigment genes. Marriages between mulattoes and either whites or Negroes give mostly children intermediate between the parents in their skin color.

"Blending" Inheritance. Polygenic inheritance was the last type of hereditary transmission to be analyzed in terms of genes. The more multiple genes participate in the formation of a trait, the smaller are the visible effects of each separate gene, and the more difficult is the analysis of the "blending" of the characters which is observed. The inheritance caused by polygenes certainly resembles what was popularly believed to be heredity through "blood." As pointed out above, the difference in the skin color between Negroes and whites is caused by probably more than three pairs of genes. Different "whites" vary in skin color—from albinotic to tan—and this variation quite apart from the color variations due to skin exposure to sunlight. African Negroes are likewise variable in skin color. It is probable that some pigment genes are scattered in white populations and some genes for lightness of the skin in Negro populations. Races differ mostly in relative frequencies of genes in their populations (see Chapter 7).

Varieties and breeds of agricultural plants and animals and also races and species of all organisms differ most often in traits caused by polygenes. Classical Mendelism dealt chiefly with clearly alternative traits, which can easily be described as present or absent in a given individual. Most men are either tasters or non-tasters of PTC, either albinos or non-albinos, either brachydactylous or with normal fingers, etc. Polygenic traits are usually matters of "more or less" of some quality. Such *quantitative characters* are described by measurement or weighing, and studies of their inheritance require application of often recondite statistical techniques, which have been evolved and perfected especially in recent years.

The polygenes and the genes with discrete major effects are not basically different kinds of genetic units. All conceivable intermediate situations exist. Substitution of a gene for its allele may cause a drastic change in the organism; or the change may be slight; or it may be so minute that statistical techniques are needed for its detection. The difference between major genes and polygenes lies not in their nature but in the techniques used for their study.

Suggestions for Further Reading

Sinnott, E. W., Dunn, L. C., and Dobzhansky, Th. 1950. *Principles of Genetics.* 4th Edition. McGraw-Hill, New York.

This is one of the several available textbooks of general genetics, containing an outline of the main facts and concepts of this science.

Mendel, G. J. 1866. *Experiments on plant hybridization.*

Translated from the original German by William Bateson. This paper appears as an Appendix in the book by Sinnott, Dunn, and Dobzhansky, referred to above. Mendel's paper is a true classic, and it should be read by every student of genetics and of evolution as a splendid example of the application of scientific method in modern experimental science.

Gates, R. R. 1946. *Human Genetics.* Macmillan, New York.

Neel, J. W., and Schull, W. J. 1954. *Human Heredity.* University of Chicago Press, Chicago.

Sorsby, A. (Editor). 1953. *Clinical Genetics.* Butterworth, London.

Stern, C. 1949. *Principles of Human Genetics.* W. H. Freeman, San Francisco.

These four books are concerned specifically with the genetics of man, although Stern's contains an excellent outline of general genetics as well. Sorsby's book, as its name implies, is devoted chiefly to the description of the genetically conditioned diseases. Gates' book is useful as an extended compilation and bibliography of human genetics up to the time of the Second World War.

Mather, R. 1949. *Biometrical Genetics.* Dover Publications, New York.

Lerner, I. M. 1950. *Population Genetics and Animal Improvement.* Cambridge, London.

The books by Mather and Lerner deal with the rapidly developing field of study of quantitative or polygenic traits, and the mathematical and statistical methods used in this study.

3

Chromosomes as Gene Carriers

Almost 400 years ago the versatile philosopher Montaigne admitted being completely baffled by the mystery of heredity. He thought that he had inherited from his father a disease—a stone in the bladder; but his father suffered from this disease some years after Montaigne was born. How, then, could the father transmit to his son something which he himself did not have at the time the son was conceived? And, besides, the semen was believed to be mere liquid. How could a liquid transmit a stone in the bladder?

To dispel even a part of the mystery which worried Montaigne much biology had to be learned. At present we would say that Montaigne did not inherit a stone in the bladder; what he inherited were genes which engendered a constitution, a development pattern, which included a predisposition towards formation of bladder stones. Furthermore, we know that the genes have a physical basis in the chromosomes in the nuclei of the sex cells, which are highly organized structures with complex and orderly behavior that makes heredity possible. The physical basis of heredity is necessarily also the physical basis of evolution.

Sex Cells and Fertilization. Leonardo da Vinci (1452–1519), who was so much ahead of his times in so many things, realized the basic fact that the father and mother contribute equally to the heredity of the child, as shown by the following quotation: "The black races of Ethiopia are not the products of the sun: for if black gets black with child in Scythia, the offspring is black. But if a black gets a white woman with child, the offspring is gray. And this shows that the seed of the mother has power in the fetus equally with that of the father." From Aristotle on, until as late as the eighteenth century, most people

44

believed that the mother furnishes inert matter and the father imparts the motion to the new life. Spallanzani (1729–1799) found, however, that this "motion" was not due to some immaterial essence in the seminal fluid of the male, as others supposed; he showed that the seminal fluid of the frog lost its ability to fertilize the eggs after a passage through a filter. The fertilizing agent is not a simple liquid.

We could not go much beyond this without making use of a new instrument invented and gradually perfected a generation before Spallanzani's—the microscope. Using microscopes, Leeuwenhoek, Swammerdam, and others discovered that the seminal fluid contains "animalcules"—spermatozoa (see Chapter 10). At about the same time, de Graaf and others found that female mammals produced eggs like birds and frogs, only much smaller. But more than a century had to elapse, and more powerful microscopes had to be manufactured, before Oskar Hertwig (1849–1922) finally, in 1876, saw the eggs of a sea urchin being fertilized by spermatozoa, and was able to discern that the most significant event in the process is the union of two about equal nuclei, that of the egg and that of the sperm. Very soon thereafter Weismann, Roux, Hertwig himself, and others realized that the phenomenon of the fusion of the nuclei during fertilization explains the equal potency of the female and the male in the transmission of heredity from parents to the progeny. The sex cells, eggs and spermatozoa, in most organisms are as strikingly unlike as cells can be. Yet they contain similar parts—their nuclei and chromosomes. The inference was then clear: the material basis of heredity resides primarily in the nuclei and their chromosomes.

The quarter of the century immediately preceding the rediscovery of Mendel's laws, roughly from 1875 till 1900, saw a rapid development of *cytology,* the study of the cell. The following quarter of a century, approximately 1900–1925, brought an even more rapid progress of *cytogenetics,* a synthesis of the findings of cytology and genetics concerning the mechanisms of the transmission of heredity.

Nuclei and Chromosomes. Cell nuclei were described by Brown in 1831, even before the promulgation of the cell theory by Schleiden and Schwann in 1839. Soon thereafter (in 1848) Hofmeister observed the process of division of living cells in the plant spiderwort (Tradescantia). He saw in the nuclei of dividing cells rod-like bodies, which later were found to stain deeply in fixed preparations by certain dyes, and called since 1888 *chromosomes* (stainable bodies). These staining reactions are now known to be due to the class of substances called nucleoproteins, and particularly desoxyribose nucleic acids (DNA), which all chromosomes contain.

The number of chromosomes in a nucleus was found, with few exceptions, to be constant for a species. In many organisms different chromosomes in the cell nuclei are recognizably different from each other. This led Boveri (1862–1915), Wilson (1856–1939), Navashin, and others (around 1900) to the correct inference that chromosomes are unlike in their genetic contents (Figures 3.1 and 3.2).

Strasburger, Bütschli, Fleming, Roux, and others found that cells divide usually by a remarkably precise mechanism called *mitosis* (Figure 3.3). Mitosis begins with a *prophase* stage, when chromosomes appear in the nucleus as slender threads, which are often composed of bead-like *chromomeres*. The chromomeres may be of different sizes and shapes, making each chromosome in a nucleus recognizable by a definite sequence of large and small chromomeres following each other in a longitudinal file. The constancy of the chromomere pattern is visible evidence of the chromosome being longitudinally differentiated into qualitatively different segments. This differentiation reflects the constant linear arrangement of the genes (see page 58).

The chromomere structure of the chromosomes is particularly evident in the giant chromosomes of cells of the salivary glands of larvae of certain flies (Figure 3.4). These giant chromosomes, first described by Balbiani in 1881, and correctly interpreted by Heitz, Bauer, and Painter in 1933, are used extensively in genetic and evolutionary research.

The prophase stage is followed by *metaphase*. The chromosomes shorten and thicken (by being thrown into a fine spiral). A spindle-shaped figure, composed of thin fibers or threads, arises in the cytoplasm. The nuclear membrane disappears, and the chromosomes become arranged, usually in a single plane, midway between the poles of the spindle. The chromosomes now divide longitudinally into exactly equal halves, and during the *anaphase* the halves pass to the opposite poles of the spindle. The cell also divides, the chromosomes enter the *telophase* and form the nuclei of the daughter cells (Figure 3.3).

In most organisms the disjunction of the daughter halves of the chromosomes and their distribution to the poles of the mitotic spindle are governed by the *centromeres*. A centromere is a specialized segment of the chromosome, permanently fixed in position, which seems to act as the insertion point of the fiber connecting the chromosome with the pole of the spindle.

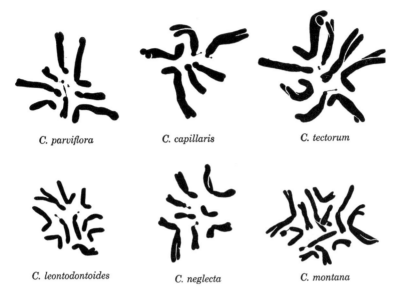

C. parviflora   C. capillaris   C. tectorum

C. leontodontoides   C. neglecta   C. montana

Figure 3.1. Chromosomes of six species of Crepis (plants of the sunflower family). Each pair of chromosomes differs from all others in its relative size and in shape. (After Babcock.)

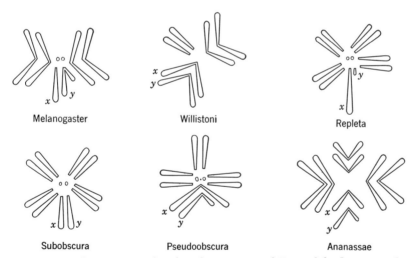

Melanogaster   Willistoni   Repleta

Subobscura   Pseudoobscura   Ananassae

Figure 3.2. Chromosomes of males of six species of Drosophila flies. x and y denote the X- and Y-chromosomes. (After Patterson and Stone and other sources.)

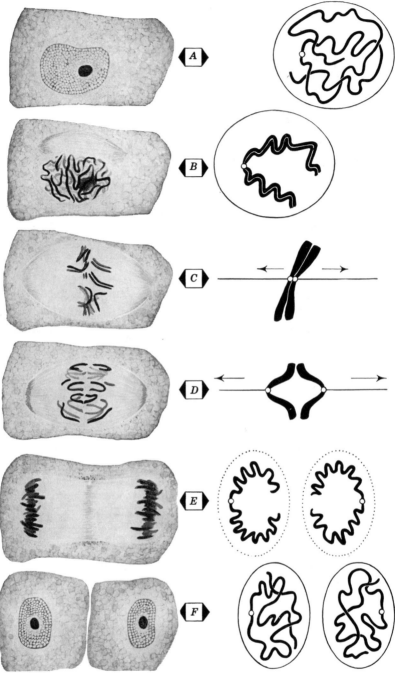

Figure 3.3. Mitotic cell division in root tip of the common onion (*Allium cepa*). The diagrammatic drawings represent the behavior of a single chromosome at different stages of mitosis. *A*, interphase; *B*, prophase; *C*, metaphase; *D*, anaphase; *E*, telophase; *F*, the daughter nuclei. (After Belar, modified.)

Between the successive mitoses the cell nucleus is in the *interphase*. The chromosomes become diffuse and usually not visible as discrete bodies. During interphase the genes reproduce themselves, that is, synthesize their copies. This can be inferred, among other things, from the fact that the DNA content of the nucleus becomes doubled

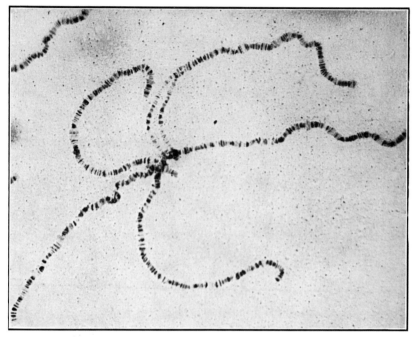

Figure 3.4. The giant chromosomes in a cell of the salivary gland of a larva of the fly *Drosophila melanogaster*. (Courtesy of Dr. Jack Schultz.)

during the interphase. The name, "the resting stage," applied to the interphase by old cytologists is, then, most inappropriate. The lack of the visible activity during the interphase, activity which is so obvious during mitosis, is contrasted with intense physiological work. Mitosis is an impressively efficient mechanism which insures accurate distribution of genes from one cell generation to the other.

Meiosis. Fertilization brings about fusion of the nuclei of the uniting sex cells or *gametes*. The uniting gametes normally contain *haploid* sets of chromosomes. In man the haploid nucleus contains 24 chromosomes, in the fly *Drosophila melanogaster* 4 chromosomes, in corn (maize) 10 chromosomes. A zygote which arises from the union

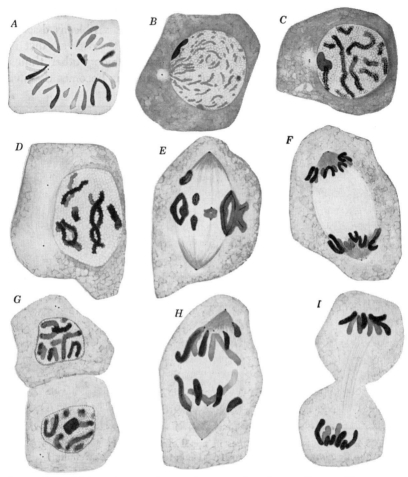

Figure 3.5.　Meiosis in a male grasshopper (Stenobothrus).　A. Chromosome complement in a spermatogonial cell, showing the diploid set of chromosomes. B. Early prophase in a primary spermatocyte.　C. Pachytene stage in a primary spermatocyte, showing the paternal and maternal chromosomes united in pairs. D. Diplotene stage, showing the paired chromosomes (bivalents) held together by chiasmata.　E. Metaphase or early anaphase of the first meiotic division, showing the bivalent chromosomes on the spindle.　F. Telophase of the first meiotic division, the halves of the bivalents have disjoined and passed to the opposite poles of the spindle.　G. The two cells (secondary spermatocytes) resulting from the first meiotic division.　H. Anaphase of the second meiotic division, showing a haploid set of chromosomes passing to each pole.　I. Telophase of the second meiotic division, resulting in formation of cells (spermatids) containing single chromosomes of each kind which the species possesses. (After Belar, modified.)

of the gametes contains the sum of the chromosomes which were carried in the gametes. The *diploid* chromosome numbers are 48 in man, 8 in *Drosophila melanogaster*, 20 in corn.

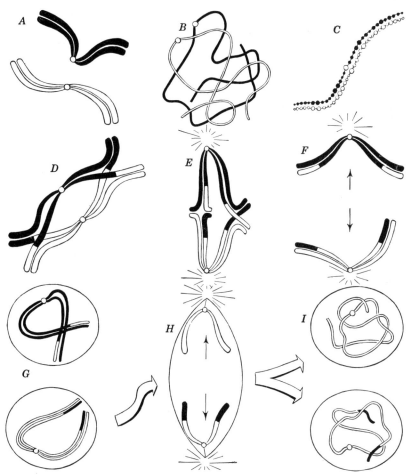

Figure 3.6. Diagrammatic representation of the stages of meiosis shown in Figure 3.5. The diagrams show only a single pair of chromosomes, the paternal chromosome being represented black and the maternal white. The centromeres are shown as white circles.

Sooner or later the diploid zygote must give rise to haploid gametes. This change is accomplished by a remarkable modification of the mitotic cell division, known as *meiosis*. In scme lower organisms meiosis occurs almost immediately after the formation of the zygote by fertilization; in higher organisms the body consists of diploid cells, and meiosis takes place in the sex glands or in the flower buds. However, the essential features of meiosis, like those of mitosis, are similar in otherwise diverse organisms. We are evidently dealing here with a fundamental life process.

The events which constitute meiosis may be seen in Figures 3.5 and 3.6. A diploid cell enters what resembles at first a mitotic prophase, but at the *pachytene* (or *zygotene*) stage the corresponding (homologous) maternal and paternal chromosomes approach each other and pair side by side. Where the chromosomes are differentiated into chromomeres it can be seen that the pairing is very exact: the homologous chromomeres lie side by side. The attraction forces which bring together the homologous chromomeres must be amazingly specific. Every one of the many genes in the nucleus finds without fail its proper partner. In any case, the chromosome pairing reduces the diploid number of single chromosomes to a haploid number of paired *bivalents.*

At the transition between the pachytene and the *diplotene* stages (Figures 3.5 and 3.6) the chromosomes become visibly divided. The bivalents consist now of two pairs of chromosome strands. In most, although not in all, organisms the pairs of strands can be seen to be held together by *chiasmata.* A chiasma involves an exchange, or crossing over, of sections between the paired chromosomes, and produces chromosome strands composed of parts of the maternal and the paternal chromosomes. Because of the chiasma formation the chromosomes are not inherited as units. Blocks of genes are exchanged between homologous chromosomes (see below).

After the diplotene, the chromosomes shorten (*diakinesis*), and the nucleus undergoes two *meiotic divisions* during which no further division of the chromosomes takes place (Figures 3.5 and 3.6). Consequently, each of the four nuclei resulting from meiosis contains a haploid chromosome complement. The fate of the four nuclei is different in different cases. In the spermatogenesis of animals each nucleus gives rise to a spermatozoon; in oögenesis three of the four nuclei are thrown out into "polar bodies," and only the fourth becomes the nucleus of the egg; in higher plants meiosis gives rise to macrospores and microspores, which produce respectively the embryo sacs with the ovules and the pollen grains. But in all cases the gametes come to contain haploid sets of chromosomes.

Correlation of Genes and Chromosomes. Linkage. In 1902 Sutton in the United States and Boveri in Germany independently pointed out that the behavior of chromosomes as seen under the microscope parallels the behavior of genes as deduced from the Mendelian ex-

Figure 3.7.   T. H. Morgan (1866–1945).

periments on segregation and recombination. If we assume that genes are borne in the chromosomes, the segregation and assortment of genes follow as a consequence. The developments of this basic idea have unified the once independent sciences of cytology and genetics in a single body of knowledge.

In 1910 Morgan (Figure 3.7) commenced his classical experiments on the fly, *Drosophila melanogaster*. This species has four pairs of chromosomes (diploid). But very soon Morgan had considerably more than four variants (mutants), differing in various visible body traits, which showed Mendelian inheritance in crosses with normal flies and with each other. However, in some of these crosses certain traits failed to show the expected independent assortment. Examples of such crosses are shown in Figures 3.8 and 3.9.

When a fly with vestigial wings but with a normal, gray, body color is crossed with a fly which has a black body but normal wings, the F_1 hybrids are wild-type, that is, have normal wings and a normal body color. Vestigial wings are, then, recessive to normal wings, and black is recessive to the normal gray. Let these hybrids be backcrossed to a double recessive strain with vestigial wings and black bodies. According to Mendel's second law, the hybrids should produce four kinds of gametes in equal numbers, and the progeny of the backcross should consist of black-vestigial, black, vestigial, and wild-type flies in equal proportions (1 : 1 : 1 : 1).

This expectation is not realized. When F_1 hybrid *males* are backcrossed to black vestigial females the offspring are vestigial gray-bodied and black long-winged flies in equal numbers (Figure 3.8). When F_1 hybrid *females* are used, the four expected classes appear in the offspring, but not in equal numbers. The parental combinations of genes, that is, the vestigial gray and the black long-winged flies constitute about 83 per cent of the progeny. The products of recombination of genes, wild-type and black vestigial flies, make up only about 17 per cent of the progeny.

Morgan saw that this infringement of Mendel's second law is expected if the genes for the black body color and for vestigial wings are borne on the same chromosome. The F_1 hybrids shown in Figures 3.8 and 3.9 carry one chromosome with the normal allele of vestigial and the gene for black. The genes in a chromosome are *linked* in inheritance. At present more than 500 genes are known in *Drosophila melanogaster*. They fall into four linkage groups, corresponding to the 4 chromosomes in the haploid set of this species. In maize ten linkage groups are known that correspond to the ten chromosomes in the haploid set. In the mouse thirteen linkage groups are known; seven more linkage groups remain to be discovered, since the haploid set consists of 20 chromosomes.

Linear Arrangement of Genes. The linkage of genes located in a chromosome need not be absolute. In the vestigial $\times$ black cross 17 per cent of recombination appeared in the offspring of F_1 hybrid females (Figure 3.9). The occurrence of chiasmata (page 52), of the exchanges of sections between the paired paternal and maternal chromosomes at meiosis, is responsible for this recombination of linked genes. Morgan advanced the hypothesis that the frequency of recombination is a function of the distance between the genes in the chromosome. Other things being equal, the farther apart the genes are, the more likely it is that a chiasma will be formed between them. Neighboring genes in a chromosome are strongly linked; those farther apart are exchanged more frequently. Of course the likelihood of chiasma formation depends on many things besides the distance between the genes. It happens that in the spermatogenesis of male Drosophila no chiasmata are formed in the chromosomes. Accordingly, no recombination of linked genes takes place in the offspring of hybrid Drosophila males.

Morgan's hypothesis was amply confirmed and developed by Bridges, Muller, Sturtevant, and others. Numerous experiments were carried out in which the recombination of linked genes was studied in hybrids of Drosophila and in other organisms. Sturtevant found a regularity which holds strictly for rather closely linked genes: namely, if the frequency of recombination between genes A and B is x, and between B and C is y, then the recombination between A and C is either $x + y$ or $x - y$. Such a relationship is expected if the genes A, B, and C are arranged in the chromosome in a single linear file. Although complications arise with loosely linked genes, the experimental data as a whole are consistent with the theory.

This theory has enabled geneticists to map the distribution of genes in the chromosomes of genetically well-known species. Figure 3.10 shows maps of this sort for the most thoroughly studied form, *Drosophila melanogaster*. These "genetic" maps indicate which genes belong to each linkage group; the order in which the genes of a given linkage group are arranged in the chromosome; and the "distances" between the genes, expressed in "map units," which, in turn, represent the frequencies of recombination between the genes expressed in percentages.

Genetic chromosome maps, all of them less detailed than those shown in Figure 3.10, now exist for several species of Drosophila, for maize, for peas (Pisum), sweet peas (Lathyrus), beans, morning glory, the fungus Neurospora, the mouse. Very sketchy maps, showing the location of very few genes, exist for some chromosomes of about two dozen more species of plants and animals, including man.

Sex Chromosomes. During the early years of the current century, Wilson, Sutton, McClung, Montgomery, Stevens, and others investigated some remarkable differences observed between the chromosomes of females and males in many organisms. In some grasshoppers and

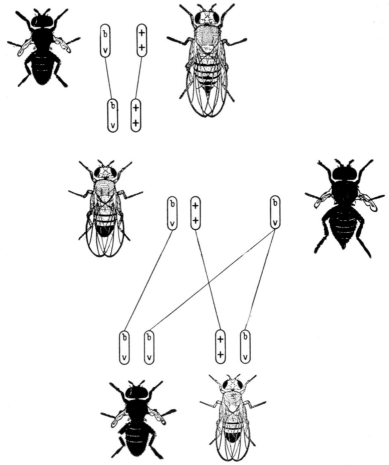

Figure 3.8. Linkage of the genes for the black body color (b) and vestigial wing (v) in *Drosophila melanogaster*. The alleles of these genes giving the normal gray body color, and normal wings are symbolized by +. The linkage in this cross is complete because the F_1 hybrid heterozygote is a male. (From C. Stern.)

bugs the males have one chromosome fewer than the females. The chromosome numbers in females are even; those in males are odd. At meiosis in spermatogenesis one of the chromosomes is left unpaired, and at the meiotic divisions passes into half of the cells. As a result, half of the spermatozoa carry the unpaired chromosome, called the X-chromosome, and the others are free of it. In oögenesis, meiosis is

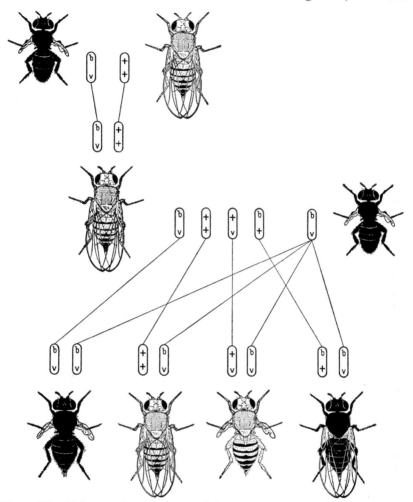

Figure 3.9. Linkage and crossing-over of the genes for the black body color and vestigial wings in *Drosophila melanogaster*. The meaning of the symbols is like that in Figure 3.8. Crossing over occurs in the F_1 hybrid heterozygous female. (From C. Stern.)

normal, all the chromosomes form pairs, and all the eggs have the same chromosome complements, including the X-chromosome.

The X-chromosomes are concerned with sex determination. If an egg is fertilized by an X-carrying spermatozoon, the resulting individual will have two X-chromosomes, and will be a female. But if a spermatozoon without an X fertilizes an egg, the result is an odd number of chromosomes, a single X-chromosome, and a male.

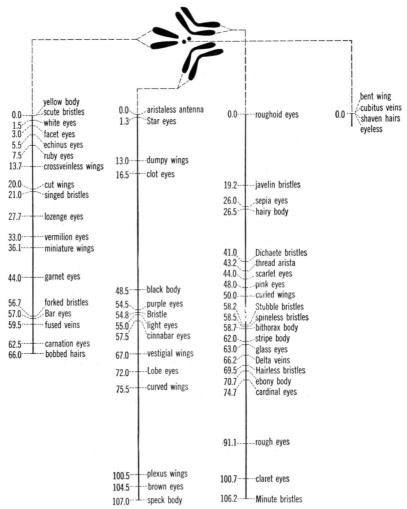

Figure 3.10.   Genetic maps of the chromosomes of *Drosophila melanogaster*, showing the relative positions in the chromosomes of some of the genes known in this organism.

In many organisms, the chromosome number is equal and even in both sexes, but the male has one of the chromosome pairs which consists of unequal members (Figure 3.2). This is the case in many flies, including Drosophila, in many beetles, and in mammals, including man (Figure 3.11). The female has two X-chromosomes, and all eggs con-

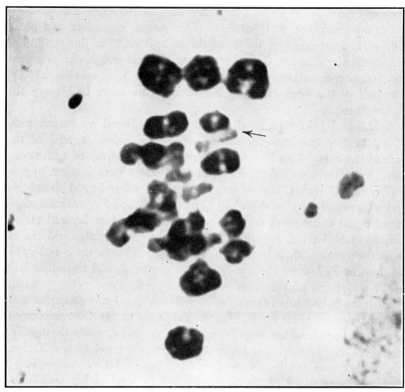

Figure 3.11. Human chromosomes, shown as meiotic bivalents in a spermatocyte. The bivalent containing the sex-determining X- and Y-chromosomes is indicated by an arrow. (Courtesy of Dr. Jack Schultz.)

tain a single X. The male has one X- and one Y-chromosome. At meiosis the X and the Y pair and form an "unequal bivalent." At the meiotic divisions the X and the Y separate and pass to different cells. Half of the spermatozoa carry the X-chromosome, and the other half carry the Y. When an egg is fertilized by an X-bearing spermatozoon the result is an XX zygote, which is a female. A spermatozoon with a Y-chromosome gives an XY individual, which is a male.

For example, in man half of the spermatozoa carry 24 chromosomes, including an X-chromosome, and half contain 24 chromosomes, including a Y. All the eggs have 24 chromosomes, one of which is the X-chromosome. Fertilization restores the diploid chromosome complement, 48; but in about half the cases this complement will contain two X-chromosomes, and will give a girl. The other half of the fertilized eggs will carry an X- and a Y-chromosome, and will give a boy.

Curiously enough, in birds, butterflies, moths, some fish, and probably in at least some of the amphibians and reptiles, the conditions are reversed. Namely, it is the male which has two X-chromosomes and forms spermatozoa all of which carry an X. Females are XY, and half of the eggs carry an X, whereas the other half carry the Y-chromosome.

Sex-Linked Inheritance. In 1910 Morgan found a mutant individual of *Drosophila melanogaster* which had white instead of the normal red eyes. This fly was the progenitor of a strain of white-eyed flies. When white-eyed females from this strain were crossed to normal red-eyed males, the offspring consisted of red-eyed daughters and white-eyed sons, as shown in Figure 3.12. The F_2 generation had about equal numbers of white-eyed and red-eyed females and males. The reciprocal cross, normal, red-eyed females to white-eyed males, gave the result shown in Figure 3.13. The F_1 flies were red-eyed, whereas in F_2 half of the males were white-eyed, and the other half of the males and all the females were red-eyed.

This sex-linked inheritance follows if the dominant gene for red, and its recessive allele for white, eyes are borne in the X-chromosomes. The Y-chromosome has no allele of this gene. A male derives his single X-chromosome from his mother; a female receives one X from her mother and another X from her father. A father transmits his X-chromosome to all of his daughters but to none of his sons. The Y-chromosome is transmitted from father to sons only in the male line.

An interesting historical detail is that in 1910 Morgan's hypothesis did not appear to be free of difficulties. Proposing this hypothesis required a great deal of courage. Indeed, it so happened that, before the studies of Drosophila, sex-linked inheritance was discovered in a species of moth. But moths, as indicated above, have a sex-determining mechanism which is the reverse of that in Drosophila, XX males and XY females. Accordingly the sex-linked inheritance in moths is also reversed: a female transmits her sex-linked genes to all of her sons but to none of her daughters. In 1910 the sex chromosomes of Drosophila and of moths had not been studied cytologically, and all the insects which had been examined had XY males (or XO males, devoid of Y-chromosomes). The inheritance of genes and the inheritance of chromosomes did not seem to agree very well.

Since 1910 a great deal of information relevant to the theory has been accumulated. In poultry and certain other birds, males were found cytologically to have two X-chromosomes and females an X- and

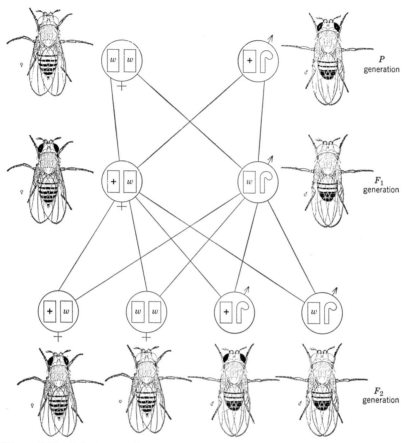

Figure 3.12. Inheritance of a gene carried in the sex chromosome. A white-eyed female of *Drosophila melanogaster* is outcrossed to a red-eyed male, and the F_1 progeny are inbred. The symbols w and $+$ stand for the genes for the white and the red eye colors, respectively; the X-chromosomes are shown rectangular and the Y-chromosomes hook-shaped.

a Y-chromosome. In accordance with this, the sex-linked inheritance in birds is of the same kind as in moths. Drosophila, man, and many other organisms, including some dioecious plants (with separate sexes), were found cytologically to have an X- and a Y-chromosome in males, two X-chromosomes in females. In man the vision defect known as color blindness, the blood disease known as hemophilia, and certain other normal and pathological traits exhibit the sex-linked inheritance and are, accordingly, localized in the X-chromosome.

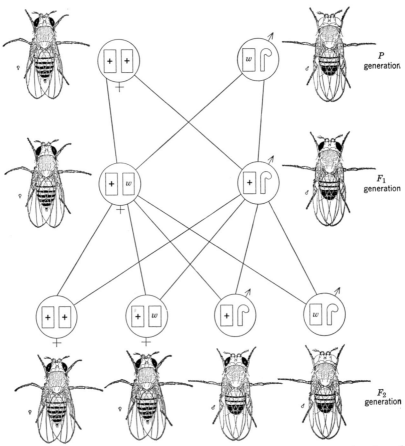

Figure 3.13.   Inheritance of a gene carried in the sex chromosome.   A red-eyed female of *Drosophila melanogaster* is outcrossed to a white-eyed male, and the F_1 progeny are inbred.   The symbols are like those in Figure 3.12.

Non-disjunction of Sex Chromosomes as Proof of the Chromosomal Theory of Heredity. In *Drosophila melanogaster* the crosses of white-eyed females and red-eyed males give the outcome shown in Figure 3.12 in most, but not in all, cases. About one white-eyed female fly appears in the F_1 generation among 2000 to 3000 red-eyed ones; about one red-eyed male may be found among similar numbers of white-eyed ones. The frequency of such "exceptional" individuals is appreciably increased if the parents are treated with X-rays or temperature shocks. In 1916 Bridges (1889–1938) published his classical work analyzing these exceptions.

Bridges reasoned that a white-eyed daughter of a red-eyed father must possess two X-chromosomes (since she is a female), both carrying the gene white (since she has white eyes). She can have received these X-chromosomes only from her mother. A red-eyed son must have a single X-chromosome (since he is a male), derived from his father (since he has red eyes). How can such distribution of the sex chromosomes take place? Bridges's hypothesis was that the process of meiosis in the females goes wrong in about one among 2000 to 3000 cells (Figure 3.14). Instead of the two X-chromosomes of the female disjoining normally, both of them either remain in the egg or are eliminated in the polar body. This failure of the chromosome disjunction yields "exceptional" eggs with two X-chromosomes or with no X-chromosome.

An egg with two X's may be fertilized by a Y-bearing spermatozoon and will give rise to a white-eyed female. This exceptional female must, if the hypothesis is correct, differ from normal females by having a Y-chromosome in addition to her two X-chromosomes. Normally, of course, the Y-chromosome is found only in males. Here, then, is an opportunity to test the validity of the hypothesis. Bridges proved cytologically that the exceptional females have the extra Y-chromosome as predicted. An exceptional egg with no X-chromosome, fertilized by an X-bearing spermatozoon, will give a red-eyed "exceptional" male. The exceptional males, however, must lack the Y-chromosome. This prediction also proved correct.

The exceptional eggs with two X's, fertilized by an X-bearing sperm, will give individuals with three X-chromosomes. Such individuals are poorly viable, but they occasionally survive as so-called superfemales. They were identified by Bridges in another experiment. The eggs devoid of X-chromosome, fertilized by a Y-bearing sperm, are inviable; such dying eggs were identified in the experiments of Li and of Poulson. Bridges analyzed also the progeny of the exceptional, XXY, females crossed to normal males; he was able to make certain predictions regarding the composition of these progenies which were found to be correct.

Changes in Chromosome Numbers. Occasional failures of the normally very precise processes of mitosis and meiosis may have important consequences. Non-disjunction gives rise to cells with one of the chromosomes represented more, or fewer, times than the other chromo-

somes of a set.   Individuals with extra chromosomes, or with some
chromosomes missing, are termed *aneuploids.*
In organisms with small numbers of chromosomes aneuploids are

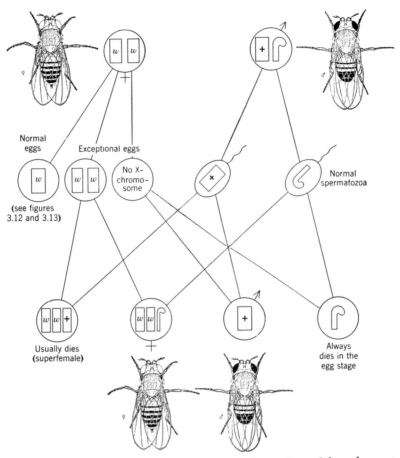

Figure 3.14.   The inheritance of the white eye color in *Drosophila melanogaster*
caused by accidental failures of the X-chromosomes of a white-eyed mother to
disjoin at meiosis.   Compare with Figures 3.12 and 3.13.

usually inviable, but in forms with many small chromosomes the
aneuploids survive more easily.   In certain grasses, such as the blue
grass, Poa, which produce seeds without fertilization, aneuploids are
common in natural populations.
Even more important are polyploids, which carry more than two
entire chromosome sets in their cells.   Both at mitosis and at meiosis

the cell division may fail, despite the chromosomes' having normally split into daughter halves. Such failures of the cell division occasionally occur in apparently normal individuals. Within the last two decades chromosome doubling without cell division has been induced artificially with the aid of certain drugs, particularly the alkaloid

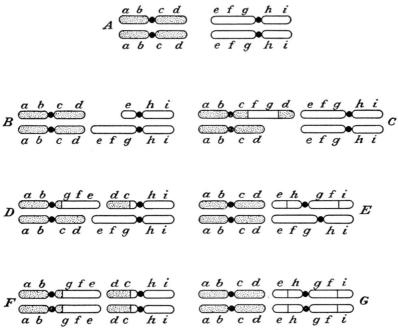

Figure 3.15. A scheme showing different kinds of chromosomal aberrations. *A.* Two pairs of original or "normal" chromosomes. *B.* Deficiency. *C.* Duplication. *D* and *F.* Heterozygous and homozygous translocations, respectively. *E* and *G.* Heterozygous and homozygous inversions, respectively. (From Sinnott, Dunn, and Dobzhansky, courtesy of the McGraw-Hill Book Company.)

colchicine. As a result of the chromosome doubling, sex cells arise which carry a diploid instead of the normal reduced, or haploid, chromosome set. Whole individuals are thus obtained with three (*triploid*), four (*tetraploid*), or higher polyploid chromosome complements. Polyploidy is of considerable importance in the evolution of the plant kingdom (Chapter 9).

Changes in Gene Dosage. Most genes are represented once and only once in the haploid chromosome complement. However, from time to time individuals appear which have a block of genes lost (*deficiency*) or present in excess (*duplication*) (Figure 3.15). Just as with aneuploids, deficiencies and duplications for large sections of chromosomes are often inviable. It is interesting that the organism withstands the duplication of a block of genes generally more easily than a deficiency of the same genes. In particular, the loss of a gene or a group of genes from both chromosome sets in a diploid organism (a homozygous deficiency) is usually lethal. This fact strongly suggests that almost every gene which the organism has must be present at least once to permit life and development.

Deficiencies, and especially duplications, have doubtless played important roles in evolution. The evolutionary development of the living world has, on the whole, led from simple to more complex forms of life. It is reasonable to suppose that this progression from the simple to the complex was accompanied by an increase in the number of genes which a species carries. Duplication and polyploidy are the only known methods whereby such increase could occur, since the appearance of self-reproducing genes from non-self-reproducing cell structures seems improbable. When a duplication occurs, the genes in the repeated sections are, to start with, merely copies of each other. In the process of evolution, however, they may suffer divergent changes (by mutation) and thus become different genes.

Changes in Gene Arrangement. The linear arrangement of genes in the chromosomes is usually constant in all individuals of a species. However, changes in the chromosome structure occasionally occur; their frequency is materially increased in the offspring of X-ray-treated individuals. The starting point of these changes is breakage of the chromosomes. Suppose, for example, that two different normal chromosomes, which carry the genes *ABCD* and *EFGH*, respectively, break into fragments *AB*, *CD*, *EF*, and *GH*. The fragments are usually lost unless the broken-off ends re-establish connections with other broken-off ends. New connections may, however, arise thus: *ABGH* and *EFCD*. Such exchange of segments between different chromosomes is known as *translocation* (Figure 3.15).

A single chromosome may be broken at two or more points. Thus the chromosome *ABCD* may give fragments *A*, *BC*, and *D*. The middle fragment may rotate through 180 degrees, and a new chromosome may have a section inverted compared with the original arrangement: *ACBD*. This is known as *inversion* of a chromosome section (Figure 3.15).

There are some simple rules which govern the formation of translocations and inversions. In organisms in which the chromosomes have localized centromeres, each rearranged chromosome must have one and only one centromere. Chromosome fragments devoid of centromere become lost. Similarly, new chromosomes formed by the union of fragments are lost if they include two centromeres. Cytological examination of dividing cells exposed to strong doses of X-rays usually shows chromosome fragments which are eliminated from the nuclei on account of failure to include a centromere. Such cells come to contain deficiencies for blocks of genes and eventually die off. This effect of X-rays on chromosome breakage is responsible for a major part of the radiation damage to living tissues, as well as for the regression of X-ray-treated cancerous growths.

Genetic and Cytological Study of Chromosomal Aberrations. Comparative genetic and cytological investigation of deficiencies, duplications, translocations, and inversions has yielded final proof of the validity of the theory of linear arrangement of the genes. Every one of these chromosomal aberrations can be diagnosed in genetically well-known organisms by making crosses with strains containing suitable genetic "markers." And in organisms favorable for cytological investigations the aberrant structure of the chromosomes can be seen under the microscope.

Consider, for example, the study of the Notch deficiency in the fly, *Drosophila melanogaster*, made by Mohr (1923). Females heterozygous for Notch have a notched wing margin, and there are certain disturbances in the arrangement of the small bristles on the thorax of the fly. Males which receive the X-chromosome containing Notch from their mothers are inviable. Notch is, accordingly, a sex-linked condition which has a dominant effect on the wings and bristles when heterozygous, and a recessive lethal effect in the male.

Mohr crossed Notch females to males with white eyes. As we know, white eyes in Drosophila are due to a recessive sex-linked gene (Figure 3.12). As expected, half of the females in the F_1 generation of this cross showed Notch wings; the other half had normal wings. But, unexpectedly, the F_1 Notch females also had white eyes, whereas the non-Notch females had normal red eyes. In the presence of Notch the white eye color behaves as though it were dominant to the normal red. Another normally recessive trait, namely, facet eye, also acted as a dominant in Notch flies, but other recessive sex-linked traits behaved quite normally (see the "map" of the X-chromosome in Figure 3.10). Mohr concluded that Notch is not due to a change in a single gene, but represents a deficiency in the chromosome comprising a block of genes which includes white and facet.

Under the microscope a deficiency can be detected most easily in the giant chromosomes of the salivary glands. Pairing of the maternal and the paternal homologues is very intimate, disc by disc, in these chromosomes. The discs which correspond to the genes missing in the deficiency chromosome have, then, nothing to pair with, and they form a "buckle" of a kind shown in Figure 3.16. If the genes which are missing are known from genetic study, like that carried out by Mohr, it is reasonable to conclude that these genes are located in a normal chromosome which forms the "buckle." Thus the location

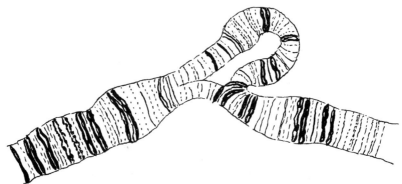

Figure 3.16. A section of a chromosome in the larval salivary gland cell of *Drosophila pseudoobscura*, showing a deficiency "buckle." The giant chromosomes in the salivary gland cells consist of the corresponding paternal and maternal chromosomes tightly paired. The individual represented in this figure lacked a block of genes. The corresponding section in the normal chromosome has formed the "buckle."

of the genes becomes known not only on the genetic "map" but also in the actual chromosomes visible in the microscope.

In genetically well-known organisms, such as Drosophila flies or corn plants, knowledge of the behavior of a given chromosomal aberration in crossing experiments permits prediction of the chromosomal configurations to be found by cytological study. Conversely, the appearance of the chromosomes under the microscope permits prediction of the outcome of certain crosses. Obviously, this correlation of genetical and cytological findings attests the correctness of the chromosomal theories of heredity which make the predictions possible.

Position Effects. There is an important difference between the deficiencies and duplications on one hand and translocations and inversions on the other. The former two types of chromosomal aberrations involve subtraction or addition of some genes or gene blocks, that is, changes in gene dosage or the *gene balance.* Individuals heterozygous or homozygous for deficiencies or duplications are usually different from normal in external appearance, and sometimes inviable. But translocations and inversions involve changes only in the arrangement of genes in the chromosomes. Translocation and inversion heterozygotes and homozygotes should have the same genes as individuals free of these chromosomal aberrations, even though these genes are differently arranged in the chromosomes.

It might seem that the appearance of the organism and its physiological functions should not be changed by the occurrence of translocations or inversions. This is, indeed, often the case. But many exceptions are known, particularly in Drosophila. In some instances normally dominant genes lose their dominance when placed in the chromosomes with changed gene order. In other instances the rearrangement of the genes results in some of these genes' behaving as though they had suddenly become very unstable and had undergone frequent changes, or mutations, during the development of the organism. This last type of behavior gives rise to "spotted," or "mosaic," distribution of colors and other traits, not uncommon among garden varieties of some ornamental plants. Finally, some translocations and inversions are poorly viable or lethal when homozygous.

The above *position effects* are forcing geneticists to revise their ideas about the relationships between the genes and chromosomes. Until the discovery of the position effects there was nothing to contradict the assumption that a chromosome is an aggregate of completely independent units, genes, arranged in a fortuitous linear order. This was certainly the simplest hypothesis that we could make, and it served well for a time; but the real situation is not quite so simple. The genes which lie in the chromosome next to each other are neighbors because their proximity makes them act together well. A chromosome is not just a container for genes but a harmonious system of interacting genes. The arrangement of genes in a chromosome has developed gradually during the evolution of the organism to which the chromosome belongs; the structure of a chromosome, like the structure of any organ, is a product of adaptive evolution.

Evolution of Heredity. Among the now-existing organisms possibly only the simplest viruses may be simple self-reproducing molecules, or "naked genes." All other organisms have many genes. It is tempting to speculate that life appeared at first in the form of virus-like molecules which caused formation of their copies from non-living substances in the environment. These primordial viruses then became diversified in response to the variety of environments which could sustain their self-reproduction (Chapter 5). The next step in the progressive evolution involved association of two or several unlike simple viruses into compounds; development of a mutual usefulness and interdependence; and final integration of the associated viruses, or genes, into organismic units, which might have been primitive cells. Cells again formed colonies. At first the colonies consisted of equivalent and later of differentiated members. The latter became multicellular organisms.

Association of interdependent self-reproducing bodies, or genes, raised biological problems which the "naked genes" did not have to face. Consider what happens when a complex of interdependent units, such as a cell, gives rise to a progeny. The progeny must be endowed with a fixed number of copies of each of the constituent units. The reproduction of compound units must be accurate. In the process of evolution this problem of precision was solved by assembling genes into aggregates, known as chromosomes, and elaboration of mechanisms of cell division, or *mitosis*.

The sexual process brought with it the evolutionary advantage of continuous production of ever-new gene combinations (Chapter 11). Sexual reproduction, however, requires mechanisms that would alternately place together gene sets derived from different parents and recombine and sort out new gene complements. This requirement became satisfied with the appearance and perfection of the mechanisms of fertilization and of reduction division, or meiosis. Aggregation and interdependence of genes in complex organisms thus led to the evolution of the genes being supplemented by the evolution of chromosomes.

Suggestions for Further Reading

Sinnott, E. W., Dunn, L. C., and Dobzhansky, Th. 1950. *Principles of Genetics.* 4th Edition. McGraw-Hill, New York.

Chapters VII–XI of this textbook of genetics discuss the basic facts of cytogenetics.

White, M. J. D. 1954. *Animal Cytology and Evolution.* 2nd Edition. Cambridge University Press, London.

This is the best available outline of cytogenetics of animals and of its bearing on evolutionary problems.

Riley, H. P. 1948. *Genetics and Cytogenetics.* John Wiley, New York.

A textbook of genetics with an emphasis on plant cytogenetics.

Wilson, E. B. 1928. *The Cell in Development and Heredity.* 3rd Edition. Macmillan, New York.

Though antiquated, this is a classic worth reading to anybody interested in genetics or cytogenetics.

Morgan, T. H. 1919. *The Physical Basis of Heredity.* Lippincott, Philadelphia.

This is another classic which played a tremendously important role in the correlation of genetic and cytological findings.

4

Heredity, Environment, and Mutation

Everyday language uses the word "heredity" both for biological inheritance and for legal inheritance of property. The statement that a person has inherited from his parents a dark, or a light, skin color does not mean the same thing as the statement that this person has inherited from his relatives a house or a farm. Inherited houses and farms are buildings or pieces of land which change their owners; the skin color is not transferred in this manner. The narrow bridge which connects parents and offspring is formed by the sex cells, and human sex cells have no color, and for that matter no skin. Inheritance of skin color refers to a developmental pattern which leads to the formation of a certain amount of pigment in the skin.

Just how much skin pigment is formed depends, however, not only on the presence of certain genes but also on the environment in which the carriers of these genes live. Exposure of the skin to sunlight, or to ultraviolet rays of certain wavelengths, darkens the skin color. The trait (skin color) that develops is thus determined by interaction of the heredity and the environment.

The environment concerned, however, is not only that prevailing at a given moment, but also the whole sequence of environments which the organism met during its lifetime. The color of my skin today is determined not only by the sunshine or its absence now but also by the amount of time spent outdoors and indoors during the preceding months. The personality of every human being is determined by his heredity, upbringing, education, relationships to other persons, disease, nutrition, etc. Every one of us is a product of his life experience, his biography. Nobody can escape his past. Living organisms are time-binding machines; they are products of their histories.

72

Heredity in Different Environments. All organisms, from simplest viruses to man, build their bodies, and those of their offspring, from materials derived from the environment. Every organism can reproduce itself from a certain range of food materials, and under a variety of environmental conditions. An organism that could exist in only a single environment would not remain alive for long, because the environment does not remain the same from one instant to the next. Every organism, therefore, is adapted to live in a certain variety of environments. How can this adaptedness be retained in changing environments?

Let A stand for a self-reproducing entity—a gene, a virus, or the sum total of the genes which an organism carries (the genotype, see below). Suppose that A builds its replicas in different environments or from different materials (foods) B_1, B_2, B_3, etc. The process of self-reproduction may, then, be visualized as follows:

$$A + B_1 = 2A + C_1$$

$$A + B_2 = 2A + C_2$$

$$A + B_3 = 2A + C_3$$

C_1, C_2, and C_3 may stand for by-products of the gene reproduction, or for the non-self-reproducing cell parts, or for the bodily forms which are the outcomes of the development of the organism in different environments. The essential point of this scheme is that, so long as the environment is capable of maintaining life of a given kind of gene or of gene system, the genes reproduce their copies (A becomes $2A$), or else they do not reproduce at all. In contrast to this, the organisms (C) produced in different environments vary.

Genotype and Phenotype. The fundamental nature of the distinction between A and C in the above scheme was perceived in 1909 by Johannsen (1857–1927). He called the heredity received by an organism its *genotype,* and the appearance of this organism its *phenotype.* The phenotype changes continuously so long as the organism remains alive. A series of photographs, taken at intervals from infancy to old age, illustrates the changes in the phenotype of a person.

On the other hand, the genotype of a person is relatively constant. It is presumably much the same during manhood as it was in youth and in childhood and as it will be during senescence. The nature of this constancy must be clearly understood. Although the chemistry of the gene reproduction is unknown, it is quite certain that synthesis of nucleoproteins must entail a complex series of chemical reactions.

Far from being inert and insulated from the environment, the genes are perhaps the most active cell constituents. The constancy of the genes is, then, singularly dynamic—they interact with the environment to transform a part of it into their own copies.

Germplasm and Soma. Even before Johannsen, Weismann (1834–1914) drew the distinction between the *germplasm* and the *soma*. The germplasm has its seat in the sex cells and the cells of the reproductive organs which give rise to the sex cells. The soma is the rest of the body. The germplasm is potentially immortal; indeed, every sex cell is able, under favorable conditions, to give rise to a new individual with another crop of sex cells. The soma is mortal; it is the body which houses the sex cells, and which is cast off in every generation owing to death.

Weismann's concepts of germplasm and soma were an important landmark in the process of understanding heredity and evolution. But they should not be confused with the modern genotype-phenotype concepts. Not all the genes are carried in the reproductive cells; they are present as well in every body cell, in other words also in Weismann's soma.

Norm of Reaction. The question whether the genotype or the environment is more important in the formation of the phenotype or the personality is evidently meaningless (although frequently and acrimoniously discussed). The phenotype is the outcome of a process of organic development. There is no organic development without an organism, and no organism without a genotype. Equally, every organism exists in an environment and at the expense of an environment. As pointed out above, any organism is the product of its genotype and of its life experience or biography.

The genotype determines the course which the development may take in any environment. In other words, the genotype of an individual determines the *norm of reaction* of the individual in all possible environments (Figure 4.1). A newborn infant has a great range of possible futures; which of these possibilities are realized and become actualities depends upon the succession of the environments gradually unfolding during the lifetime. The ranges of possibilities are, however, different for carriers of different genotypes. For example, the genotype of an albino causes little or no pigment to form regardless of the amount of skin exposure to sunlight. The genotypes of most "whites" make the skin colors vary within wide limits, depending upon exposure to sunlight. And the genotypes of Negroes make the skin pigment develop rapidly within a few days after birth, and the skin to become dark independently of sun exposure.

The norm of reaction of a genotype is at best only incompletely known. Complete knowledge of a norm of reaction would require placing the carriers of a given genotype in all possible environments, and observing the phenotypes that develop. This is a practical im-

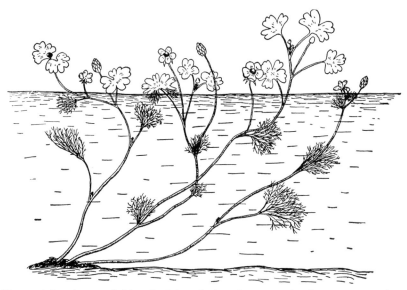

Figure 4.1. A remarkable plasticity of the phenotype in the water crowfoot (*Ranunculus aquatilis*). The norm of reaction of this plant is such that the leaves submerged in water develop to look very different from the leaves which are above the water level. (After Weaver and Clements, from Robbins and Weier.)

possibility. The existing variety of environments is immense, and new environments are constantly produced. Invention of a new drug, a new diet, a new type of housing, a new educational system, a new political regime introduces new environments. It would be very useful to know how various human genotypes would respond to all these environments.

Adaptive and Non-adaptive Modifications. Our ancestors of only a century ago lived under conditions radically different from our own. The environment changes also within the lifetime of an individual; it is never the same for two individuals, or for one individual on two successive days. This is true not only for man, but also for any species. In order to survive an organism must respond to changing environments in ways that enable it to secure its livelihood. The survival depends upon the norm of reaction.

In Chapter 1 (pages 13–14) it has been pointed out that many, although not all, modifications of the phenotype produced by changes in the environment are adaptive. The organism reacts to many environmental changes by homeostatic modifications of the developmental patterns, which favor the perpetuation of life in the changed environments.

However, different genotypes often differ in their ability to produce adaptive responses to environmental changes. The albinos in man do not develop the protective sun tan, and may suffer dangerous sunburns. The albino genotype is not well adapted to environments with intense sunshine. The genotypes of most "whites" develop the protective tan if their carriers are exposed to sunshine, but the pigment is lost after a prolonged lack of sun exposure. This last reaction is also believed by some authorities to be adaptive, since unpigmented skin may facilitate the formation of vitamin D (the "sunshine vitamin") in climates and during seasons when sunshine is scarce. The genotypes of "whites" are, then, adaptive in seasonally changeable climates, such as those of northern and central Europe. It is no accident that most human races which inhabit the tropical and subtropical regions have dark skins. These are the regions of abundant and intense sunshine (see Chapter 13).

Superior and Inferior Norms of Reaction. When carriers of a genotype are placed in an environment to which their genotype is not adapted they react by loss of health or by death. Hereditary defects and diseases are genotypic variants which react to environments usual for the species or race by production of ill-adapted phenotypes. There is, consequently, no hard and fast distinction between "hereditary" and "non-hereditary" diseases. Most or all human beings may come down with measles if exposed as children to an environment containing the virus of measles. On the other hand, only some people develop diabetes. Accordingly, we call measles a non-hereditary and diabetes a hereditary disease. But there may be some persons genotypically immune to measles. And a person with hereditary diabetes may enjoy good health if he receives injections of proper amounts of insulin at regular intervals. Either genotype may produce disease in some and health in other environments.

We should beware of assuming that some genotypes are always "normal" and others "abnormal," except in the sense that some are met with more and others less often in nature. The more frequent genotypes, by and large, are those which are better fit to survive under usual, frequently met with, environmental conditions. But it may be misleading to say that the carriers of a certain genotype must reach certain "intrinsic" height, or weight, or skin color, or intelligence level. Any height or weight or intelligence a person may have is "intrinsic," in the sense that the phenotype observed is the necessary outcome of the development brought about by a certain genotype in a certain succession of environments. We can never be sure that any of these traits have reached the maximal development possible with a given genotype. The performance of a genotype cannot be tested in all possible environments, because the latter are infinitely variable.

Non-inheritance of Acquired Characters. It is a matter of every-day experience that children resemble their parents; the influence on organisms of nutrition, climate, and living conditions is also evident. Putting these facts together, popular imagination concluded that environmental modifications of the bodies of parents are transmitted by heredity to the offspring. The belief that acquired characters are inherited was originally not a scientific theory; it was, and still is, a part of the folklore.

Buffon (1707–1788) was one of the precursors of evolutionism, who believed that the environment may change the nature of organisms ("denature" them, as he preferred to put it). He took it for granted that the changes induced by the environment in what we would now call the phenotype would be inherited. Lamarck (1744–1829), the first thorough-going evolutionist, emphasized particularly the fact that, in animals, extensive use or exercise of organs strengthens them, whereas continued disuse weakens them. For example, muscles become larger and stronger as a result of exercise, and are reduced by prolonged disuse. It seemed evident to Lamarck that such acquired changes would be transmitted to the offspring. Darwin (1809–1882) considered natural selection (Chapter 6) the fountainhead of evolution. Nevertheless, he accepted the inheritance of acquired modifications as an important, if subsidiary, force, a view that was shared by most of Darwin's immediate followers. For example, the Negro race was considered "a child of the African sun." The tanning of the skin by exposure to intense sunlight over many generations was believed to produce a progressive darkening, which becomes fixed in the heredity of the inhabitants of Africa. Similarly, the absence of eyes in many subterranean animals was ascribed to inheritance of the effects of long-continued disuse of the eyes, owing to the life in darkness.

The assumption that acquired characters are inherited was finally challenged by Weismann (whose principal work was published in 1892). Weismann's famous experiment consisted in cutting off the tails of newborn mice in a series of successive generations. The tails were no shorter in the progeny of experimental mice. This experiment seems rather naïve at present, but it is only fair to say that heritable degeneration of an organ as a result of its amputation in the parents is even now an accepted belief among some of the followers of Lamarck.

Many experiments were carried out in the closing decade of the nineteenth, and the first two decades of the current century, to test the hypothesis of inheritance of acquired traits. The results of these experiments were overwhelmingly negative. Most biologists came to the conclusion that the hypothesis must be rejected.

One of the last alleged instances of such inheritance created something of a stir, because it was espoused by the eminent physiologist Pavlov (1849–1936) in Russia and McDougall in America. In McDougall's experiments rats were dropped into a water tank with two exits, one lighted and the other dark. The rats had to learn to use the dark exit, the lighted one being provided with a mechanism which gave an electric shock to an animal attempting to use it. Different rats require different numbers of "lessons" to be taught. It was contended that the offspring of trained rats were taught more easily than those of the untrained ones, apparently an inheritance of acquired training. Repetition of these experiments disclosed a more complex situation than was originally suspected. Among rats there exist strains which differ genotypically in their response to training. The original experiments involved an unconscious selection of rats with norms of reaction favorable to training as parents of the next generations.

The Hypothesis of Pangenesis. The view that the earth is round was not accepted without struggle, because everybody could so easily see that the earth is flat. Scientific theories gain acceptance with difficulty if they contradict popular beliefs. The negative outcome of experiments on the inheritance of acquired traits failed to convince some people. Is it possible that the outcome of such experiments would be different if the action of the environment inducing the traits were continued ten times, or a thousand times, longer than it actually was? Perhaps the most satisfactory answer to such doubts is that the mechanism of heredity revealed by modern genetics makes inheritance of acquired characters highly improbable.

How, indeed, can the skin color produced by sun exposure influence the genes in the sex cells which will determine the skin color of the next generation? An imaginative solution of this problem was suggested by Maupertuis (1698–1759), made popular by one of Darwin's bitterest critics, Samuel Butler, in 1879, and worked out in detail by the vitalist Semon (1904). They compared biological heredity to memory. The sex cells, as it were, "remember" the structure of the body which produced them, and choose materials from the environment which can build a similar body. The acquired characters are simply "remembered." The trouble is that this ingenious theory fails to explain anything. Ascribing memory to sex cells, like ascribing a vital force to the living matter, merely takes for granted the natural phenomena which have to be explained.

Darwin, who, as we know, also believed in the inheritance of acquired characters, proposed in 1868 his "provisional hypothesis of pangenesis." He assumed that all organs of the body, perhaps all cells, produce diminutive vestiges of themselves, called gemmules or pangenes. The gemmules are shed into the blood stream, and are transported by blood to the sex glands, where the gemmules of different organs are assembled to form sex cells. Body cells modified by the environment might produce modified gemmules which will reproduce the modification in the next generation (see Figure 4.2).

The hypothesis of pangenesis had the virtue of being easy to test. Galton in 1875, and other investigators later, made experiments of blood transfusion, or of transplantation of ovaries, between white and black varieties of rabbits and of poultry. The hypothesis would lead us to expect the birth of spotted, black and white, offspring from experimental animals. This expectation was not fulfilled.

The hypotheses of pangenesis, and of heredity as "organic memory," are invalid. The reason why they are discussed at all is that, as pointed out by Zirkle (1946), variants of these hypotheses are, explicitly or implicitly, a necessary part of every belief in the inheritance of acquired traits. The Russian agriculturist Lysenko has gained much notoriety owing to the suppression of genetics in the USSR. Lysenko is a believer in the inheritance of acquired traits, and, apparently unaware of Darwin's authorship, he propounds an hypothesis of pangenesis as his own invention. Similarly, he ascribes a power of memory to the sex cells.

In reality, the genes do not arise from gemmules cast off by the body cell; they reproduce by synthesizing their own copies. The self-reproduction of the genes sets the norm of reaction of the organism in different environments.

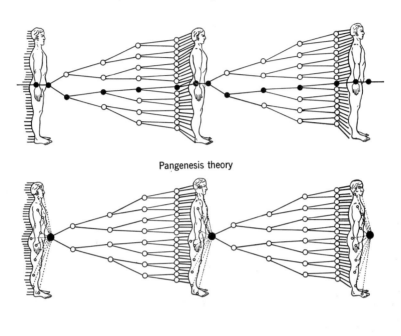

● Germ cell   O Somatic cell   ∘ Gemmule

Figure 4.2.   The relationship between the germ cells and the body cells according to the gene theory and the theory of pangenesis.   According to the former theory the germ cells (sex cells) arise by division of other cells of the germ line; according to the latter theory the germ cells are compounded of particles (gemmules) produced by body cells.

Gene Destruction and Gene Change.   Can genes be changed by the environment?   Assuredly they can.   The problem, however, is what are the consequences of gene change.   Proteins, including nucleoproteins, are easily changed, denatured, by high temperature, salts of heavy metals, hydrogen-ion concentration, etc.   These factors undoubtedly change the genes also.

To give a crude example, when an egg is boiled for breakfast, the genes contained in its chromosomes are altered so radically that they never divide again.   This is, indeed, the most frequent consequence of induced gene change: failure of the changed structure to perpetuate itself by self-reproduction.   But a gene that does not reproduce itself is no longer a gene.   Conceivably, methods will some day be discovered which will permit destruction of specific genes without disturbing the rest. Thus, we could produce a deficiency for the gene white in Drosophila flies (see pages 67–68), or remove the genes responsible for the skin pigment in man, but at present such methods are unknown.

It is only a special, and rare, type of gene change that interests biologists. A gene may be altered without losing the ability to reproduce itself, and the altered structure is copied when the reproduction occurs. Such changes are *gene mutations*. Mutations give rise to variants, alleles, of the gene. Individuals which carry a mutant gene possess a new norm of reaction to the environment. Usually they can be recognized by their external appearance.

History of the Mutation Concept. Plant and animal breeders have observed from time to time the appearance of sudden hereditary

Figure 4.3. A short-legged mutation in domestic sheep (left) and an individual with normal legs (right). (From Weimer.)

changes or "sports." A lamb with short, dachshund-like, legs was born on a New England farm late in the eighteenth century (Figure 4.3). This single lamb became the progenitor of the Ancon breed of sheep which was for a time popular with farmers, but was eventually lost. Another lamb with similar legs was born, from normal parents, in Norway some thirty-five years ago. In 1853 a girl who had a black skin irregularly splotched with white was born to Negro parents with uniformly dark skin. About half of the children of this girl by a black man also had pied skins. The girl born in 1853 was heterozygous for a dominant mutant gene for white spotting.

Darwin considered "sports" too rare to be of much importance in evolution. He ascribed more importance to the small, "fluctuating," inheritable differences which occur between individuals of any species. Men, even members of the same family, differ in height, shades of skin, hair, and eye colors, shape of the head and face, and many other traits.

De Vries (1848–1935) took the opposite view; in his *Mutation Theory* (1901) he maintained that evolution proceeds by large, discrete, and sudden changes, which he called mutations. He supported his thesis with observations on the evening primrose, *Oenothera lamarckiana*, which in his garden produced several mutations. De Vries regarded mutations as new species of plants, and their real nature was discovered only much later. Some of them represented chromosomal aberrations: triploids, tetraploids, or aneuploids. Others were homozygotes for recessive genes for which the parents were heterozygous. Only a minority were due to mutational changes in the genes which took place in the experimental plantings.

Is Evolution Continuous or Discontinuous? After the publication of de Vries's work there was much discussion between Darwinists and mutationists. Darwinists contended that evolution resulted from gradual shifts in the characteristics of a species over a long series of generations. Mutationists thought that evolution consists of relatively rare but drastic mutations. At present, we know that this issue was a spurious one.

Beginning in 1910, Morgan and his collaborators described many mutations in species of vinegar flies, Drosophila. Some of the mutations produce striking changes: flies with vestigial wings or with no wings at all, with eyes of bizarre shapes or without eyes, with yellow or with black bodies instead of the normal gray, etc. Some mutations are so drastic that they kill the organism; such mutations are called *lethal*. But many, in fact most, mutants produce changes so slight that an expert eye is necessary to notice them at all. Mutations range all the way from minute to drastic changes. Evolution is a gradual and continuous process, but it results from the summation of many discontinuous changes, mutations, a great majority of which are small. Mutationism is certainly not opposed, but supplementary, to Darwinism.

Mutations in Different Organisms. Mutations have been observed in diverse organisms, from man to the simplest viruses. When the mutants can be crossed to the ancestral form, the mutant traits are usually inherited according to Mendel's laws. Most mutations appear to be changes in single genes. The mutant alleles are sometimes dominant ones, but more often recessive to the ancestral condition. Some mutations, however, produce changes in the chromosome structure, chromosomal aberrations (Chapter 3).

Contrary to de Vries's opinion, mutations do not produce new species. The mutants of Drosophila are still flies which belong to the same species of Drosophila to which their ancestors belonged (see, however, the species formation through polyploidy, Chapter 9).

Mutational changes affect all organs of the body and all kinds of traits. Drosophila mutants differ in the color of the body, of the eyes, and of some internal organs; in size and shape of the whole body, of the eyes, wings, bristles, legs, eggs, larvae, and pupae (Figures 4.4 and 4.5). The viability, length of life, fertility, and behavior of the flies may be altered. Physiological and biochemical traits may be affected.

Because of the work of Beadle and others, numerous biochemical mutants have recently been found in the fungus Neurospora, in yeasts, and in some bacteria. These mutants show a great variety of metabolic patterns. They require the presence in their food of vitamins, amino acids, or other substances, which are not needed for normal growth of the ancestral form or of other mutants. The cells of the mutants accumulate chemical substances which in the ancestral forms are intermediate products of certain metabolic reaction chains. Such biochemical mutants are invaluable for the study of cell physiology. A new branch of science, biochemical genetics, is evolving on the borderline between genetics and chemical physiology. Apart from its intrinsic interest, this science promises also valuable technological applications.

Lethal mutants cause the death of their carriers. Death may occur, in different lethals, at any stage of the development, from cleavage of the fertilized egg to the adult organism. Poulson, Hadorn, and others have studied the causes of death in some lethals in Drosophila; and Dunn, Landauer, and others in mice, poultry, and other animals. Some of the lethal "syndromes" resemble certain human hereditary diseases. Gene changes by mutation may drastically modify the basic developmental processes of the organism.

Homeotic Mutants. Fundamental, as well as superficial, traits are under the control of genes, and are subject to mutation. Of course the distinction between the "fundamental" and the "superficial" is, to a large extent, arbitrary. This is particularly clear in *homeotic* mutants, which transform some organs into others. In at least three species of Drosophila mutants are known which turn the "balancers" of the fly into a second pair of wings (Figure 4.5). The order of flies, Diptera, to which Drosophila belongs, differs from other insect orders, among other things, by the presence of one pair of wings and one pair of balancers. Yet the "tetraptera" mutant can be crossed to a normal fly; the mutant condition is recessive to normal and seems to be produced by a change in a single gene.

Other homeotic mutants in Drosophila have the antennae of the fly

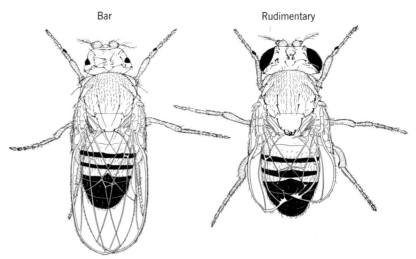

Figure 4.4. The mutants bar eyes (left) and rudimentary wings (right) of *Drosophila melanogaster*. (Originals drawn by E. Wallace.)

turned into legs, or eyes replaced by antennae, or a third pair of wings formed on the prothorax (where no other living insect has wings, but some fossil insect had), or the mouth parts of the fly radically changed in structure. These and similar mutants are fascinating materials for morphological studies. Whether they are of much significance in evolution is a different matter. Most evolutionists are of the opinion that the development of the living world rarely if ever involved major changes produced by single mutational steps. Among recent authors, Goldschmidt (1940), however, has defended the opposite view. To him the homeotic mutants illustrate the possible mode of origin of novel types of body structure, and, hence, of new families, orders, and perhaps classes of organisms.

Frequency of Mutation. The surest way to observe mutations in any organism is to examine large numbers of individuals. Most cultures of Drosophila contain no mutants, but an occasional culture may yield a single fly with white eyes, among many normal red-eyed sibs. Another culture may contain an individual with a yellow body, or with cut wings, or with forked bristles, etc. Some genes mutate more frequently than others. Table 4.1 shows the frequency of mutation of

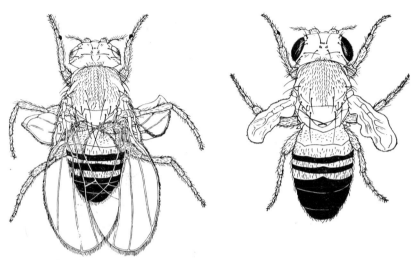

Figure 4.5. The mutants bithorax (left) and vestigial wings (right) of *Drosophila melanogaster.* (After E. Wallace, redrawn.)

several genes in maize (corn). The gene *R* is relatively mutable, whereas the gene *Wx* has failed to mutate in a million and a half individuals studied.

Haldane, Morch, Penrose, Neel, and others have made estimates of the frequency of mutation of human genes which produce certain hereditary diseases. One of these diseases is hemophilia (bleeding), which is due to a recessive gene carried in the X-chromosome (a sex-linked gene, Chapter 3). According to Haldane, two to three out of 100,000 human sex cells which carry an X-chromosome contain a hemophilia gene newly arisen by mutation. There is reason to think that the British queen Victoria had such a newly mutated gene, which she transmitted to some of her progeny. The dominant gene for chondrodystrophy (dwarfism due to shortness of the arms and legs, with head and trunk of normal size) arises by mutation more frequently than that for hemophilia. The gene for epiloia (tuberous sclerosis) mutates less than once in every 100,000 sex cells.

TABLE 4.1

MUTATIONS OBSERVED IN SEVEN GENES IN MAIZE

(After Stadler.)

Gene	Individuals Examined	Mutations Observed	Mutations per 1,000,000 Individuals
R (color factor)	554,786	273	492
I (color inhibitor)	265,391	28	106
P₂ (purple color)	647,102	7	11
Su (sugary)	1,678,736	4	2.4
Y (yellow seeds)	1,745,280	4	2.2
Sh (shrunken seeds)	2,469,285	3	1.2
Wx (waxy seeds)	1,503,744	0	0

Mutations in any single gene may be rare. But since a chromosome complement contains thousands or tens of thousands of genes (Chapter 3), many mutations arise in most species in every generation. In *Drosophila melanogaster*, approximately 2 out of every 1000 X-chromosomes acquire a new lethal mutant gene per generation. Mutations which produce small changes are doubtless more numerous than lethals. The frequency of such small mutations is little known, since it is hard to notice them all, although they are doubtless more frequent than lethals.

Thus it comes about that Timofeeff-Ressovsky (1939) has estimated that, in *Drosophila melanogaster*, 2 to 3 per cent of individuals in every generation carry one or more newly arisen mutant genes. Muller's estimate for man is even higher. Ten to 40 per cent of human sex cells in every generation carry a newly arisen mutation. The stability of the gene as a self-reproducing unit is compatible with the production of numerous mutants which serve as raw materials for evolutionary changes.

Environment and Mutation. For more than half a century biologists have tried to discover the causes which bring mutations about, and the problem is still far from being solved. We do not know how to produce a given kind of mutation where and when desired.

Mutations appear as a rule in single individuals so that only one of the many sex cells produced by the parents of a mutant carries a gene which suffers a given kind of mutational change. Mutation in a diploid cell affects only one chromosome, although two chromosomes of the same kind, with more or less similar genes, are present in the cell. This isolated occurrence of mutations is suggestive. The immediate causes, whatever they may be, which make the gene mutate are strictly localized within a cell, in the immediate vicinity of the gene which undergoes the change. It may be, although this is not proven, that mutations occur when the genes reproduce themselves. One or both copies of a gene formed by the self-reproduction process may differ from the original in structure.

However that may be, several environmental factors are known which speed up the mutation process. Muller, who was later awarded a Nobel prize for his discovery, announced in 1927 that X-rays are *mutagenic* (mutation inducing). Muller observed many mutations in the progeny of X-rayed Drosophila. Depending upon the amount of X-rays applied, mutations may be tens and even hundreds of times more frequent in the progeny of irradiated flies than in the non-irradiated control flies.

X-rays are mutagenic in all animals and plants which have been experimented with, and there is every reason to think that they are mutagenic in all organisms, including man. The fact that the number of mutations induced is proportional to the amount of the rays reaching the sex cells is important. X-rays are now used extensively in medicine, and many people are becoming exposed to the radiations produced by the release of atomic energy. Misuse of X-rays may raise the specter of uncontrolled increase of the mutability in human populations, a disaster for public health.

Chemical and Biological Mutagens. Several strongly mutagenic chemical compounds are now known. Experimenting with Drosophila, Auerbach (1949) found that mustard gas is a powerful mutagen. It is one of the "war gases" ($Cl \cdot CH_2 \cdot CH_2$)$_2$S. When applied in concentrations just short of those which kill the flies, this gas increases the mutation rates almost as much as the strongest practicable X-ray treatments. Several chemicals are mutagenic when mixed with the food on which Drosophila larvae grow and develop. Among them, the effects of formalin and urethane are best ascertained. Demerec has discovered (1952) that the mutation rates in certain bacteria are greatly increased by treatments with manganous and ferrous compounds. Organic peroxides are also mutagenic, at least in bacteria.

An environmental factor that may be important as a mutagen under natural conditions is high temperature. Muller and Timofeeff-Ressovsky (1935) found that, in Drosophila, mutation rates are doubled or trebled with every 10°C rise in temperature. Although this is a relatively small increase compared with what can be produced by

X-ray treatments, it may be important for evolution if the mutation rates remain high for many generations.

Doubtless important, and yet little studied, are the genetic modifiers of the mutability. Ives (1950) found that different strains of the same species of Drosophila show different mutability in the same environment. In some instances it was possible to show that such differently mutable strains differed in a single gene, which did not have any visible effects on the flies other than the modification of the mutation rates. The mutability of a gene depends, therefore, not only upon its own structure but also upon other genes which the organism carries. The physiological mechanisms which bring about such modifications of the mutability are completely unknown.

Spontaneous and Induced Mutations. When mutants appear in the progeny of parents which were not treated with any known mutagens, the mutations are said to have arisen *spontaneously*. Of course, the word "spontaneous" applied to any natural phenomenon means only that the actual causes of this phenomenon are unknown. After the discovery of the mutagenic effects of X-rays and similar radiations, a suspicion arose that the spontaneous mutability may be caused by cosmic rays and other high-energy radiations. The amounts of such radiations, however, proved sufficient to account for less than one per cent of spontaneous mutations.

It is important to remember that X-rays, and all other mutagens so far discovered, merely increase the frequency of the same kinds of mutations which also arise spontaneously. In other words, when we apply a mutagen to a culture of Drosophila or of bacteria, the treatment is likely to give in different individuals all sorts of mutations in all genes, instead of definite mutations in genes of our choice. Although the discovery of these mutagens has been a great achievement of biological science, we cannot help wishing that means would be found to transform genes in desired ways. In theory, there is no reason why specific transforming principles could not be found. The search for them has indeed met with some success.

Cytoplasmic Heredity. Apart from the genes carried in the chromosomes, some self-reproducing units exist also in the cytoplasm of some, and perhaps of all, cells. Examples of such units are the chloroplasts, the chlorophyll carriers of green plants. The chloroplasts arise from self-reproducing primordia in the cytoplasm. In recent years evidence has been accumulating that the cytoplasm of many organisms contains *plasmagenes*, self-reproducing structures too small to be seen even with the aid of microscopes.

When a cell divides, the genes in the chromosomes are apportioned to the daughter cells by means of the high-precision mechanism known as mitosis (Chapter 3); but there is no mechanism of comparable accuracy for the division of the plasmagenes. A cell usually carries several or many plasmagenes of each kind, and at cell division each daughter cell receives roughly half of the plasmagenes present in the mother cell.

Sonneborn, Beale (1949), and others have observed remarkable transformations in the infusorium, *Paramecium aurelia.* When infusoria of this species are injected into rabbits, the blood serum of the rabbit comes to contain antibodies which paralyze the infusoria placed in a drop of liquid containing this serum. Different strains of infusoria, however, induce formation of different antibodies, so that the infusoria can be classified into groups, or "serotypes," A, B, C, D, etc. Under standard culture conditions, each strain of infusoria breeds true as to its serotype. But the serotype can be changed.

The most potent agency to induce the change is exposure of the infusoria to the serum with antibodies of the proper type. The concentration of the serum must not, of course, be strong enough to kill the infusoria. The simplest way to explain these changes is to suppose that the infusoria carry in their cytoplasm plasmagenes of several serotypes. However, at any one time, one kind of plasmagene outnumbers the others, and the most frequent kind determines the actual serotype to which an infusorium belongs. If this plasmagene is suppressed or destroyed by the antibodies in the serum, one of the other kinds of plasmagenes multiplies instead; the change in the serotype is the result.

It should be strongly emphasized that the induced transformations do not resemble the inheritance of acquired characters as imagined by the early evolutionists (or by Lysenko in Russia). An "acquired character" is a modification of a part of the body, such as the darkening of the skin under the influence of sunlight. To be inherited the modified body part must produce some substance that would reach the genes in the sex cells, and cause a *specific transformation of those, and only those, genes which determine the traits of the same body part in the offspring.* There is not a trace of evidence that such transformations occur. Moreover, this view tacitly assumes that there is a one-to-one correspondence between a gene and an organ or a part of the adult body; this, however, is not true. Genes determine developmental patterns of the whole organism in different environments. In other words, genes determine which traits will appear in a given environment, but the genes are not determined by the traits which happen to be realized.

Suggestions for Further Reading

Burks, B. S. 1942. *A study of identical twins reared apart under different types of family relationships.* In McNemar and Merrill's *Studies of Personality.* McGraw-Hill, New York.

Cattell, R. B. 1950. *Personality.* McGraw-Hill, New York.

Haldane, J. B. S. 1938. *Heredity and Politics.* Norton, New York.

Hogben, L. 1941. *Nature and Nurture.* Norton, New York.

Osborn, F. 1951. *Preface to Eugenics.* Harper, New York.

Penrose, L. S. 1949. *The Biology of Mental Defect.* Sidgwich & Jackson, London.

Scheinfeld, A. 1950. *The New You and Heredity.* Lippincott, Philadelphia.

Stern, C. 1949. *Principles of Human Genetics.* W. H. Freeman, San Francisco.

The above books and articles are representative of modern points of view concerning the relationships of heredity and environment, particularly in man.

Zirkle, C. 1946. *The early history of the idea of the inheritance of acquired characters and of pangenesis. Transactions of the American Philosophical Society,* Volume 35, pp. 91–151.

This is an excellent outline and analysis of one of the mistaken ideas which nevertheless played an important role in the history of biology.

Zirkle, C. 1949. *Death of a Science in Russia.* University of Pennsylvania Press, Philadelphia.

A documented review of the so-called Lysenko controversy and its background.

Dobzhansky, Th. 1951. *Genetics and the Origin of Species.* 3rd Edition. Columbia University Press, New York.

Chapter II of this book deals with the problem of mutation in its relation to evolution.

Genes and mutations. 1951. *Cold Spring Harbor Symposium on Quantitative Biology,* Volume 16.

This volume contains articles by fifty-four authors, representing various approaches and points of view concerning the study of genes and mutations.

5

Elementary Evolutionary Changes or Microevolution

Adaptedness and Adaptation. Darwin wrote in 1859: "We see beautiful adaptations everywhere and in every part of the organic world." Indeed, the capacity of life to master even most inhospitable environments is remarkable. During summer months, margins of permanent snow fields in high mountains may acquire a pinkish color, owing to the presence of the alga *Sphaerella nivalis.* This alga is adapted to live and reproduce at temperatures close to freezing. In contrast to it, some algae inhabit hot springs of Yellowstone Park with temperatures up to 85°C (185°F), which are well above the limit of toleration for most organisms. The emperor penguins inhabit the Antarctic ice, and breed during the long and bitterly cold winters. No nests are constructed; the birds incubate the eggs by placing them on their feet and covering them by a skin fold which they have on the belly. Both sexes and all members of a colony compete for the privilege of incubating the eggs, regardless of whether they are the actual parents.

The universal adaptedness of life to its environment is, next to the nature of life itself, the greatest problem which biology has to face. Darwin has attempted to explain the process of adaptation as an outcome of natural selection impinging upon organic variation. In our present terminology this means that the conservatism of heredity is counterbalanced by the dynamism of mutation and sexual reproduction. Some of the genotypes generated by these processes are adaptive in certain environments, and are perpetuated by natural selection; other genotypes fail to be perpetuated. Some simplest examples of evolutionary adaptation are discussed in the following pages.

91

Resistance of Bacteria to Bacteriophages. D'Herelle (1917) discovered organisms, too small to be seen in ordinary microscopes, which were called bacteriophages, or simply phages. Under electron microscopes phages appear as tiny spheres, with or without a minute "tail" (Figure 5.1). If a suspension of bacteriophages is added to a culture of bacteria, the phages penetrate and multiply inside the bacterial cells. The bacteria break down, and large numbers of phages are released, ready to attack new bacteria. Phages, then, are parasites preying on bacteria. Many studies have been carried out on phages which attack colon bacteria, *Escherichia coli*, which occur in the intestinal tract of man and of other animals.

If a culture contains many bacteria, one or several bacterial cells may prove resistant to bacteriophage attack. If the bacteria are kept on a solid nutrient medium in a Petri plate, the resistant cells multiply and form colonies of bacteria, which are seen with the naked eye as white specks on the surface of the medium (Figure 5.2). From such colonies, new cultures of bacteria may be started which are completely resistant to the phage. The resistance is a genotypic trait of the bacterial strain which is retained indefinitely when the strain is transferred to fresh cultures.

The origin of bacterial strains resistant to bacteriophage attacks has been studied by many investigators, among whom Burnet (1929), Luria and Delbruck (1943), and Demerec and Fano (1945) are the pioneers. Two working hypotheses can be considered. (1) The resistance arises by spontaneous mutation in any bacterial culture, regardless of whether that culture is or is not exposed to the phage. Suppose that a resistant cell appears about once in ten million to one hundred million bacterial cell divisions. Cultures which contain hundreds of millions of bacteria are, therefore, likely to have one or several resistant cells. In the absence of phages, the resistant cells are simply lost among great masses of normal cells. When a phage is introduced all normal cells fall prey to its attacks; only the few resistant cells survive and reproduce, forming the resistant colonies which are easily picked out. (2) The resistance may, conceivably, be induced in a small proportion of the cells by their contact with bacteriophages. The cells that become resistant survive, and the susceptible ones are destroyed.

According to the first hypothesis, the origin of resistant mutants is independent of the phages, which act simply as selecting agents, a sort of sieve which retains only the resistant cells. According to the second hypothesis, exposure to the phage is the cause which trans-

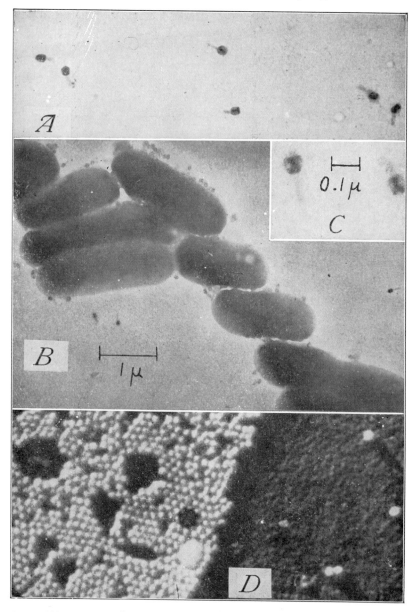

Figure 5.1. Bacteriophages which attack colon bacteria, *Escherichia coli*. *A*. Bacteriophage particles magnified about 29,000 times, and in *C* magnified about 75,000 times. *B*. Bacteria cells with bacteriophages adhering to their surface at a somewhat lower magnification. *D*. Particles of a plant virus "shadowed" by a metal spray. (After Luria, from Curtis and Guthrie.)

forms some susceptible cells into resistant ones. A test of the validity of these working hypotheses has been made by a statistical analysis of the experimental findings. If the second hypothesis were correct, a bacterial culture would contain no resistant cells until and unless exposed to the phage. The first hypothesis assumes that resistant mutants appear in the cultures before they are exposed to the phage.

Let us, then, take several bacterial cultures, each grown from a

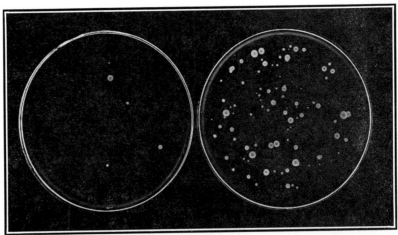

Figure 5.2. Two Petri plates with colonies of colon bacteria (*Escherichia coli*) which have acquired by mutation a resistance to the attacks of bacteriophages. The number of mutants on the plate on the right is obviously greater than on that on the left. (Courtesy of Dr. M. Demerec.)

single or a few cells. All cultures are simultaneously exposed to phages, and the numbers of resistant cells which survive are counted. According to the second hypothesis, the cultures should contain a certain mean number of mutants, subject only to the variation due to statistical errors of sampling. The mathematical theory of probability shows that these sampling errors will obey a simple rule, namely, that the variance (the sum of squared deviation from the mean, divided by the number of observations) will be about as great as the mean itself. If the first hypothesis is correct, the numbers of resistant cells in different cultures will be far more variable. If the mutation takes place early when the growing culture contains few cells, the mutant cell will multiply and produce a large progeny. By the time the bacteriophage is introduced in the culture, many resistant bacteria may be present. On the contrary, a mutation taking place just before the application of the phage will yield a single resistant cell. Statistically, the result will be that the variance of the number of resistant bacteria will be greater than the mean number of such bacteria in different cultures. Experiments have shown that the variances are indeed much greater than the means. This is a rigorous proof of the validity of the first hypothesis, that of spontaneous mutation.

Ability of Bacteriophages to Attack Bacteria. If a phage suspension is applied to a culture of colon bacteria, a mutant line of the bacteria can be obtained which is resistant to the phage. Several strains of phages, however, have been discovered which differ in their appearance under electron microscopes and in certain physiological characteristics. Now, a line of bacteria resistant to one phage strain may be fully susceptible to other phages. The resistance in the bacteria is specific to the phage strain which was applied as the selector of the resistant mutant cells.

A line of bacteria which had become resistant to one phage strain may be made resistant also to other phages. To do so, the bacteria are exposed successively to different phage strains, and the resistant mutants are isolated. Bacteria have been obtained which are resistant to several phages. The simplest explanation of this situation is that the colon bacteria carry many genes, and that the resistance to different phage strains is due to mutation of different genes. Multiple resistance is due to occurrence of several mutations.

The selection of resistant mutants adapts bacteria to live in environments in which phages also occur. The phages meet this situation by a similar adaptive process. If a large number of phage particles are added to a bacterial culture which is resistant to that particular phage, a new strain of the phage may be obtained which can prey on these bacteria. The new phage strain can be maintained on cultures of sensitive bacteria. The bacteria may, however, become resistant to the "new phage" by another mutation, and the phage may overcome that second resistance by still another mutational step.

The changes in the bacteriophages, like those in the bacteria, seem explicable on either of the two hypotheses outlined above for bacteria (page 94). First, mutations which enable phages to attack previously resistant bacteria may arise spontaneously in phage cultures, and may be selected when resistant bacteria are exposed to the mixture of mutant and original phages. Second, the ability of the phage to attack resistant bacteria may be acquired only through contact with such bacteria. In 1945 Luria demonstrated that the first hypothesis is correct. Hershey then estimated that the mutations which overcome the resistance of the bacteria occur, on the average, in two to three out of every billion phage particles.

Resistance of Bacteria to Antibiotics. Discovery of chemotherapeutic and antibiotic drugs has been a great advance in modern medicine. These drugs kill certain disease-creating microorganisms, often when applied in extremely small doses. Their efficacy, however, may be severely reduced by the development of strains of microorganisms resistant to the antibiotics. Resistant bacteria appear in laboratory cultures in which the bacteria are kept on nutrient media to which a certain antibiotic has been added. They can be isolated also from experimental animals or from human patients who were repeatedly treated with a chemotherapeutic or antibiotic drug.

A concentration of the antibiotic streptomycin as low as 25 milligrams per liter of the nutrient medium stops the growth of the colon bacteria, *Escherichia coli*. However, if several billion bacteria are placed on streptomycin-containing medium, one or several cells continue to grow and divide, and form colonies from which strains permanently resistant to even very high doses of streptomycin may be established. The situation is quite parallel to that described above for the development of bacteriophage-resistant strains of the same bacteria. Demerec found that mutations to streptomycin resistance arise in about one out of a billion divisions of the bacterial cells. The mutations are not induced by streptomycin. The role of the streptomycin is that of a selecting agent; it removes vast numbers of non-resistant cells, and permits only mutant cells to survive.

"Training" of Bacteria. The development of resistance to penicillin in the bacterium *Staphylococcus aureus*, studied by Demerec, appears at first sight less easy to account for on the basis of the mutation-selection hypothesis. If about one hundred million cells of these bacteria are placed on a nutrient medium containing 0.1 of an "Oxford unit" of penicillin per cubic centimeter (milliliter) of the medium, usually less than ten cells survive and reproduce. But the progeny of these cells survives well on this medium, and a few cells per billion survive at concentrations of penicillin up to 0.2 of an Oxford unit per milliliter of the medium. These relatively resistant survivors can now be exposed to still higher concentrations of penicillin. By stepping up the concentrations of penicillin five times, bacteria are obtained which can grow in the presence of as much as 250 units of penicillin per milliliter of the medium.

This gradual "training" of the bacteria to withstand the presence of penicillin comes through summation of several mutational steps, each of which taken separately confers only partial resistance on the bacteria. Demerec estimates that these mutations occur spontaneously at a rate of about one per one hundred million bacterial cells (10^{-8}). Suppose, then, that four or five such mutations must occur to make the bacteria completely resistant to penicillin. Simultaneous mutation of two such genes in the same cell is likely to occur about once in a number of cell divisions expressed by a figure with sixteen zeros (10^{-16}). Simultaneous mutation of five genes has an utterly negligible probability of occurrence. And yet rigorous selection accumulates such mutations so efficiently that the experiments on induced resistance are easily reproducible.

Resistant Bacteria in Animal Hosts. Hundreds of reports have been published in recent years on patients developing drug-fast infections as a result of treatment with antibiotic and chemotherapeutic drugs. It is now recognized that most infections treated with streptomycin must be brought under control by sufficient doses of the drug within a few days from the beginning of the treatment. If the doses of the drug used are too small to accomplish this end, the infection is likely to become streptomycin-resistant; and further treatment with this antibiotic is ineffective.

When many people are treated with chemotherapy, resistant mutants of pathogenic bacteria acquire so great an advantage over susceptible bacteria that the drugs become effective in fewer and fewer patients. This is what happened as a result of mass application of sulfonamide drugs for treatment of certain venereal diseases. The proportion of cases of disease which failed to respond to sulfonamide treatment has increased. An unpremeditated experiment of this kind was also made in certain training centers of the Navy during the last war. An attempt was made to reduce the incidence of diseases produced by Streptococcus bacteria by giving to large numbers of men small doses of a sulfonamid drug. The result was what any competent geneticist could have predicted: a sharp increase of infections with sulfonamid-resistant strains of streptococci.

There has been much discussion as to whether the drug-resistant bacteria arise in the treated patients, or are always present in bacterial populations. This is a spurious problem. Any mutation has a certain probability of occurrence; the application of the antibiotics does not influence the rate of origin of the resistant mutants. Nevertheless, the antibiotics are responsible for the spread of such mutants, giving them an adaptive advantage which they do not possess outside the environments in which the drugs are present.

Reversibility of the Effects of Mutation and Selection. Mutant bacteria resistant to bacteriophages or to antibiotics are superior to sen ,i-
tive bacteria in environments in which bacteriophages or antibiotics
are present. Sensitive bacteria are killed off, the resistant ones survive. Yet resistant mutants are not induced by the phages or the antibiotics; they arise regardless of whether the environmental selecting
agents favor them or not. Why, then, are most colon bacteria found
outside of laboratories still susceptible to bacteriophage attacks and
sensitive to streptomycin? Why have the resistant mutants not
crowded out the sensitive genotypes? The theory leads us to infer
that the resistant mutants must in some respects be at a disadvantage
compared to sensitive bacteria in the absence of phages and antibiotics.

This theoretical inference is strikingly verified in some experiments.
Close to 60 per cent of the streptomycin-resistant mutants in colon
bacteria are also streptomycin dependent; these mutants are unable
to grow on culture media free of streptomycin. A substance which is
poisonous to normal sensitive bacteria is essential for life of the resistant mutants! E. H. Anderson has shown that some bacteriophage-
resistant strains of colon bacteria require for growth certain food substances which are not needed for the growth of sensitive bacteria. The
resistant mutants will be wiped out in environments in which the
required foods are not available.

Just what puts some mutants at a disadvantage in competition with
"normal" types is unknown at present. Some streptomycin-resistant
mutants can grow without streptomycin, and some phage-resistant
mutants are not known to possess special food requirements. It should
be noted, however, that advantages and disadvantages which are
easiest to discover are of the all-or-nothing type: all streptomycin-
sensitive bacteria are killed in the presence of streptomycin, and all
streptomycin-dependent bacteria die in the absence of this substance.
But the advantages and the disadvantages may also be quite small
and yet very effective in the long run. Suppose that a mutant grows
slightly slower than the parental type in a certain environment. The
mutant will then be quite rare, and yet it may not be easy to discover
the nature of the handicap which keeps it rare.

Where the advantages and disadvantages are of the all-or-none type,
the importance of the environment in selecting the best-adapted genotypes can be demonstrated with remarkable clarity. Demerec and his
collaborators showed that the changes from streptomycin sensitivity
to resistance and dependence are reversible. A large number of colon

bacteria of a streptomycin-dependent strain are placed on a Petri plate with nutrient medium free of streptomycin. Only the mutant cells which can grow without streptomycin survive and form colonies of streptomycin-independent bacteria. The mutation from streptomycin dependence to independence occurs about forty times per one billion divisions of the bacterial cells.

Virulence of Pathogenic Microorganisms. Disease-producing microorganisms often lose their ability to infect their normal hosts after prolonged cultivation on artificial media in laboratories, but the virulence of such "degenerate" bacteria may sometimes be restored. For this purpose a large number of the bacteria which lost their virulence are inoculated in a host susceptible to the disease. If the bacteria are able to multiply in such a host, a new virulent strain may be isolated.

Fowl typhoid, a disease often fatal to chickens, is caused by the bacterium *Salmonella gallinarum*. In an experiment by Gowen, an originally highly virulent strain of these bacteria lost its virulence after some months of cultivation in the laboratory. Inoculation of about 100,000 bacteria of the virulent strain in a bird results in disease which is fatal to some 70 per cent of the birds; the same dose of avirulent bacteria produces no disease. A thousand times greater (100,000,000) dose of avirulent bacteria results in the death of only 34 per cent of the chickens. The full virulence, however, is restored by inoculating about two billion avirulent bacteria into each of several chickens; after a week, new cultures of the bacteria are re-isolated from the infected birds. Such "passage" of the bacterial strain through living hosts was repeated six times. New virulent strains of bacteria were obtained.

The simplest interpretation of the loss and reacquisition of the virulence is that different genotypes are advantageous in bacteria which live as parasites in living hosts, and multiply in laboratory test tubes. When bacteria grow on laboratory media, mutants are selected which enable them to live most successfully in this artificial environment, even though the mutants lose the ability to invade a host's body. Conversely, when laboratory strains of bacteria are inoculated in a host's body, the mutants which restore the ability to overcome the resistance of the host acquire a clear survival advantage.

Genetics and Epidemics. Mankind has always dreaded the recurrent scourge of epidemics. Some 25 million people perished from black death in Europe in 1347 and 1348, between a quarter and a third of the population. Outbreaks of infections occur also in wild and in domestic animals and plants.

We have seen that mutations in pathogenic microorganisms make them more or less virulent, and more or less sensitive to antibiotics. There exist also genetic variations in the susceptibility to diseases among the hosts which the pathogens attack. Perhaps the clearest example is the resistance of varieties of the common onions to attacks by the smudge fungus, Colletotrichum. Onion varieties which have white bulbs are easily infected with the fungus; cream-colored or yellow bulbs are slightly susceptible; and deeply colored red or purple bulbs are resistant. The resistance is due to the presence in the scales of the colored bulbs of catechol and protocatechuic acid, substances which can be shown to be poisonous to the spores of the fungus. Walker and his students have shown that the color of the bulbs, the presence in them of catechol and protocatechuic acid (which are colorless substances), and the resistance or susceptibility are manifestations of the same genes. The gene I, when homozygous (II), makes the bulbs white and susceptible to the infection. The heterozygotes, Ii, are yellow and only slightly susceptible, whereas the homozygotes, ii, are deeply colored and resistant.

There is no doubt that genetic variations in the susceptibility to infection occur also among higher animals and among men. Gowen has described strains of chickens some of which were more resistant than others to the fowl typhoid, resulting from infections with Salmonella (see above). Genetic resistance interacts, of course, with the immunity to certain diseases acquired by individuals as a result of the formation of protective antibodies in their blood. The formation of protective antibodies may be induced by a previous infection or, artificially, by vaccination. The genotype determines, as we know, the responses of the organism to the environment. The actual resistance or susceptibility of an individual (his phenotype) will depend upon his genetic constitution as well as upon his previous contacts with the disease.

An epidemic, then, will affect at first those individuals in the host's population which are phenotypically and genetically most susceptible to the infection. An epidemic may start when a strongly virulent strain of the pathogen appears. The spread of the infection will be more and more rapid as the number of its victims increases, but the point will be reached when a majority of the highly susceptible individuals will be either dead or recovered from the disease. An epidemic grows so long as each victim transmits the infection, on the average, to more than one new victim. When the frequency of the transmission drops below one, the epidemic subsides. The outcome of an epidemic may be a genetic change in the composition of the populations of both the host and the parasite.

Rust Fungi Attacking Wheat. As far as man is concerned, the foregoing picture of the genetic background of epidemics is rather hypothetical. It is, however, borne out by observations particularly on the diseases of certain crop plants. The rust fungus, *Puccinia graminis tritici,* is responsible for one of the most serious diseases which affect wheat plantings. This species of rust contains some 200 varieties (called "physiological races" by the students of these fungi). The rust varieties are distinguished from each other by their ability to infect different varieties of wheat. Most wheat varieties are susceptible to infection by some, but resistant to other varieties of the rust.

The spores of the rust are distributed by winds and air currents. Since the degree of infestation of wheat fields by the rusts influences the yield of the crop, annual census of the relative frequencies of the spores of different rust varieties is made in the United States and in other wheat-growing countries. The incidence of the different rust varieties undergoes striking changes with time (Table 5.1).

TABLE 5.1

FREQUENCIES (IN PER CENTS OF THE TOTAL) OF THE SPORES OF THE DIFFERENT VARIETIES OF THE RUST FUNGUS *Puccinia graminis tritici* IN THE UNITED STATES

(After Stakman and Others.)

Variety Number

Year	11	17	21	34	36	38	49	56
1930	4	0.3	7	0.6	36	30	20	0.2
1931	22	0.6	4	2	28	15	25	1
1932	5	1	2	0.9	10	46	27	2
1933	2	1	4	7	4	33	37	4
1934	0.6	0.6	7	22	21	3	1	33
1935	19	1.5	2	18	6	5	1	44
1936	12	4	0.8	4	3	22	1	47
1937	8	6	0.6	1	6	9	7	56
1938	2	3	1	0.8	1	16	0.9	66
1939	3	10	0.4	0.6	0.8	24	0.6	56
1940	4	34	0	0.5	2	10	0.1	44
1941	1	51	0	0	2	6	2	32
1942	0.3	27	0	0.2	2	27	4	31
1943	0.1	23	0	0.1	0.4	24	0.3	49
1944	0	21	0	0	0.2	26	0.2	43

The changes in the relative frequencies of the rust varieties are largely due to the introduction of new varieties of wheat for mass planting by the farmers. Wheat breeders are constantly trying to create new kinds of wheats resistant to infection by the rusts. They are often successful, to the extent that new wheat genotypes are obtained by hybridization and selection which are resistant to the rust varieties that are prevalent at the time when the breeding work is done. These new kinds of wheat are then multiplied and planted by many farmers. At first, the yields of wheat are satisfactory. But the new wheats begin to be attacked by rust varieties which were hitherto unknown or rare, and soon the rust infestations become so heavy that the wheat yields decline. Eventually it becomes necessary to use another assortment of wheats for planting.

For example, the outbreak of rust variety 56 in 1934 and thereafter (see Table 5.1) seems to be connected with large-scale planting in the United States of the wheat variety called Ceres. In 1925 this high-yielding wheat was planted on a large scale. About ten years later Ceres was so heavily attacked by rust that its plantings rapidly shrank in number. This is a genetic and epidemiological experiment conducted on a grand scale. Introduction by man of a new host plant initiates a process of selection of genotypes in the parasite which can invade this host, with the result that the adaptedness of the host genotypes declines. An unstable equilibrium is temporarily restored by a genotypic change in the host.

Insect Pests Resistant to Poisons. Experiments on adaptation through selection of useful mutants have been made chiefly with bacteria and other microorganisms because the experimenter can easily manage huge numbers of individuals and of generations, which would be out of the question with larger creatures. Similar adaptive processes occur also in higher organisms, although usually more slowly. Many insecticides, poisons which kill insect pests, have been discovered. A particularly powerful insecticide is dichloro-diphenyl-trichlorethane, popularly known as DDT. This substance is highly poisonous to most insects in such low concentrations as to deserve being placed among the "wonder drugs." The struggle of man against insect pests has nevertheless not ended, owing to the emergence of DDT-resistant varieties of insects.

The housefly, *Musca domestica,* is often controlled by DDT sprays. Yet Missiroli and Weismann reported independently in 1947 that houseflies from certain localities in Italy and in Sweden, respectively, had become relatively resistant to DDT. The concentrations of DDT which in previous years were sufficient to destroy most of the house-flies in these localities no longer were effective when applied in the customary way. Since 1947 similar reports have come from Denmark, England, Greece, Egypt, Peru, Venezuela, Mexico, and parts of the United States as widely separated as New Jersey, Florida, California, and Oregon. In many places DDT can no longer be relied upon to bring housefly infestations under control.

Strains of houseflies resistant to DDT have been obtained also in laboratory experiments. Lindquist and Wilson exposed a normal sensitive strain to a dose of DDT which killed about 90 per cent of the individuals, and used the survivors as parents of the next generation. A significant resistance to DDT appeared after three generations of such selection.

There is no agreement among different investigators about how permanent is the resistance once acquired by a fly strain. In some instances the resistance has been retained for ten or more generations without renewed exposures to DDT; in others the resistance has been alleged to become weaker or lost. This situation may be interpreted in several ways. It is possible that the DDT resistance is due to a single mutation, analogous to that which confers the streptomycin resistance on bacteria (page 98). It may also be that the resistance is produced by a combination of several genes which are normally present in most fly populations. In either case, a "resistant" strain may actually be a mixture of more or less resistant and of sensitive genotypes. The average resistance may vary greatly from generation to generation, and it may be more or less fixed or changeable in different strains.

Theoretically, we might expect the resistant houseflies to be adaptively inferior to the sensitive ones in the absence of DDT treatments. Indeed, some investigators have found that resistant flies take more time to develop than the normal ones. If confirmed, this difference may be very significant, since a rapid development may be advantageous to the flies in their normal habitats. Other investigators have found indications of important physiological differences between sensitive and resistant flies.

The emergence of strains of insect pests resistant to various insecticides has assumed, in recent years, the proportions of a major problem to those concerned with pest control. Resistances to DDT treatments have been described in several species of mosquitoes, in filter flies (Psychoda), cockroaches, body lice, bedbugs, and bark beetles (Scolytus). Even before the advent of the DDT, strains resistant to fumigation with hydrocyanic gas were known to have developed in at least three different species of scale insects (Coccidae) in the fruit orchards of California. Similarly, the codling moth (*Carpocapsa pomonella*), the larva of which is responsible for the "wormy" apples, has developed in Colorado and in New York State races resistant to lead arsenate sprays. From South Africa have come reports that ticks which infest cattle are becoming resistant to arsenic baths. New cases of resistance of various pests to insecticides are constantly reported in the literature. Genetically oriented studies in this field are urgently necessary.

Industrial Melanism. Perhaps the most striking and longest known examples of observed evolutionary changes concern the development

Figure 5.3. Light-colored and dark varieties of the moths *Amphidasys betularia* and *Odontoptera bidentata*. The dark varieties have greatly increased in frequencies in some industrial districts of England and other European countries. (After W. Bowater.)

of dark, melanic, varieties in several species of moths in the industrialized regions of western Europe, particularly in England. Each of these moth species has two varieties, one relatively light and the other dark (Figure 5.3). The two varieties differ in a single Mendelian gene, the dark variety being usually dominant to the light one. The light varieties are the "normal" ones, in the sense that until recently the moths were represented in nature by light individuals, the dark ones being exceptional or altogether unknown. But beginning in the middle of the nineteenth century, the dark varieties have been recorded as occurring more and more often, especially in the vicinity of large industrial centers. In many industrial regions the incidence of dark varieties has grown rapidly from decade to decade; some of the populations now consist of dark individuals, with or without an admixture of light ones.

The most satisfactory interpretation of the spread of the melanic varieties has been suggested by Ford, who believes that the dark varieties are in general more vigorous than the light ones. In one species, *Boarmia repandata,* he was able to demonstrate the superior vigor of the melanic forms experimentally. Why, then, are the dark varieties crowding out the normal light ones only in industrial regions and not everywhere? Ford's answer is that the light varieties compensate for the deficient vigor by being protectively colored. In other words, they are camouflaged by matching the coloration of their surroundings, and escape being detected and eaten by their enemies, insectivorous birds, more often than do the more conspicuous dark varieties. The situation is different in industrial regions, where the countryside is contaminated by soot and other waste products. Here, on darker backgrounds, the light varieties are no longer camouflaged, whereas the dark varieties may more nearly match the colors of their surroundings. Industrialization of a region removes, then, the disadvantages of the dark varieties, which spread and eventually supplant the light ones.

Deleterious Character of Most Mutations. Most mutants which arise in any organism are more or less disadvantageous to their possessors. The classical mutants obtained in Drosophila usually show deterioration, breakdown, or disappearance of some organs (Figures 4.4 and 4.5). Mutants are known which diminish the quantity or destroy the pigment in the eyes, and in the body reduce the wings, eyes, bristles, legs. Many mutants are, in fact, lethal to their possessors. Mutants which equal the normal fly in vigor are a minority, and mutants that would make a major improvement of the normal organization in the normal environments are unknown.

And, yet, modern theories of evolution consider the process of mutation to be the source of the raw materials from which evolutionary changes may be constructed. The deleterious character of most mu-

tants seems to be a very serious difficulty. A more careful consideration shows, however, that the difficulty is much less formidable than
it may appear at first sight.

Are the mutations which make the colon bacteria resistant to bacteriophages or to streptomycin harmful or useful? Is the resistance to
DDT sprays deleterious or advantageous to the houseflies? Obviously,
these questions are meaningless when the nature of the environments
in which the mutants are placed is not specified. On media containing
bacteriophages or streptomycin, the resistance is necessary to the bacteria, since the carriers of the non-resistant genotypes are destroyed.
Flies or scales resistant to the DDT or to hydrocyanic gas have evident
advantages in localities sprayed or fumigated with these poisons, but
the same genotypes are disadvantageous when phages, antibiotics, and
insecticides are absent.

Useful Mutations. Useful mutations, therefore, are known. They
are in fact not uncommon when organisms are placed in environments other than those in which these organisms usually occur, but
in environments in which the species normally lives useful mutations
are not observed. A closer consideration will show that this is, indeed,
as it should be. Every kind of mutation that a biologist observes in
his experiments has a certain probability of occurrence, and it has
occurred repeatedly in the history of the species. The mutations
which improve the adaptedness of the species to its normal environments were tried out by natural selection, and have become incorporated into the "normal," that is, frequently met with, genotypes. The
"normal" genotypes are compounded of just such useful mutations.
Hence the mutations that take place are deleterious.

But when the environment changes, the adaptedness of the organism
is disrupted, and the harmony between the environment and its inhabitants can be restored only through a genotypic reconstruction.
Some mutations prove useful in new environments and in combination with new components of the species genotype. The mutant genes
replace the genes that were "normal" in the old environment, and
become the new adaptive "norm." Although the old genes may re-
appear from time to time by mutation, they will now be deleterious
and will be eliminated. This is what happens when colon bacteria
resistant to streptomycin are kept on media with high streptomycin
content. The mutants which restore the sensitivity to strepomycin
are destroyed.

The Price of Adaptation. Many mutants which are deleterious in
a certain environment may be useful in altered circumstances. It does

not follow, however, that every mutant which occurs in any species must necessarily be useful in some environment; numerous mutants in Drosophila and in man produce hereditary diseases which can hardly be useful in any environment. It is difficult to imagine an environment which would make hemophilia or the amaurotic idiocy useful.

There is nothing surprising in the appearance of such adaptively worthless mutants. A mutation is essentially a dislocation taking place in the delicate self-reproducing mechanism of the gene. Random changes in any complex mechanism, such as a watch or an automobile, are more likely to injure than to improve it; and yet watches and automobiles are changed for the better, step by step, in their historical development, just as the organisms are in their evolutionary development. The improvements in non-living mechanisms are due to the skill of the engineers; those in living beings are established by natural selection perpetuating the useful mutants and gene combinations, and failing to perpetuate the useless ones.

But why, it may be asked, should useless mutations be produced at all? It would be vastly better if the organisms produced only useful mutations where and when needed. A little thought will show how naïve such a question really is. The normal colon bacteria produce bacteriophage-resistant and streptomycin-resistant mutants, a great majority of which are lost, because they are useless in the absence of phages and of streptomycin. In order to produce only phage resistance in the cultures to which phages are applied, only streptomycin resistance in the cultures which are brought in contact with streptomycin, and neither mutant in cultures which remain in normal environments, bacteria would have to possess a prescience of the future. When the phages attack it is too late: the non-resistant bacteria perish. All kinds of mutants are produced regardless of whether any of them will prove useful. A living species that would suppress the mutation process, by making the gene reproduction absolutely accurate, might gain a temporary advantage. In a static environment such a non-mutable species would not beget the useless and harmful mutants, but when the environment changed and made some of the mutants better fit than the old norm to survive, a non-mutable species would be the loser. In the long run, mutability is a useful trait, even though most mutants are harmful in any one environment. Herein lay the fundamental error of the belief in the inheritance of acquired traits: it assumed that the genes are made to mutate in a determined direction by every change in the development of the body.

Suggestions for Further Reading

Darwin, Ch. 1859. *On the Origin of Species by Means of Natural Selection.*

This is one of the greatest books of all time, and an acquaintance with it is a "must" for every student of evolution. There are numerous editions of this work. The first edition (1859) has recently been reprinted by the Philosophical Library, New York, with a foreword by C. D. Darlington (1951).

Catcheside, D. G. 1951. *The Genetics of Microorganisms.* Pitman, New York.

Braun, W. 1953. *Bacterial Genetics.* Saunders, Philadelphia.

The books of Catcheside and of Braun review the experiments on the genetics of microorganisms.

Dunn, L. C. (Editor). 1951. *Genetics in the Twentieth Century.* Macmillan, New York.

This is a symposium held in 1950 to commemorate the fiftieth anniversary of the rediscovery of Mendel's work and of the birth of genetics. Several papers in this symposium are pertinent to the topics discussed in the present chapter, especially *Genetic studies in bacteria,* by J. Lederberg; *Genetics and disease resistance,* by J. W. Gowen; *Genetics and plant pathology,* by J. C. Walker.

Natural Selection
and Adaptation

It is a commonplace observation that every living being is so constructed that it is able to live in a certain environment (Figure 6.1). A fish is adapted to live in water, a bird is an efficient flying machine, a cow and a deer have digestive organs which enable them to feed on herbage and foliage, the human mind permits man to acquire and transmit culture. The origin of this apparent purposefulness of biological organization is a riddle which several generations of biologists have attempted to solve. Some have taken the easy way out by supposing that every living species is endowed by the Creator with those features which it needs in order to live in the habitats in which it is actually found. This is, however, a spurious solution; it implicitly blames the Creator also for all the imperfections and all the sufferings found in human and biological nature.

So far the only scientifically tenable solution of the riddle was proposed by Darwin in 1859. According to Darwin, organisms become adapted to the environment in the process of evolution; this process is controlled by natural selection of genetic variants which are relatively better fitted than others to survive and to reproduce in certain environments. The theory accepted by a majority of modern evolutionists is clearly derived from Darwin's theory; however, it is just as clearly not identical with the Darwinian prototype. The changes in the theory are due to the mass of new evidence discovered by biologists since 1859. The modern theories are often referred to as *neo-Darwinism,* which would be a good name if it were not for the fact that it was applied also to the theories developed by Weismann and others around 1900, and they are as different from the modern ones as they were from Darwin's. *Synthetic theory* and *biological theory* of evolution

Figure 6.1. Different kinds of birds are adapted to different foods, different types of country, and different ways of life. The figure shows examples of this "adaptive radiation" in modern birds, together with the primitive, and possibly ancestral, form Archaeopteryx, which is known only as a fossil. (From Colbert.)

are better names, because they emphasize that modern theories are a result of synthesis of the findings of many biological disciplines—genetics, systematics, comparative morphology, paleontology, embryology, ecology, etc.

History of the Idea of Natural Selection. Some historians believe that a germ of the theory of natural selection is as old as the myths of the Greek philosopher Empedocles (fifth century B.C.) and the Roman poet Lucretius (first century B.C.). According to these myths, parts of human bodies, heads, trunks, arms, and legs appeared in the world before complete human beings. These isolated parts proceeded to combine at random, giving rise to many inviable combinations which were lost, and to complete human bodies which survived and reproduced their likes.

According to Darwin himself, the idea of natural selection was suggested to him by the *Essay on the Principles of Population,* published in 1798 by the English country parson and amateur sociologist and mathematician T. R. Malthus. Malthus pointed out that human populations tend to increase in numbers in geometric progression; that growing populations sooner or later outrun their food supply; that more children are born than live to maturity, because of the *"struggle for existence"*; hunger, war, and disease keep the population numbers in check. Darwin saw that this is obviously true for any living species, from a microbe to the elephant. Indeed, an oyster produces up to 114,000,000 eggs in a single spawning; under favorable conditions, some bacteria can double in number in less than half an hour. Higher animals, mammals and birds, produce only few young, but on the average always more than two per pair of parents. Given enough time, the number of individuals of any species could become too large for the earth to support them.

In reality, the populations of most species oscillate within rather narrow limits, and only rarely do some populations grow as fast as their reproductive powers might permit. The struggle for existence causes a part, and often a very large part, of the progeny to die before reaching sexual maturity. Living beings "fight" against the physical environment—excessive cold, heat, dryness, wind, etc. They are destroyed by predators, parasites, and diseases. And they "compete" with individuals of their own and other species for food, for shelter, and for mates.

Darwin saw further the relation between the Malthusian struggle for existence and the fact that agriculturists have since time immemorial improved the quality of domestic animals and plants by selecting for reproduction those individuals which possessed the qualities which were useful or desirable to the breeders. Now, the survivors in the struggle for existence are likely to differ in their genotype from the victims which succumb in this struggle. Provided that the survivors differ in heredity from those who do not survive, the struggle for existence will automatically result in *natural selection* of the fitter genotypes. The hereditary endowment of the succeeding generations will differ from that of the preceding generations in the direction of superior fitness.

Competition and Cooperation. The logic of Darwin's reasoning was unassailable. Nevertheless, he and his theories were attacked by those who believed that the recognition of man as a part of nature is subversive to religion and insulting to human dignity. In the ensuing polemics some unfortunate overstatements were made. Herbert Spencer said that the struggle for existence led to the *"survival of the fittest."* The use of the superlative gave a subtle overemphasis to the supposed struggle and competition—as though only one fittest survived and all the rest died. Spencer's statement sounded very much like the concept of Superman, advanced by the German philosopher Nietzsche, which in turn played a role in the development of racist and Nazi ideas.

Phrases such as "struggle for existence," "nature red in tooth and claw," "eat or be eaten" were very freely used, especially by popular writers on evolution, in the late nineteenth and early twentieth centuries. This phraseology seemed to appeal to the emotions of many people of those days. With the development of genetics and with a change of the intellectual climate during the current century, it began to be realized that the fierceness of the struggle for existence leading to natural selection was greatly exaggerated. It is simply the fit, rather than the "fittest," who survive.

Evolutionary success is determined by the ability of the carriers of a given genotype to transmit their genes to the greatest possible number of individuals in the following generations. "Struggle," "competition," and like expressions have a metaphorical meaning when applied to the process of natural selection which should not be confused with their usage when applied to human affairs. Thus trees "struggle" against the danger of being felled by wind by developing stronger root systems; mammals and birds "struggle" against cold by developing heat insulation, temperature regulation, or by remaining dormant during winter months; desert plants "struggle" against dryness by having leaves transformed into spines. Plants and animals "compete" for food when food is scarce, but they do not necessarily fight against one another.

Among the early critics of Darwin, the English writer, Samuel Butler, and particularly the Russian political philosopher, Kropotkin, sought to replace Darwin's theory of "struggle" by one which made cooperation and mutual help the principal agents of evolution. Recently this idea was developed further and modernized by Allee and by Ashley Montagu. As a corrective against the abuse of Darwinism by political propagandists, this emphasis on the importance of cooperativeness in natural selection is very useful. Indeed, pugnacity and aggressiveness are often less conducive to biological success than is inclination to "live and let live" and to cooperate with other individuals of the same and of other species. The fact is that both competition and cooperation are observed in nature. Natural selection is neither egotistic nor altruistic. It is, rather, opportunistic: life is promoted now by struggle and now by mutual help. Thus parental care and defense of the offspring are obviously advantageous for the survival of the species; and yet members of an established colony of a certain species of ant in Australia destroy the daughter colonies as soon as the latter appear on the surface of the ground in the vicinity of the parental nest.

Johannsen and Pure Lines. Less spectacular but more important than the misunderstanding of the relative importance of competition and cooperation in natural selection was another difficulty of Darwin's theory. As pointed out above, Darwin realized quite clearly that natural selection will produce permanent improvements only provided that the surviving "fit" differ in genotype from the eliminated "unfit." If the individuals which breed and those which are prevented from breeding are alike in genetic endowment, their progenies should be alike and selection should be ineffective. This matter was clarified long after Darwin's death by the Danish botanist Johannsen (1857–1927).

Johannsen (1909) started his experiments with garden beans by choosing seeds of different sizes and weights from a commercial variety, and keeping the progenies of the plants grown from each seed separately (Figure 6.2). The garden bean is a plant species which, like Mendel's pea, reproduces mostly by self-pollination. Progenies obtained from a single individual of such species by self-fertilization are called *pure lines*, and individuals which belong to the same pure line usually have similar genotypes. The pure lines obtained by Johannsen from larger beans produced, on the average, larger seeds than did the pure lines bred from smaller beans, when planted under similar environmental conditions. This amounts to saying that the original variety contained a variety of genotypes. Next, Johannsen

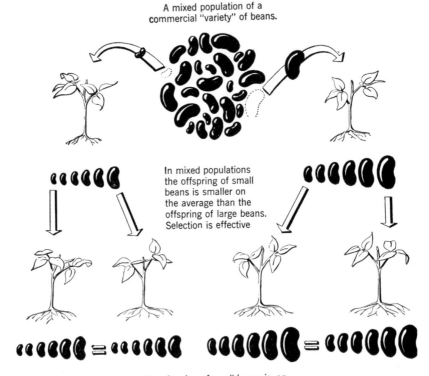

A mixed population of a commercial "variety" of beans.

In mixed populations the offspring of small beans is smaller on the average than the offspring of large beans. Selection is effective

The offspring of small beans is, on the average, of the same size as the offspring of large beans. In the pure lines selection is ineffective.

Figure 6.2. The main results of Johannsen's experiments on pure lines in beans. The commercially planted "varieties" of beans are mixtures of lines with different genotypes. From such a variety, genetically different pure lines with larger or smaller seeds can be isolated by selection. But the offspring of large or small beans from any one pure line are similar.

selected the largest and the smallest seeds *within* each of his pure lines. When planted under similar conditions, the offspring of the large and the small beans had the same average size. This experiment proved that selection is ineffective within a pure line. The differences in size between seeds produced by plants of the same pure line are not genotypic; they are acquired because of the unavoidable minor variations in the environmental conditions under which the plants grow; they are within the norm of reaction of the genotype of the pure lines.

Johannsen's work was confirmed by other investigators working with pure lines and with *clones*. A clone is the offspring of a single individual obtained by asexual means, such as simple fission and budding. Clones can be easily obtained in most microorganisms and in some plants and animals which can reproduce asexually. Selection is ineffective in a clone (unless mutation intervenes; see below).

In effect, the work of Johannsen proved only that acquired characters are not inherited (see Chapter 4). Indeed, phenotypic differences between genotypically uniform individuals are acquired through environmental modification, but in the 1910's these results were interpreted as a blow to Darwin's theory of natural selection. For Johannsen found that selection was effective only in the original material, which was a mixture of several genotypically different pure lines. Selection, then, has done nothing "creative"; it has merely isolated some of the genotypes which were already present in the original mixture. In the absence of pre-existent genotypic differences, selection is powerless to effect evolutionary changes.

The modern solution of the foregoing difficulty is simple enough. Selection operates with genetic raw materials supplied by mutation and sexual reproduction. Mutation and sex produce an abundance of genetic variability, interacting with which selection becomes a creative process (see Chapter 14). But before this solution could be reached, another, and apparently even more formidable, difficulty of the Darwinian theory had to be removed.

Gene Frequency and Gene Pool. According to the "blood" theory of heredity, which was quite generally accepted in Darwin's day, the heredity of a child is a solution, or an alloy, of the heredities of the parents. Consider, then, what happens in a population which contains genotypes that produce, in a certain environment, individuals of a middle stature, genotypes which produce tall and short people, and a few genotypes which produce giants and dwarfs. In the genetic sense, a population, a *Mendelian population*, is a community of sexually reproducing individuals among whom marriages are concluded. Suppose, furthermore, that our Mendelian population is *panmictic* with respect to stature; in other words, that the likelihood of an individual's marrying a partner of any stature is proportional to the relative frequencies of these statures in the population. It is easy to see that, in such a panmictic population, individuals who are taller than

Figure 6.3.　Charles Darwin (1809–1882).

the average will often marry partners who are shorter than themselves, whereas persons who are shorter than the average will usually marry mates who are taller than they are.

If the blood theory of heredity were true, the heredity of children would be a compromise between the heredities of their parents. A panmictic population would then become less and less variable in stature, and in other characters, as one generation followed the other. In other words, a sexual panmictic population would become more and more uniform, and eventually it could reach the point where all individuals composing the population would be uniform in hereditary endowment. Such a genetically homogeneous population could be called a pure race.

Darwin realized that a necessary consequence of the acceptance of the blood theory of heredity was the belief that sexual reproduction tended to level off any genetic variability that might be present in a sexual population. And yet, if evolution is to occur, populations must always possess a supply of hereditary variability. Darwin admitted that the contradiction was insoluble in his time. At present it is known that the contradiction was spurious, because, as shown so clearly by Mendel, heredity is transmitted by genes rather than by "blood." The problem was solved in 1908, independently by Hardy in England and by Weinberg in Germany.

Suppose that a sexually reproducing population lives isolated from other populations of the same species, for example, on an oceanic island. Suppose, furthermore, that the population consists of individuals homozygous for a gene AA, and of individuals homozygous for aa. Let the proportion of AA individuals in the population be represented by a fraction q, and the proportion of aa by $(1 - q)$. If the population is panmictic with respect to this gene, there will be q^2 matings $AA \times AA$, which will produce AA children; $(1 - q)^2$ matings $aa \times aa$, which will give aa children; and $2q(1 - q)$ matings $AA \times aa$, which will give heterozygous, Aa, progeny.

Instead of considering the genotypes of the parents who mate, it is more convenient to consider the sex cells which they produce. Suppose, then, that all individual members of a sexual population are equally fertile and contribute equal numbers of sex cells or gametes to the "*gene pool*" of the population. If the population is panmictic, these sex cells unite at random, so that A and a eggs are fertilized by A and a sperms in proportion to their frequency in the gene pool. Let the fraction of the sex cells which carry A be q, and the fraction of sex cells a in the gene pool be $(1 - q)$. The progeny, consequently will be:

		Eggs	
		qA	$(1 - q)a$
Sperms	qA	q^2AA	$q(1 - q)Aa$
	$(1 - q)a$	$(1 - q)q\,Aa$	$(1 - q)^2aa$

In other words, there will be respectively q^2 and $(1 - q)^2$ of homozygous AA and aa, and $2q(1 - q)$ of the heterozygotes Aa. The important problem is what the distribution of the genotypes will be in the next generation. Let us again consider the composition of the gene pool. The homozygotes AA and aa produce only A and a gametes, whereas the heterozygotes Aa produce equal numbers of A and a sex cells. The total frequencies of the A and a gametes in the gene pool will accordingly be:

$$A = q^2 + q(1 - q) = q^2 + q - q^2 = q$$
$$a = q(1 - q) + (1 - q)^2 = q - q^2 + 1 - 2q + q^2 = 1 - q$$

The frequencies of the genes A and a in the gene pool will thus remain constant at the levels q and $(1 - q)$, and the distribution of the genotypes among the zygotes in the population will be:

$$q^2AA : 2q(1 - q)Aa : (1 - q)^2aa$$

This is the Hardy-Weinberg formula, which describes the equilibrium condition in a sexually reproducing population and is the cornerstone of modern population genetics. The gene frequencies, q and $(1 - q)$, remain constant in sexually reproducing populations. Consider again the example of a human population consisting of persons different in stature. Some people are tall and others short, owing to the presence in the population of genes affecting the stature. Each of these genes, which may be called A and a, B and b, etc., has a certain frequency in the gene pool. In the absence of any of the factors changing the gene frequencies described below, the population will always have some tall, average, and short persons, as well as some giants and dwarfs.

Factors Which Change Gene Frequencies. The Hardy-Weinberg theorem describes the statics of a Mendelian population. If all gene frequencies in all populations remained constant, evolution would not take place. Evolution may be defined in a most general way as a *change in gene frequencies.* In reality, agents are known which may alter the gene frequencies in populations. The dynamic forces are as follows:

(1) *Mutation.* If the allele A changes into *a,* or vice versa, the frequencies q and $(1 - q)$ may become altered.

(2) *Selection.* The Hardy-Weinberg theorem assumed that the carriers of all genotypes contribute equally to the gene pool of the following generation. This is not necessarily the case. Some genotypes may be more fecund than others, or they may have different viabilities, different longevities, some may be sexually more active than others, etc. Most differences of this kind cause variations in the *adaptive values* of carriers of genotypes, and may bring about changes in gene frequencies.

(3) *Migration.* Relatively more carriers of the gene A than of *a* may emigrate from or immigrate into a population.

(4) *Genetic Drift.* The assumption implicit in the Hardy-Weinberg theorem is that the population consists of so many individuals that chance variations in gene frequencies are negligible. Strictly speaking, this condition could obtain only in ideal, infinitely large populations. In reality, all populations are finite, and some populations are small.

In deriving the Hardy-Weinberg formula it was assumed that the populations are panmictic. For some natural populations this assumption does not hold true. For example, many higher plants and some hermaphroditic animals reproduce by self-fertilization. In wheats, oats, beans, peas, and some other crop plants the ovules are fertilized mostly by pollen from the same flower. Inbreeding, mating of close relatives, and self-fertilization lead to increased frequencies of homozygotes, and decreased frequencies of heterozygotes, compared to panmictic populations. Gene frequencies are not usually altered by deviations from panmixia.

Adaptive Value, Darwinian Fitness, and Selection Coefficient. The carriers of some hereditary endowments are more viable and reach the reproductive age more often than do carriers of other genotypes. Representatives of different genotypes vary also in fecundity (numbers of young born, or of eggs or seeds produced), in sexual activity, in the duration of the reproductive period, and in other properties which favor the reproductive success of the organism. The viability and the reproductive success determine the contribution which the carriers of a genotype make to the gene pool of the next generation of the species or of a population. This contribution is a measure of the *adaptive value,* or *Darwinian fitness,* of the genotype. Thus, if a genotype produces, on the average, 100 surviving offspring where another genotype produces 90 offspring, the adaptive value of the former is 1.00 and of the latter 0.90. It is also said that the second genotype is opposed by a *selection coefficient* of $s = 0.10$.

An Example of Estimation of the Speed of Selection. Haldane, Fisher, Wright, and other investigators have analyzed mathematically the changes which occur in populations under the influence of various forms of selection. It will be sufficient here to consider a single example. About 70 per cent of the American white population feel a bitter taste in certain solutions of the PTC substance, whereas about 30 per cent are non-tasters. The non-tasters are homozygous for a recessive gene *t*; the tasters are either homozygous or heterozygous for the dominant *T* (*TT* or *Tt*, cf. Chapter 2, page 30). Since people do not usually know whether they are tasters or non-tasters of PTC, the population may be assumed to be panmictic with respect to this trait. According to the Hardy-Weinberg formula, the frequencies of the tasters and non-tasters should be $q^2 TT : 2q(1-q)Tt : (1-q)^2 tt$. Since the non-tasters, *tt*, constitute 0.3 (30 per cent) of the population, the frequency of the gene *t* in the gene pool should be $(1-q) = \sqrt{0.3} = 0.548$. The frequency of the gene *T* in the gene pool is, then, $q = 1 - 0.548 = 0.452$. The frequencies of the three genotypes will, then, be:

$$q^2 TT = 0.204; \quad 2q(1-q)Tt = 0.495; \quad (1-q)^2 tt = 0.300$$

Assume now that all non-tasters, *tt*, are removed from the population or are prevented from reproduction. The genotype *tt* will, then, have an adaptive value zero, and will be opposed by a selection of $s = 1.00$. What will be the frequency of tasters in the next generation? The homozygous tasters will contribute only *T* sex cells to the gene pool of the next generation, whereas the heterozygous tasters will produce equal numbers of *T* and *t* gametes. The gene frequencies in the next generation will be 0.65 of *T* (0.204 + 0.247 = 0.451, or 65 per cent of the total) and 0.35 of *t* (0.247, or 35 per cent of the total).

Supposing that the non-tasters of PTC are prevented from reproduction generation after generation, the frequency of the *t* gene in the gene pool of the population will decrease as shown in Table 6.1. An im-

THE PROGRESS OF SELECTION AGAINST A RECESSIVE GENE

(The table shows the frequency in the gene pool of a human population of the gene for taste-blindness (t) expected if all taste-blind persons are prevented from reproduction in several generations.)

Generations of Selection	Gene Frequency	Generations of Selection	Gene Frequency
Initial	0.55	10	0.085
1	0.35	15	0.059
2	0.26	20	0.046
3	0.21	30	0.026
4	0.17	40	0.024
5	0.15	50	0.019
6	0.13	100	0.010
7	0.11	500	0.002
8	0.10	1000	0.001
9	0.09		

portant conclusion to be gleaned from Table 6.1 is that selection against a recessive gene is less effective the rarer that gene is in the population. Two generations of selection suffice to reduce the frequency of the gene t from the original 0.55 to less than half of the original—0.26; but four generations are needed to cause another halving of the gene frequency, to 0.13. Starting with a frequency of 0.010, we need 400 generations to depress the frequency down to 0.002. This shows the immense difficulty which would be encountered by selection against rare recessive defects or diseases in man, contemplated by some eugenical programs. Taking into consideration that the length of a human generation is at present some 25 years, such eugenical measures would have very little effect in a predictable future.

In the example just considered, the selection was supposed to be absolutely thorough ($s = 1.0$). With less intense selection, when only a part of the recessives is debarred from reproduction (s less than 1.0), the progress would be slower still. And yet, no matter how small the selection may be, it will, given enough time, change the gene frequencies in the direction favored by the environment or by the breeder. This is important to know, because one of the objections made against Darwin's theory of selection was that selection in nature will have no effect since most variable traits of organisms are neither very useful nor very harmful to their possessors. In reality, even small genetic advantages and disadvantages may be important in evolution.

Adaptive Value and the Environment. Differences in the adaptive value may be of diverse origin. Adaptive value, or Darwinian fitness, is not the same thing as bodily strength, vigor, or bravery. The "fittest" may actually be a relative weakling if he gives birth to more children than his hale and hearty neighbor.

Furthermore, the adaptive value of a genotype depends on the environment in which it lives, as examples given in Chapter 5 abundantly show. Here we may consider only the situation in domesticated animals and plants and in man. Primitive cattle breeds yield only two or three quarts of milk per cow per day; modern dairy breeds produce several times more (as much as 10,000 pounds of milk and 300 or more pounds of butterfat per cow per year). On the other hand, primitive cattle can live well with little care under harsh conditions, whereas their modern counterparts require special feeding and attention. Has, then, the selection practiced for centuries by cattle breeders improved or damaged the fitness of the domestic cattle? The question is evidently meaningless if the environment is not specified. Clearly, the breed which produces much milk has a superior fitness in the environment of a dairy farm, even though it becomes more fastidious in its diet, less able to resist inclement weather, and quite unable to defend itself against wolves and other enemies.

For a similar reason the often-met-with statement that natural selection has ceased to operate in modern human societies does not stand critical examination. True enough, the importance for survival and reproduction of such qualities as the ability to withstand cold without protective clothing, to find and kill wild animals with bare hands or with stones, to eat uncooked food, and to give birth without obstetrical help is presumably less in modern man than in his remote ancestors. The importance of possession of a nervous system which permits learning complex techniques and withstanding the wear and tear of modern "tempos" is presumably greater for modern man. Modern medicine has transformed some diseases that were fatal in primitive man into passing annoyances in modern man, but modern life requires a greater plasticity of behavioral traits than was needed before (cf. Chapter 14). In any case, whatever traits are favored or discriminated against under civilized conditions are by definition the traits which increase or diminish the fitness of their possessors in civilized environments. Calling selection "natural" only if it selects traits which we deem desirable is a lax use of words.

Modern theories of evolution consider the environment to be the directive force in the evolutionary process. But the environment does not change the organism from without, as some theorists of the past believed. The environment furnishes the challenge, to which a living species may respond by adaptive transformations of its gene pool. Whether the species does or does not respond to the challenge depends on the presence in the gene pool of the proper raw materials, mutant genes and gene combinations. Thus a culture of colon bacteria exposed to a bacteriophage produces a bacteriophage-resistant strain only if it happens to contain resistant cells previously arisen by mutation. No strains of colon bacteria capable of growing at a temperature of 80 to 85°C have been found, and this species apparently does not produce mutants which could resist such temperatures. Nevertheless, algae which live at such temperatures are known in the hot springs of Yellowstone Park.

Natural Selection and Self-reproduction. Natural selection is universal in the living world. It is implicit in the process of living. The origin of life on earth meant the appearance of self-reproducing units which tended to transform the susceptible materials (food) in the environment into their own copies. However, the process of self-reproduction is not absolutely perfect, and deviating, mutant, copies appear from time to time. If the mutants reproduce themselves less efficiently than the ancestral units, they are eliminated. If the mutants are more efficient, they crowd out the ancestral form. Finally, if the mutants can maintain themselves in an environment unsuitable to the ancestor (that is, can subsist on a new food), the ancestral form and the mutant may continue to exist side by side. Thus life is diversified.

Self-reproduction brings in its train natural selection, and the two together result in evolutionary progress. Self-reproduction, therefore, may reasonably be regarded the fundamental property of life (Chapter 1).

Selection in Asexual and Self-fertilizing Organisms. It will be shown in Chapter 7 that "pure races" do not exist, and never have existed, in man or in other organisms which reproduce sexually and by cross-fertilization. But "pure races" can be formed in organisms which propagate asexually, by parthenogenesis, or by self-fertilization. In such organisms the entire offspring usually have the same genotype as the mother. Unless mutation intervenes, clones and pure lines are formed which consist of individuals with identical heredity. As shown by Johannsen (cf. page 113), selection may be observed at its simplest in organisms which form clones or pure lines. A field of wheat, or of barley, or of beans, or a culture of bacteria usually consists of mixtures of pure lines or clones. When a breeder picks out a seed from the sturdiest plant in his field, he isolates a single pure line, which may give rise to a new variety. Some of the most valuable varieties of the self-fertilizing crop plants are descendants of single selected individual progenitors. Within a pure line or a clone, selection is, according to Johannsen, without effect, since the selected individuals are not genetically different from the rest.

When a mixture of pure lines or clones is exposed to natural selection, the multiplication of some lines may be favored and other lines may be discriminated against. Harlan and Martini planted the same mixture consisting of equal parts of eleven varieties of barley in several regions of the United States having different climates and other environmental conditions. For several years thereafter the mixture was harvested and replanted again in the same regions. The proportions of the varieties in the mixture have become radically altered: some varieties were eliminated altogether, others increased in frequencies. Interestingly enough, different varieties were favored by selection in different regions. Thus the variety Hannchen was victorious in Minnesota, the variety White Smyrna in Montana and Oregon, Manchuria in New York State, etc. (see Table 6.2).

TABLE 6.2

SURVIVAL OF BARLEY VARIETIES FROM THE SAME MIXTURE AFTER REPEATED
SOWINGS IN DIFFERENT ENVIRONMENTS

(After Harlan, Martini, and Stebbins.)

Varieties	Virginia	New York	Minnesota	Montana	Oregon	California
Coast & Trebi	89.2	11.4	16.6	17.4	1.2	72.4
Hannchen	0.8	6.8	61.0	3.8	0.8	6.8
White Smyrna	0.8	0	0.8	48.2	97.8	13.0
Manchuria	0.2	68.6	0.4	4.2	0	0
Gatami	2.6	1.8	3.2	11.6	0	0.2
Meloy	0.8	0	0	0.8	0	5.2
Others	5.6	11.4	18.0	14.0	0.2	2.4

Note. The figures show the percentages of the different varieties which resulted from selection.

When a single "pure race" is isolated the progress of selection comes to an end. However, the occurrence of a mutation in a pure line or a clone may open a new field of action for selection, just as the occurrence of a mutation to streptomycin resistance in bacteria permits selection of a resistant strain (Chapter 5). The variety of oranges known as "Navel" arose by mutation on a single tree found at Bahia, Brazil, in 1870. The many thousands of Navel oranges cultivated in California and elsewhere are direct descendants of the original mutant propagated by grafting (that is, asexually). The smooth-skinned peaches (nectarines) and some varieties of apples and other fruit trees are descendants of single "lucky" mutants.

Selection in Sexual Cross-fertilizing Populations. The situation in organisms which reproduce sexually and by cross-fertilization is very different from that in species which form clones or pure lines. The chief biological consequence of sexuality is emergence of an endless variety of genotypes in sexual populations. As shown in Chapter 2, an individual heterozygous for n genes is able to produce 2^n kinds of sex cells carrying different combinations of the parental genes. The result is that in sexually reproducing species no two individuals are likely to have the same genotype.

A relatively more constant characteristic of a sexual population is its gene pool, in which various genes are represented, each with a definite frequency. Except for identical twins, no two persons are likely to have the same genotype, but every human population can be described as having certain frequencies of the blood group genes, of genes for tasting and non-tasting certain chemical substances, for different eye colors, skin colors, etc. (see Chapter 7 for further discussion of this point). Natural or artificial selection may increase the frequencies of some genes, and decrease the frequencies of others, in the gene pool of a sexual population. Since new genotypes are constantly produced by the sexual process, selection has always new materials to work with. The "improvements" brought about by selection in sexual populations may, therefore, far exceed the limits of variation in the original materials, even if no mutation intervenes. Surely, no wild hen ever laid as many eggs as do modern poultry breeds, and no wild boar reached weights which are usual for hogs on Iowa farms. Long-continued application of artificial selection has brought about radical changes in the genotypes of domesticated animals.

Table 6.3 shows the results of a selection experiment carried by corn breeders and geneticists at the Illinois Agricultural Experiment Station for more than half a century. The original variety with which the work was started in 1896 had an average protein content of 10.92 per cent and an average oil content of 4.70 per cent in its seed. Selection was carried both in the direction of increasing and in the direction of decreasing the protein and oil contents. By 1949 lines were obtained

TABLE 6.3

PROGRESS OF SELECTION FOR HIGH AND FOR LOW CONTENTS OF PROTEIN AND OF OIL IN CORN

(After Woodworth, Lang, and Jugenheimer.)

	High Lines		Low Lines	
Generation	Per Cent Protein	Per Cent Oil	Per Cent Protein	Per Cent Oil
Initial	10.9	4.7	10.9	4.7
5	13.8	6.2	9.6	3.4
10	14.3	7.4	8.6	2.7
15	13.8	7.5	7.9	2.1
20	15.7	8.5	8.7	2.1
25	16.7	9.9	9.1	1.7
30	18.2	10.2	6.5	1.4
35	20.1	11.8	7.1	1.2
40	22.9	10.2	8.0	1.2
45	17.8	13.7	5.8	1.0
50	19.4	15.4	4.9	1.0

having as much as 19.45 per cent protein and 15.36 per cent oil, and lines with as little as 4.91 per cent protein and 1.01 per cent oil. It does not seem that the selection has yet reached the limits of its effectiveness.

Selection and Hybridization.   The success of selection depends upon the presence of genetic variability in the population to which the selection is applied.   As we have seen, among asexual or self-fertilizing organisms selection can only isolate the best genotypes already present when the selection is started.   Sexual crossing and recombination of genes among hybrids yield a vast supply of ever-new genotypes, some of which may be superior to the old ones.   This is the reason why many valuable varieties obtained by modern breed-ers are isolated from among hybrids between two or several older varieties.   For example, the Thatcher wheat variety which now grows on many millions of acres of wheat fields has a combination of genes derived from the varieties Iumillo, Marquis, and Kanred.

In sexual organisms hybridization is, in a sense, the regular method of reproduction.   Any heterozygous genotype is a hybrid genotype. In this sense, any human being is a hybrid, and any marriage a hy-bridization.   But the word "hybridization" is also used to describe crossing of more or less dissimilar parents: different breeds, races, and species.   The more dissimilar are the parents crossed, the greater is likely to be the number of differences between them, and the greater the diversity of genotypes resulting from segregation in hybrid progenies. Breeders of domestic animals and plants often resort to more or less remote hybridization. Thus the "Thoroughbred" horse arose several centuries ago from hybrids between the light Arabian and Barbary, and the heavier European horses (see Chapter 9). To take a more recent example, the Santa Gertrudis cattle are derivatives of a cross between shorthorn and the Indian (zebu) cattle.

Introgressive Hybridization. In making use of hybrids between dissimilar varieties and species, the breeders have borrowed a method which is of some importance also in evolution in nature, at least in the plant kingdom. The work of botanists (in recent years particularly of Anderson and of Stebbins) has shown that distinct species of plants, when they inhabit the same territory, occasionally cross and produce fertile offspring. Of course crossing within a species remains more frequent than that between species. Interspecific crosses, however, cause a diffusion, or introgression, of genes from one species to another. The gene transfer augments the genetic variability and furnishes great opportunities for natural and artificial selection.

Iris fulva and *Iris hexagona* are two species of irises studied by Riley in southern Louisiana. They differ in a number of ways: in the former species the tube of the flower is golden yellow, and in the latter it is green; in the former the sepals are coppery red and relatively short, in the latter they are blue-violet and relatively long, etc. Furthermore, *Iris fulva* grows chiefly on drier lands, in woods, and on slopes of ridges; *Iris hexagona* occurs on low lands, on wet clay, and in full sun. It appears that before man came and started to cut the forests and to drain the marshes for pastures and fields, the two species of irises kept well separated in their respectively different habitats. Man's activities have created new habitats on which both species, as well as hybrids between them, can grow. Riley has found colonies of irises in which varying proportions of individuals were clearly of hybrid origin, containing mixtures of genes of both species. Another example of hybridization, involving the cultivated corn (maize), will be discussed in Chapter 9.

Genetic Drift. Another agency which cooperates with natural selection in bringing about evolutionary changes is genetic drift, the action of which was studied mathematically in a series of important works chiefly by Sewall Wright. The nature of this agency is simple enough. Since a sex cell contains only half the chromosomes present in the diploid organism, a parent transmits to each child only half of his genes, and fails to transmit the other half. In a stationary population (that is, a population which neither expands nor contracts in numbers in successive generations) every pair of parents produces on the average two surviving offspring. With two children, half of the parental genes will be represented once each, one quarter will be represented twice each, and one quarter will be altogether lost. In the next generation some of the genes will again be reduplicated and others will be lost. In the course of many generations some "lucky" genes will be considerably increased in frequency, but many others will no longer exist. For this reason, it can be said that only a fraction of the genes which were present in the gene pool of the human species in, for example, the time when the pyramids were being built, or during the Stone Age, still exist in the now-living mankind. But these genes have become, barring mutation, greatly increased in numbers.

In reality, even in a stationary population the offspring of some parents are lost, whereas other parents leave numerous progeny. Many populations (of, for example, insects) alternately expand greatly in numbers in some years, and then are decimated until only few individuals are left. The genetic consequence of such expansions and contractions is that many genes are lost and others are increasing in frequencies. The author once visited a village with a population of perhaps three hundred individuals isolated in a remote corner of Asia. The singular condition in this village was that most of the inhabitants had the same family name. The explanation of this condition was simple—apparently an early settler happened to raise a large family consisting mostly of boys, and his sons were in turn fathers of large families. The genes of the early settler have become, within perhaps half a dozen generations, incorporated in many individuals. If this settler lived in a large city, the multiplication of his family name would not be conspicuous, since the carriers of this name would be scattered among other people. In a village the result seemed striking. Suppose, then, that the early settler carried a gene or a chromosome structure which is rare in the general population. The village in question has come to have a population in the gene pool of which this gene or chromosome could be unusually frequent.

As pointed out on page 119, the Hardy-Weinberg theorem of constancy of gene frequencies presupposes that the population consists of infinitely many breeding individuals. The individuals of a given generation may be said to come from a random sample of sex cells taken from the gene pool of the preceding generation. Suppose that this gene pool had equal numbers of the genes A and a, $q = (1 - q)$

= 0.5. Suppose, next, that the sample consists of one million sex cells (500,000 individuals). The gene frequency in the next generation may deviate from 0.5 by a standard error which will be equal to $\sqrt{0.5 \times 0.5 : 1,000,000} = 0.0005$. This standard error is only one-thousandth of the gene frequency, and, consequently, the gene frequency may be said to be unchanged. The situation will be different in a sample of 100 sex cells (50 individuals). The standard error will now be $\sqrt{0.5 \times 0.5 : 100} = 0.05$. This is one-tenth of the original gene frequency, and the gene frequency in the next generation will probably lie between 0.45 and 0.55, but it may easily be between 0.4 and 0.6, and even as low as 0.35 or as high as 0.65.

Variations in gene frequencies due to sampling errors in finite populations are known as *genetic drift*. Mutation and selection tend to change the gene frequency in a population systematically in the same direction, generation after generation. Genetic drift has an unsystematic effect: in one generation it may pull the gene frequency upward, then downward, or leave it unchanged. Nevertheless, given enough time (enough generations), the genetic drift may produce large changes in populations consisting of small numbers of breeding individuals.

Drift and Selection in Isolated Populations. Many organisms do not occur everywhere in the countries in which they live, but form more or less isolated groups, or colonies, each containing only some tens or hundreds of individuals. Thus land animals and plants may form colonies on dry land isolated by water, whereas water-dwelling organisms often live in lakes or ponds isolated by stretches of land. Many creatures occur only on certain soils, or live only where a certain kind of food is available. At the dawn of history mankind consisted of many small nations or tribes, more or less isolated from each other, with marriages occurring mostly within a tribe.

Suppose that the isolated colonies of a species have, to begin with, similar gene pools, with a certain gene A having the frequency, for example, of 0.5. If this gene is not acted upon by mutation and selection, its frequency in the species as a whole will continue to remain 0.5, in accordance with the Hardy-Weinberg rule. But consider the separate tribes. If these tribes have small populations, the gene frequencies will, owing to genetic drift, become higher than 0.5 in some tribes and lower than 0.5 in others. In the course of time, the tribes will tend to drift apart in gene frequencies. In fact, some tribes may come to have only the gene A and others only a.

It is possible, although not proven (cf. Chapter 7), that the differences between human races in traits which seem to be adaptively neutral arose through genetic drift in small populations. Most human populations contain persons of different blood groups, tasters and non-tasters of PTC, etc.; however, the incidence of these traits varies in different parts of the world (Figures 7.6 and 7.7). These variations could have arisen through genetic drift in the isolated tribes of which early mankind was composed, and subsequently impressed upon the much larger and no longer strictly isolated modern races. Colonies and local races of many animals and plants often show minor differences in color patterns, size, shapes of various parts, etc., which also may be neither useful nor harmful to their possessors. Genetic drift in small populations is one of the possible hypotheses to account for such differences between populations.

Interesting situations arise in small populations which are acted upon simultaneously by natural selection and by genetic drift. Selection always tends to fix the frequencies of genes in the populations at values most advantageous under the environments in which these populations live. The genetic drift causes variations up and down from these values. The separate, partially or completely isolated, populations of a species act, then, as evolutionary trial parties which explore the adaptive possibilities of various genetic structures. Most of these trial parties "discover" nothing of interest, and eventually get lost and supplanted by the more successful populations. The important thing, however, is that in some populations, perhaps in only a single population, gene combinations may arise which are not very useful, perhaps even slightly disadvantageous, but possess new adaptive potentialities. Such "evolutionary inventions" are then perfected by natural selection, and occupy new ecological niches which were unattainable to the original species. The importance of the genetic drift in evolution is that its interaction with natural selection confers a greater adaptive plasticity than a living species would possess otherwise.

Conservative and Creative Aspects of Selection. Some philosophers and some biologists have doubted that natural selection can be the guiding agent in evolution because selection, allegedly, produces nothing new, and merely removes from the populations degenerate variants and malformations (cf. Chapter 14). This objection seemed particularly impressive when Johannsen demonstrated that selection does not induce hereditary variations in genotypically uniform pure lines and clones (see page 114), but the objection became invalid in the light of modern biological knowledge.

We should clearly distinguish the two basic evolutionary processes: that of the origin of the raw materials from which evolutionary changes can be constructed, and that of building and perfecting the organic form and function. Evolution can be compared to a factory: any factory needs a supply of raw materials to work with, but when the materials are available they must be transformed into a finished product by means of some manufacturing process. The raw materials of evolution are the genotypes which arise by gene and chromosome mutation and by recombination engendered in the process of sexual reproduction. But, according to the apt phrase of Sewall Wright, mutation alone would produce "an array of freaks, not evolution." It is selection which gives order and shape to the genetic variability, and directs it into adaptive channels. Some of the classical theorists of evolution believed that evolution was produced by natural selection; others thought that it was produced by mutation or by hybridization. They were equally in error, since it is the interaction of all these processes which results in evolutionary changes.

Mutation and recombination yield a supply of genetic variability, which is then organized by natural selection in accordance with the demands of the environment. Most mutants, however, are deleterious to the organism in "normal" environments; they produce defects, malformations, and hereditary diseases of various degrees of gravity. The action of selection, accordingly, has two aspects, which Schmalhausen has called the stabilizing selection and the dynamic selection. The former keeps down the number of deleterious mutant genes and gene combinations (cf. Chapter 7), and in so doing it protects and stabilizes the "normal" developmental pattern of the species. On the other hand, the environment changes in time and in space. The dynamic natural selection permits the species to keep its hold on the changing ecological niches which it occupies, and also to conquer and control new ecological opportunities.

Even the stabilizing function of natural selection involves more than a purely negative action of blocking the spread in populations of bad mutants. It is frequently forgotten that the environment which we call "normal" for a species is in reality a complex of a great many different environments. Just think how profoundly different are the environments to which any species inhabiting temperate or cold lands is exposed in summer and in winter. In order to survive, such species must of necessity be adapted to all the environments which recur

seasonally, or from time to time, in their native country. Many tropical and subtropical plants can grow well enough during the summers
in the United States, but they do not survive winters; in California
and Florida some of them survive average winters but are killed by
exceptionally severe ones. How many, if any, offspring are produced
by the carriers of any genotype depends on the reactions of this
genotype not to just one but to many different environments—in other
words, on the norm of reaction of this genotype (cf. Chapter 4).
Adaptively most valuable genotypes are those which react favorably
in all the environments to which the species is exposed in its natural
habitats. The stabilizing natural selection favors, then, the genotypes
which can withstand the environmental shocks which the organism is
likely to meet. The result of selection is the development of homeostasis (cf. Chapter 1). The organism of man, of a frog, of a Drosophila
fly, of a corn plant, and in fact of any species develops and maintains
its normal structures and functions despite the manifold and often
erratic changes in the environments. The "stabilization" of organic
development permits a great deal of genetic and evolutionary progress.

New developmental patterns become necessary, however, when the
environment changes permanently. This change may occur because
of alterations in the climate, because of ecological upsets produced
by the appearance of new diseases, parasites, predators, or competitors, because the species becomes adapted to eat new kinds of food,
to grow on different soils, and for many other reasons. Dynamic
natural selection involves, then, the establishment of new genotypes,
adapted to the new conditions. It is fair to say that selection *produces*
new genotypes, even though we know that the immediate causes of
the origin of all genotypes are mutation and recombination. It is only
in organisms which reproduce exclusively by asexual means or by self-
fertilization that selection, in the short run, merely picks out some of
the available genotypes and suppresses others. In the long run, selection is the directing agent because it determines which genotypes are
available for new mutations to occur in.

Sexual reproduction and cross-fertilization are immensely efficient
trial-and-error mechanisms which generate new genotypes. Their action in a given generation depends, however, on the composition of
the gene pool of the population, which in turn has been determined
through natural selection in the ancestral generations. Thus it comes
about that we can obtain, by selection, strains with characters which
far exceed the limits of variation in the ancestral materials (see page
125). The human species, and all other species of organisms which

live in the world at present, were not preformed in the primeval amoebae or in the primordial viruses. They have evolved gradually in the history of the earth under the control of natural selection.

Suggestions for Further Reading

Darwin, Ch. 1859. *On the Origin of Species by Means of Natural Selection.*

This is the original statement of the theory of natural selection. For further comment, see the "Suggestions for Further Reading" at the end of Chapter 5.

Osborn, H. F. 1896. *From Greeks to Darwin.* 2nd Edition. Macmillan, New York.

Although antiquated, this work remains a useful account of the early history of evolutionism.

Andrewartha, H. G., and Birch, L. C. 1954. *The Distribution and Abundance of Animals.* Chicago University Press, Chicago.

Dobzhansky, Th. 1951. *Genetics and the Origin of Species.* 3rd Edition. Columbia University Press, New York.

Schmalhausen, I. I. 1949. *Factors of Evolution, the Theory of Stabilizing Selection.* Blakiston, Philadelphia.

Stebbins, G. L. 1950. *Variation and Evolution in Plants.* Columbia University Press, New York.

These books (Andrewartha and Birch to Stebbins) should be consulted for discussions of modern versions of the theory of natural selection.

Allee, W. C. 1951. *Cooperation among Animals.* Schumann, New York.

Kropotkin, P. 1917. *Mutual Aid.* Knopf, New York.

Also available in a Penguin Books edition (London, 1939).

Ashley Montagu, M. F. 1952. *Darwin, Competition, and Cooperation.*

These three books (Allee to Ashley-Montagu) emphasize cooperation, as against struggle, as an important factor leading to natural selection.

Li, C. C. 1955. *Population Genetics.* Chicago University Press.

Lerner, I. M. 1950. *Population Genetics and Animal Improvement.* Cambridge University Press, London.

The books of Li and Lerner may be consulted for a mathematical theory of selection and of genetic drift. These books are intended for advanced students and research workers.

For a very elementary treatment of the same topics see also:

Dunn, L. C., and Dobzhansky, Th. 1952. *Heredity, Race, and Society.* 2nd Edition. New American Library, New York.

Anderson, E. 1949. *Introgressive Hybridization.* John Wiley, New York.

The author of this last book believes that introgressive hybridization is rather more important in the evolution of life than it is usually credited with being.

Another discussion of this phenomenon can be found in the book by Stebbins quoted above.

7

Individuals, Populations, and Races

Experience shows that every person we meet is different from any met before. Individual differences exist also among animals and plants, and for that matter no two material objects are completely identical. Yet human language forces the infinite variety of experience into categories symbolized by words—man, horse, dog, pine, etc. It is easy to mistake words for actual objects, and to conclude that each word refers to some metaphysical entity or "idea." Plato, the greatest philosopher of antiquity, actually taught that individual men, horses, pine trees, etc., are imperfect and temporary expressions of the eternal and unchangeable ideal Man, Horse, and Pine.

Although few modern philosophers and still fewer scientists take Plato's "ideas" literally, his way of thinking is deeply rooted in many minds. It is common to hear people speak glibly of a "typical Frenchman," or "real American," or "ideal horse." Such expressions are legitimate only so long as the speaker realizes that the "type" or "ideal" is a composite image which he endows with properties commonly met with in actual individuals or considered desirable or pleasing. The trouble is that people are frequently tempted to think of these abstractions as though they were real entities. This "typological" thinking may even be carried to the point when the imaginary Man or the imaginary American is substituted for real men and for living persons who compose a nation as objects of sympathy and affection.

Types and Classifications. The typological approach is convenient in the branches of biology which deal with description and classification of animals and plants. Just as a large library must be systematized and catalogued to be usable, so living organisms have been divided into phyla, classes, orders, families, genera, species, and subspecies or races, and each category has been given a name. A name stands for a group of individuals which have some traits in common. Thus all individuals called "fox terrier" have many properties in common; some of these properties are shared by all individuals referred to the species dog (*Canis familiaris*), to the genus Canis, the family Canidae, the order of carnivores (Carnivora), the class of mammals (Mammalia), and the phylum of vertebrates (Chordata). The properties common to each category may be represented schematically in a picture or in a description; such schemes are very useful in teaching zoology and botany.

The "types" of dog, carnivores, vertebrates, etc., do not exist, however, apart from the real animals. It was perhaps this kind of illusion which led Linnaeus to conclude that species were units created by God. In the nineteenth century the French comparative anatomist Cuvier and many others believed in types or "basic plans" which existed in some ideal world and of which the real animals and plants were but imperfect copies. The great poet Goethe created a schematic generalized plant ("Urpflanze"), of which the plants that actually grow were supposed to be variants (Chapter 10).

Much harm came from the notions of typical or "pure" white, Nordic, Germanic, and other "pure" races of man. No two men look alike, and different countries are inhabited by people who look obviously different. Some anthropologists, from the eighteenth century to the present time, have succumbed to the temptation of supposing that this great variety of human beings arose through mixture of a relatively small number of "pure" races. These anthropologists assume that the "pure" races have lived at some unspecified time in the past, and arbitrarily endow them with combinations of traits, such as stature, head shape, skin, and hair colors. Very occasionally a living person is found who more or less resembles the imaginary standard of the "pure" race, but a great majority of human beings have to be regarded as mixtures of two or of several races. Authorities seldom agree on either the number or the characteristics of the supposed "pure" races; this disagreement is not surprising since, in the words of the eminent anthropologist Howells, these races were arrived at by "a kind of divination." All this would have made trouble only for anthropologists, but politicians and bigots found the "pure" races convenient instruments to stir up race prejudice and unhealthy nationalism.

Pure Races? As shown in the foregoing chapter, pure races conforming to a single genetic type could exist in sexually reproducing organisms only if heredity were transmitted by blood instead of by genes. Then the "type" of a race or of a species could represent the limiting condition which a sexually reproducing population would reach after a prolonged period of breeding in isolation. But in reality groups of genetically uniform individuals—clones and pure lines—exist only in asexual or self-fertilizing populations. Hardy and Weinberg (see Chapter 6) have firmly established that sexually reproducing and cross-fertilizing populations do not become any "purer" with time, and that when applied to such populations the notion of "pure" race is absurd.

Although members of a sexual cross-fertilizing population are rarely, if ever, genetically identical, and although individuals of a clone or a pure line usually are genetically uniform, individuals in a sexual species are far more interdependent than those in clones or pure lines. In a clone of bacteria, every cell may give rise by division to a progeny, but individuals of a clone are independent from one another in reproduction. In sexual species, an isolated individual can leave no progeny and is lost to the species. Members of a sexual population are interdependent. They are bound together by ties of mating and parentage. Every individual derives its genes from the common gene pool of the population, and returns its genes to the same gene pool.

The word "population" is sometimes used loosely to refer to any group of living beings; thus we speak of the bird population of a forest, or of the fish population of a lake. But a *Mendelian population* is a reproductive community of sexual and cross-fertilized individuals among whom matings regularly occur and who, consequently, have a common gene pool.

In theory, Mendelian populations may be homozygous for all their genes, but this happens rarely or never in reality. Every member of a Mendelian population (identical twins excepted) is likely to have a genotype of its own, not found in any other individual. It would be meaningless to say that every individual belongs to a separate "race." It is also easy to see how little meaning, except in a purely descriptive sense, has the idea of "type" when applied to a Mendelian population. Such expressions as the "average" condition or the "typical" phenotype may be entirely misleading. For example, most human populations consist of persons with O, A, B, and AB blood groups, but there is no such thing as an "average" blood group. We can say only that in some populations persons belonging to certain blood groups are relatively more frequent than those belonging to other blood groups.

Such a statement does not, however, describe an average or a type, but the composition of the gene pool of the population.

Sympatric and Allopatric Variability. Mendelian populations may be of various orders of magnitude. In man marriages are concluded most often among residents of the same community, town, city, and country. Every individual human being encounters during his reproductive age a certain number of individuals of the opposite sex who may be regarded as his potential mates. These groups of potential mates are the elementary Mendelian populations, to which in human genetics and anthropology the term *isolates* is often applied. But the isolates are seldom completely isolated from each other. Intermarriages between isolates occur more or less frequently, giving rise to Mendelian populations of higher orders. The language which people speak, the nation and the country to which they belong, influence the frequencies of intermarriage and make larger isolates. Finally, mankind as a whole is a great Mendelian population. Any two human beings of reproductive age and of opposite sex anywhere in the world are potentially able to mate and to produce offspring. There is actually some gene flow, direct or indirect, continuous or intermittent, between all isolates of the human species.

Individuals of the same or of different species who live together in the same territory are called *sympatric*. Residents of different territories are *allopatric*. These terms may be defined more precisely as follows. The places where the parents are born are usually separated by some distance from the birthplaces of their offspring. Individuals who live within the average distance between the birthplaces of parents and offspring are sympatric, and those living at greater distances are allopatric. Matings occur usually between sympatric individuals, and these individuals are members of elementary Mendelian populations. Although this distinction is obviously not sharp, because adjacent populations commonly overlap, it is of considerable importance in evolutionary biology.

Genetic differences are observed, of course, between sympatric as well as between allopatric individuals. People in an American town differ in appearance from the inhabitants of a Japanese town, but individual Americans as well as individual Japanese differ also among themselves. But the differences between sympatric individuals arise through combination of genes coming from the same gene pool, and, unless the individual dies childless, the genes revert again to the gene pool. Allopatric populations have separate gene pools, although there may be some diffusion of genes between these pools, owing to migration and to intermarriage of people whose parents were born in remote parts of the world.

The existence of genetic differences between sympatric individuals, members of the same Mendelian population, is referred to as *individual variability* or as *polymorphism*. Genetic differences between Mendelian populations are called racial or subspecific. *Race* and *subspecies* are synonyms, the former word being used most often in connection with man, and the latter for organisms other than man. *Breeds* of domestic animals and *varieties* of cross-fertilized cultivated plants are races. It should be noted, however, that, although most races of free-living species are allopatric, breeds and varieties of domesticated species may be either sympatric or allopatric, since their mating is controlled by man. Human races were originally allopatric, but with the development of the cultural regulation of marriage they have become partly sympatric (see Chapter 13). The word "variety" has been used in so many different senses that it is at present worthless as a scientific term. It is sometimes applied to clones of asexual species and even to sympatric genotypes within a polymorphic Mendelian population, which cannot legitimately be called races or subspecies.

Some Examples of Polymorphism in Human Populations. As shown in Chapter 6, a Mendelian population may be described most adequately in terms of relative frequencies of various genes and chromosomal variants in its gene pool. For example, most human populations are polymorphic with respect to the blood groups. The American white population consists of approximately 47 per cent of persons with blood of group O, 43 per cent of group A, 7 per cent of group B, and 3 per cent of group AB. Since human populations are panmictic with respect to the blood groups (nobody chooses his mate according to the blood group), it can be deduced that the three alleles which determine the blood groups, I^O, I^A, and I^B, have the frequencies in the gene pool respectively of 0.67, 0.26, and 0.07.

Of course human populations are polymorphic with respect to many genes other than those which determine the blood groups. In the foregoing chapter it has been mentioned that some 70 per cent of American whites are tasters, and some 30 per cent are non-tasters, of the PTC substance. In the gene pool, about 55 per cent of the sex cells carry the recessive gene t for non-tasting, and the remaining 45 per cent contain the dominant gene T for tasting.

The phenotypic manifestation of the genetic polymorphism in Mendelian populations may or may not be very conspicuous. In human populations the polymorphism with respect to the blood groups is perfectly clear-cut, since, when tested by competent observers, there is never any doubt about the blood group to which a person belongs. The situation with tasting the PTC substance is a little less definite, since some persons find weak solutions of PTC tasteless but strong solutions bitter. Classification of such persons as "tasters" or "non-tasters" may be ambiguous. With many other traits, especially those determined by polygenes (cf. Chapter 2), the different genotypes fail to produce discrete phenotypic classes. Thus the pigmentation of human skin varies all the way from albino to black. Similarly, the color of the hair and eyes, the shape of the head, and countless other human characteristics vary continuously from one extreme to another.

Dominant Deleterious Genes and Hereditary Diseases. We have seen in Chapters 4 and 5 that, in any living species, there occur from time to time mutations and chromosomal changes, most of which are more or less deleterious to their carriers in the environments which are normal for the species. There exist, of course, all transitions between mutants which produce dangerous hereditary diseases and mutant genes which are neutral and even useful to the organism.

Some mutants act as dominant lethals, that is, they kill their carriers even in heterozygous condition. Thus in Drosophila many eggs deposited by an untreated female mated to a male treated with X-rays fail to produce larvae. The death of the eggs is due to induction by X-rays of dominant lethals (mostly inviable chromosome breakages) in the treated spermatozoa. An example of a spontaneously arising lethal in man is retinoblastoma, a form of tumor in the retina of the eye, which causes death usually during infancy. According to Neel and Falls, about 4 in 100,000 infants born in the State of Michigan are new retinoblastoma mutants.

Deleterious mutants which are not completely lethal may be retained in a population for several generations. This is the case with numerous hereditary defects and diseases in human populations. Thus the chondrodystrophic dwarfism (see Chapter 2, page 32) is a semi-lethal in the genetic sense. These dwarfs enjoy satisfactory health, but, according to Haldane, produce on the average only about one-fifth as many children as do normal persons.

Recessive Deleterious Genes and Hereditary Diseases. A newly arisen recessive mutant is likely to be carried in an individual heterozygous for the recessive and for the dominant normal allele. Even if the recessive mutant is lethal when homozygous, the heterozygous carriers may be normal in appearance and in health. A vast majority of genes for rare recessive hereditary diseases are carried in populations in normal-appearing heterozygotes, making it difficult to detect and to eliminate them by any plausible eugenical measures. Thus the juvenile amaurotic idiocy causes the death of the homozygotes before the onset of sexual maturity, and yet the parents of the afflicted children are normal people. Albinism in man may be classed as a mildly deleterious condition due to homozygosis for a recessive gene, but the parents of the albino are normally pigmented. Muller has estimated that a "normal" and healthy person in human populations is heterozygous, on the average, for eight recessive genes which could produce, in homozygous condition, more or less grave defects or diseases.

Perhaps most interesting at this point are human genes which are disabling or even fatal to homozygotes but are also detectable in heterozygotes. Individuals homozygous for the gene for thalassemia die of a fatal anemia, usually in childhood. The parents of the anemics may have a mild form of anemia ("thalassemia minor"), and their red blood cells show certain peculiarities detectable under the microscope. The gene is, then, lethal in homozygous and subvital in heterozygous condition. The remarkable condition is that the thalassemia occurs chiefly among people native to the Mediterranean region (Italians, Greeks, Syrians, etc.). In populations of some parts of Italy this gene reaches, however, astonishingly high frequencies—10 or more per cent of the gene pool.

Another form of lethal anemia is due to homozygosis for another recessive gene which occurs chiefly among people of African extraction. This anemia, or sickle-cell disease, causes the red blood cells to assume characteristic shapes (Figure 7.1) when placed in a medium deficient in oxygen. The heterozygous carriers of this gene are normal or very mildly anemic. The frequency of the sickle-cell gene in some Negro populations exceeds 40 per cent, although in other populations it is low.

It is certain that man is not the only species afflicted by accumulation of deleterious genes in its gene pool. Most, or all, sexually reproducing organisms share the same fate. The most detailed relevant studies, begun in 1925 by a Russian geneticist Chetverikov, have been made on natural populations of Drosophila flies. It may be noted that a fair number of mutants had been found before 1925 in Drosophila in laboratory cultures, but the outdoor populations of these flies seemed quite uniform and free of mutants. So much so, that some authorities at that time suspected that mutants are just laboratory artifacts which never occur in nature.

Chetverikov devised a technique of bringing to light the recessive mutants which are hidden in normally appearing heterozygous individuals. The principle of this technique consists in breeding the individual flies collected in nature in laboratory cultures, and obtaining progenies in which certain individuals carry in duplicate chromosomes which were present in a single dose in the free-living ancestor. The

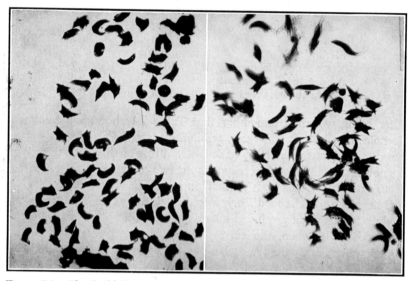

Figure 7.1. The "sickle" shapes assumed by the red blood cells of persons heterozygous (left) or homozygous (right) for a gene for sickle-cell anemia when subjected to reduced oxygen supply. (Courtesy of Professor J. V. Neel.)

results of the study were startling. Almost every "normal" fly living in the state of nature proved to be heterozygous for one or more recessive genes which are lethal, or semilethal, or cause sterility, or modify in various ways the physiological characteristics or the external appearance of the homozygous individuals. Many mutants previously found in laboratories were shown to be present also in natural populations; many new mutants were discovered.

Table 7.1 provides an illustration of the degree to which the genotype of a sexually reproducing species may be riddled with deleterious mutants. We must, of course, remember that every fly carries two second and two third chromosomes (one received from the mother and the other from the father). It is obvious, then, that few, if any, flies in nature are free of the potentially deleterious genes. On the

TABLE 7.1

PERCENTAGES OF THE SECOND AND THIRD CHROMOSOMES IN SOUTH AMERICAN
POPULATIONS OF *Drosophila willistoni* WHICH CONTAIN VARIOUS DELETERIOUS
RECESSIVE MUTANT GENES

(After Pavan and Collaborators.)

Effects in Homozygotes	Second Chromosome	Third Chromosome
Lethal or semilethal	41.2	32.1
Subvital	57.5	49.1
Sterility	31.0	27.7
Retarded development	31.8	35.7
Accelerated development	13.7	2.8
Visible abnormalities	15.9	16.1

other hand, we must remember that Table 7.1 shows the total frequencies of all kinds of lethals, semilethals, subvitals (relatively mild
hereditary diseases), sterility genes, etc. Most of these mutant genes
are not allelic, and flies heterozygous for two or even for several lethal
genes are quite viable and "normal" in appearance.

Heterosis and Balanced Polymorphism. Most of the genes considered up to this point produced heterozygotes which were similar to, or
intermediate between, the corresponding homozygotes (that is, the
heterozygotes, *Aa*, either resemble one of the homozygotes, *AA* or *aa*,
or are intermediate between them). It happens, however, that some
genes produce heterozygotes, *Aa*, which are superior in vigor or in fitness to both *AA* and *aa* homozygotes. A superiority of the hybrids,
heterozygotes, is known as *hybrid vigor*, or *heterosis*. This condition
is common in nature, and it is very important in agricultural practice.
The exploitation of heterosis in hybrid corn in the United States has
resulted in an increase of the yield of about 15 bushels per acre. It is
estimated that the aggregate increase of the yield for the whole country in 1946 was between 832 and 924 millions of bushels (see Chapter
9).

The dynamics of a population with heterotic heterozygotes can be
described as follows. Suppose that the adaptive value of a heterozygote, *Aa*, is equal to 1. The adaptive values of the homozygotes, *AA*
and *aa*, are, respectively, $1 - s_1$ and $1 - s_2$ (s_1 and s_2 are, of course,
selection coefficients, see Chapter 6). Suppose that the frequencies
of the genes *A* and *a* in the gene pool of the population are *q* and
$(1 - q)$. It can be shown mathematically that when the adaptive
value of a heterozygote is above those of both homozygotes, natural

selection will act to retain both alleles, *A* and *a*, in the population indefinitely. The population will, accordingly, be polymorphic; polymorphism maintained by selection is known as *balanced polymorphism*. The genes under the conditions outlined above will reach equilibrium frequencies at the following values:

$$q = s_2/(s_1 + s_2) \quad \text{and} \quad (1 - q) = s_1/(s_1 + s_2)$$

This little exercise of mathematics leads to interesting biological conclusions. First of all, the mechanism of balanced polymorphism will maintain in the population any gene which produces a heterotic heterozygote, no matter how poorly viable, or even lethal, may be the homozygotes. Assume, for example, that the homozygote, *aa*, is lethal ($s_2 = 1.0$) and the other homozygote, *AA*, is slightly less fit than the heterozygote (let s_1 be 0.1). Natural selection will establish an equilibrium at which the gene *a* will have a frequency of $(1 - q)$ per cent in the gene pool $[0.1/(1 + 0.1) = 0.09]$.

It is quite conceivable that the occurrence of some recessive hereditary defects and diseases in human and other species may be kept up by balanced polymorphism. There is some evidence (Allison, 1954) that heterozygous carriers of the gene for the sickle-cell anemia are less susceptible to malaria (tropical fevers) than are the "normal" homozygotes. In countries where malaria is prevalent even a relative immunity may constitute an important adaptive advantage. Natural selection will then maintain a certain incidence of the genes for the sickle-cell anemia in the population of malaria-ridden countries, despite the fact that the homozygotes for this gene die of fatal anemia.

Chromosomal Inversions in Drosophila Populations. Experimental verification of the hypothesis of balanced polymorphism proved possible in populations of Drosophila. Natural populations of some species of these flies vary with respect to a rather recondite trait, namely, the structure of their chromosomes. The arrangement of the genes in the chromosomes is visibly reflected in the giant chromosomes of the salivary glands of Drosophila larvae (Figure 7.2). Different chromosomal variants found in the same free-living population differ in inversions of blocks of genes (cf. page 66). The flies which have chromosomes with different gene arrangements interbreed freely; therefore, some flies possess two chromosomes of a pair with identical gene arrangements (inversion homozygotes), and other flies have the two chromosomes with different gene arrangements (inversion heterozygotes).

The flies homozygous and heterozygous for different chromosomal variants look externally alike. It is, nevertheless, possible to demonstrate by experiments that the inversion heterozygotes usually show hybrid vigor, that is, are superior in fitness to the homozygotes. The experiments are conducted on artificial populations living in "popu-

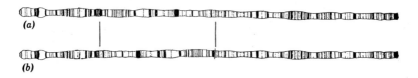

(a)

(b)

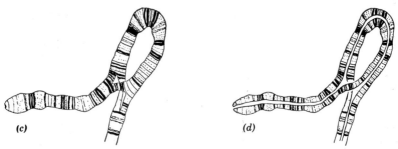

(c)   (d)

Figure 7.2. An inversion in *Drosophila pseudoobscura*. *a*. The "Standard" arrangement of discs in the third chromosome. *b*. The "Arrowhead" arrangement. *c* and *d*. The inversion loop formed in the third chromosome in the cells of larval salivary glands in individuals heterozygous for the inversion, that is, carrying one "Standard" and one "Arrowhead" chromosome. In *d* the chromosomes are drawn with a space between them, in order to show more clearly the method of pairing. (From Moore.)

lation cages" (Figure 7.3). A population of Drosophila flies with known frequencies of different chromosomal structures is placed in the cage; fresh food is introduced at intervals, and the used-up food removed; from time to time samples of the larvae are taken, and their chromosomes examined under the microscope.

If flies with chromosomes of a given kind were superior in fitness to other chromosomal types, natural selection would make the population uniform for the favored chromosomal structure. In actual experiments this uniformity occurs only rarely. More often, the population in the cage reaches an equilibrium at which two or several

Figure 7.3. A population cage, used in studies on the processes of natural selection in experimental populations of Drosophila. The cage contains fifteen cups with the nutrient medium adapted for raising Drosophila flies in laboratories. The cups with used-up medium can be removed and replaced by cups with fresh food, without losing any of the flies in the cage. (After Dobzhansky, courtesy of *Scientific American.*)

kinds of chromosomes occur side by side. Now, as shown above, such an equilibrium is expected if the inversion heterozygotes are superior in adaptive value to the homozygotes.

Figure 7.4 shows the outcome of an experiment in which a population of *Drosophila pseudoobscura* placed initially in the cage had 10

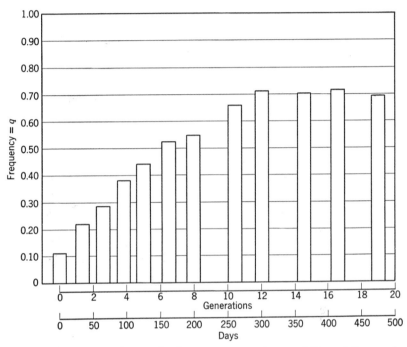

Figure 7.4.   Progress of natural selection in a population of *Drosophila pseudoobscura* kept in a population cage (see Figure 7.3). The gene pool of this population contained originally about 11 per cent of one kind of chromosome and 89 per cent of another. The bars show a gradual increase in the frequency of the chromosomes which were originally rare in the population, and an eventual attainment of a stable equilibrium.

per cent of the chromosomes with the gene arrangement called "*ST*" and 90 per cent of the chromosomes with the arrangement known as "*CH.*" The graph shows that the incidence of the *ST* chromosomes in the population rose rapidly (and that of *CH* declined). However, in about 250 days after the start of the population (corresponding to some ten fly generations), the population reached an equilibrium state, with approximately 70 per cent *ST* and 30 per cent *CH* chromosomes. The changes observed in this population indicate the following adaptive values for the different chromosomal types:

Chromosomal Types		Adaptive Value	Selection Coefficient
Heterozygotes	ST/CH	1.00	0
Homozygotes	ST/ST	0.90	$s_1 = 0.10$
Homozygotes	CH/CH	0.41	$s_2 = 0.59$

According to the formula given above (page 143), the population is expected to reach an equilibrium when the ST chromosomes amount to $q_{ST} = s_2/(s_1 + s_2) = 0.85$, or 85 per cent of the total. The frequency of ST chromosomes observed in the experimental populations a year after the start of the selection process is slightly below the predicted frequency.

Individuals and Populations as Units of Natural Selection. The experiment just described raises an interesting problem. The outcome of natural selection in a population containing ST and CH chromosomes has been to establish an equilibrium condition at which the population consists of certain proportions of the chromosomal heterozygotes, ST/CH, as well as of the homozygotes, ST/ST and CH/CH. These homozygotes, particularly CH/CH, possess a low fitness. We may say that the CH/CH homozygotes are afflicted with a grave hereditary disease; a fitness of 41 per cent means that the genotype is effectively semilethal. Natural selection, then, causes the appearance in every generation of a certain number of genetically crippled individuals. It seems very strange that natural selection should fail to eliminate from the population the unfit genotypes.

The solution of this paradox, however, is simple. Let us keep in mind that the fittest genotypes in many populations are heterozygotes endowed with hybrid vigor. But a sexual population consisting entirely of heterozygotes for a pair of allelic genes or chromosomal structures would produce, according to Mendel's first law, a progeny consisting of only 50 per cent of heterozygotes and 50 per cent of homozygotes. What natural selection does is to establish proportions of the genotypes at which the average fitness of an individual in the population is the highest attainable one, but the high fitness of the population as a whole is purchased at the price of producing some genetically unfit individuals (the homozygotes). We are compelled to conclude that, with sexual reproduction, it is the Mendelian population, as well as the individual which is the unit of natural selection and evolution.

The hybrid vigor is a very widespread phenomenon in sexually reproducing populations of both wild and domesticated animals and plants. We shall discuss it in more detail in Chapter 9. The fitness of these populations is maintained by natural selection by means of mechanisms such as are described for Drosophila populations.

Chromosomal Races in Drosophila. A population of Drosophila living in nature, like the experimental populations considered above,

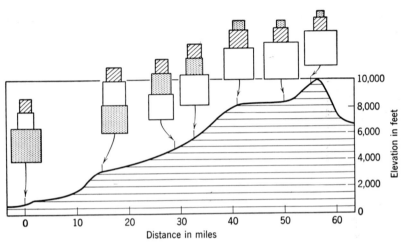

Figure 7.5. The relative frequencies (symbolized by the dimensions of the squares) of three different kinds of chromosomes in populations of *Drosophila pseudoobscura* which live at different elevations in the Sierra Nevada in or near Yosemite Park, California. Stippled, white, and shaded squares represent three different kinds of chromosomes. The fly populations which occur at different elevations are racially distinct.

may be characterized by the relative frequencies of the various chromosomal variants in its gene pool. Thus a population of *Drosophila pseudoobscura* near Mather, in the Sierra Nevada of California, contains about 32 per cent of third chromosomes with the gene arrangement called *ST*, about 19 per cent of the chromosomes with the gene arrangement *CH*, about 37 per cent with the arrangement *AR*, about 9 per cent with the arrangement *TL*, and the remaining 3 per cent with other gene arrangements. Since, as the experiments have shown, the flies carrying different chromosomes differ from each other in fitness, the populations which inhabit localities with different climatic and other conditions often show distinct differences in composition.

Figure 7.5 illustrates the composition of the populations of several localities in the Sierra Nevada not far removed from Mather, but lying at different elevations. The sizes of the squares symbolize the frequencies of the different chromosomes; stippled squares represent frequencies of the chromosomes with the *ST* gene arrangement; white squares show the frequencies of *AR* chromosomes; and cross-hatched squares refer to the frequencies of *CH* chromosomes. Now, at the locality lying at the lowest elevation above the sea level (on the left in Figure 7.5) the *ST* chromosomes are the commonest, followed by *AR*, and *CH* chromosomes are relatively rare. As one ascends the mountain range (moving to the right in Figure 7.5), the *ST* chromosomes become progressively less frequent, and *AR* chromosomes more and more frequent.

The situation observed in the lowly Drosophila fly is very instructive, for it illustrates the nature of races in many sexually reproducing organisms, including man. Consider that the population of the highest locality (elevation 10,000 feet above the sea level, the rightmost population in Figure 7.5) is very different in composition from the population of the lowest locality. But Figure 7.5 shows that localities intermediate in elevation have populations of intermediate composition. The frequencies of genes and chromosomal variants in the gene pools of adjacent populations change gradually; they form *geographic gradients* or *clines*.

Geographic Distribution of the Blood Groups in Man. The blood groups in man reveal a situation remarkably parallel to that shown by the chromosomal types in Drosophila. As we know, the three alleles of a gene, I^O, I^A, and I^B, give four blood groups: O, A, B, and AB. With the exception of some American Indian tribes which are (or were before the invasion of the Europeans) uniform for blood group O, most other human populations contain individuals of all four blood types. The relative frequencies of the four types, however, are by no means uniform, as shown in Figures 7.6 and 7.7. In the Old World, the gene I^B is most common in Central Asia and in India, and shows descending gradients both westward and eastward. The gene I^A is common in Western Europe, in some parts of Africa, in Australia, and the Blackfeet and Blood tribes of the American Indians (in Montana and the adjacent part of Canada). The gene I^O is common everywhere, especially among the American Indians.

It is clear that knowing the blood group of an individual human being (or the chromosomal constitution of an individual *Drosophila pseudoobscura*) is, with some exceptions, quite insufficient to determine his "race" or the geographic location of the population from

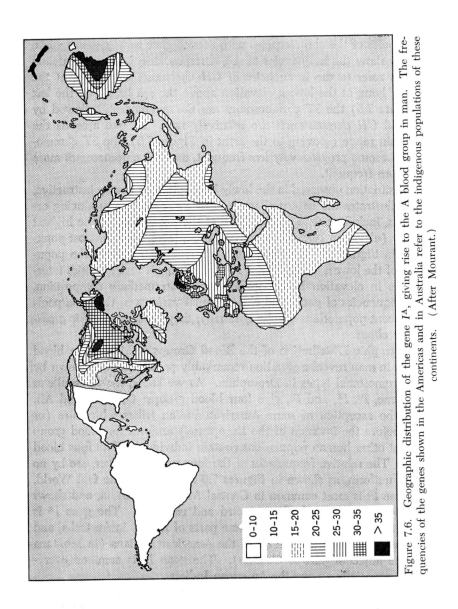

Figure 7.6.   Geographic distribution of the gene I^A, giving rise to the A blood group in man.   The frequencies of the genes shown in the Americas and in Australia refer to the indigenous populations of these continents.   (After Mourant.)

0-10
10-15
15-20
20-25
25-30
30-35
> 35

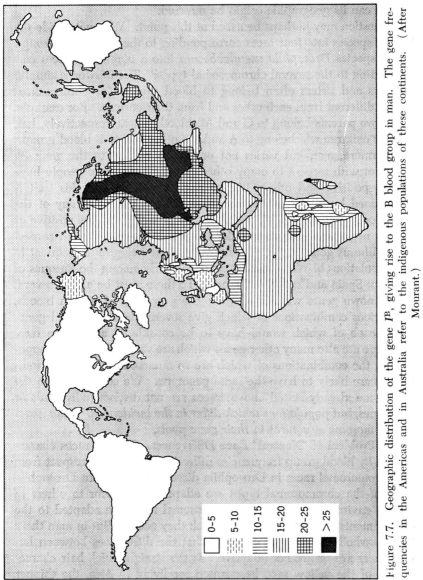

Figure 7.7. Geographic distribution of the gene *I*^B, giving rise to the B blood group in man. The gene frequencies in the Americas and in Australia refer to the indigenous populations of these continents. (After Mourant.)

0–5
5–10
10–15
15–20
20–25
> 25

which the individual came. For this purpose we must have a sample of individuals from a population, and the greater the sample, the more exactly can its geographic origin be inferred.

A question may perhaps be asked at this point. Why not divide the human species into four races corresponding to the four blood groups, or the species *Drosophila pseudoobscura* into a number of races corresponding to the several chromosomal types? The answer is simple: brothers and sisters often belong to blood groups (or chromosomal types) different from each other and from their parents. For example, if the two parents belong to O and AB blood groups, respectively, half of their children will belong to A and the other half to B blood groups. Furthermore, mankind varies not only with respect to the gene I^O-I^A-I^B but with respect to many other genes. Thus some people have Rhesus positive and others Rhesus negative blood, and this trait is determined by alleles of another gene, *Rh*. A person of any of the four blood groups, O, A, B, and AB, may be either Rhesus positive or Rhesus negative. Human populations are differentiated with respect to the Rhesus gene, the Rhesus negative allele being most frequent in the populations of Western Europe, particularly among the Basques of northern Spain and southern France. To these must be added several other known genes which determine the properties of human bloods, the various combinations of which give several thousand blood genotypes, each of which would have to be considered a separate race. But there are also many other genes which are variable in human populations, the combinations of which are so numerous that no two individuals are likely to have the same genotype. We come, then, to the conclusion already stated above: races are not distinct individuals or genotypes, but *populations which differ in the incidence of some genes or chromosome structures in their gene pools.*

The Problem of "Neutral" Race Differences. Human races characterized by blood group frequencies differ in an important respect from the chromosomal races in Drosophila discussed above. In Drosophila some of the chromosomal types are adaptively superior to others in certain environments, and the chromosomal races are adapted to the environments of the territories in which they occur. But in man there is little wholly convincing evidence that the differences between human races are or are not adaptive. Is the straight thick hair characteristic of the yellow race best suited for living in Asia, the thinner straight, wavy, or curly hair of the white race for living in Europe, and the kinky Negro hair for living in Africa? Is there any advantage in having the thick Negro lips in Africa, and thinner lips in Europe and Asia? Why should round (brachycephalic) heads be common among the inhabitants of Central Europe, and long (dolichocephalic) heads among the northern and the southern Europeans? The dark skin color of many human populations appears to be advantageous for living in hot climates, and the light color in temperate climates. And yet, although sunburns are health hazards, most persons of the white race develop the protective suntan easily enough and can withstand exposure to the tropical sun. There is a possibility that pale skin colors are advantageous when sunshine is scarce, because they facilitate the formation in the organism of the protective antirachitic vitamin D. The evidence for this is, however, not decisive.

Many races of animal and plant species differ from each other in colors, in proportions of some body parts, and in other traits which do not seem to facilitate the survival or reproduction of their carriers in the environments in which they occur. Some zoologists and botanists accordingly believe that many, or even most, race differences are adaptively neutral—they neither help nor handicap their possessors. There even was an opinion which for some years was current among both biologists and anthropologists, that the traits used to distinguish and to classify races and species should be adaptively neutral. Adaptively significant differences are, so the argument ran, too easily modified by the environment, and consequently not reliable as basis of classification. But if the differences between races and species are adaptively neutral, how could they be established by natural selection, which perpetuates useful and eliminates harmful traits? Those who believe that organic evolution is brought about chiefly through the action of mutation, gene recombination, and natural selection are inclined to think that most race and species differences are adaptive, or at least were so at the time when these races and species were in the process of formation.

The plain truth is that little research has been done to study the possible effects on fitness of the genetic differences among individuals within human populations or between the populations (races). All too often it has been assumed that all "normal" human beings function very nearly similarly. This typological thinking has doubtless prevented the discovery of the adaptive significance of numerous human traits. It should be remembered that even slight selective advantages may be important in evolution. If the possessors of darker skins produce, in the tropical climates, an average of 101 surviving children for every 100 children produced by persons with lighter skins, the tropical countries will eventually be populated by dark races.

Furthermore, selective advantages need not necessarily be expressed in robust health. Suppose that in certain cultures the possessors of curly hair will be sexually more attractive to the opposite sex than individuals with straight hair. This preference might lead to the formation of a race with curly hair.

Finally, the externally visible racial "traits" may be only outward "marks" of physiological differences which are important in adaptation. As pointed out in Chapter 2, a gene difference often produces a whole complex of traits, some more and others less striking to an observer's eye. An excellent example of such a manifold effect of genes has been discovered in the common garden onion by Walker and his collaborators (see Chapter 5). The resistance or susceptibility of the onion bulbs to smudge (a parasitic fungus) is determined by the presence or absence in the onion scales of certain chemical substances (catechol and protocatechuic acid). White onions do not contain these substances and are susceptible to the smudge; colored (red or purple) onions are resistant. The color of the onion bulb is known to be determined by several genes. Is, then, the color of the onion bulb adaptively important? It may well be that being white or purple is of no importance to the welfare of the plant. However, the "color genes" also cause resistance to smudge infections, and this resistance may be very important for the plants growing in localities in which these infections occur. It is most probable that many allegedly "neutral" genes in man will be found to induce physiological characteristics of importance in health or disease.

Experiments on Mountain and Valley Races of Plants. Although we are often unable to see the selective advantages of racial traits, there is no doubt that the process of formation of races in general serves to adapt different populations of a species to live in the environments of different countries in which these populations occur. Experiments bearing on this problem have been made on races of certain California plants by Clausen, Keck, and Hiesey.

Figure 7.8 shows races of yarrow (Achillea) from different parts of California. The race growing on the humid Pacific Coast near San Francisco is a compact plant, with a thick stem, which grows throughout the year, including the mild winters in the maritime climate of this race. In the hot and dry interior valley of California there is a race consisting of very tall plants with gray-pubescent leaves, which grow chiefly during the winter and spring seasons when there is some rain, and are dormant during the long rainless summer. In the forest belt of the Sierra Nevada grows a relatively tall race with a slender erect stem. Because the winters in its native habitat are severe the plants become dormant when the weather turns cold, and the active growth and flowering occur during the spring and summer. Finally, in the high alpine zone of the Sierra Nevada is a dwarf race which is able to grow, flower, and mature its seeds during the very short mountain summer, and to remain dormant over the long cold season.

The question which naturally arises is this: To what extent are the differences between the races of yarrow due to diversity of their genotypes, and to what degree are they induced directly by the environments which these races inhabit? With yarrows, this question can be resolved by experiments more conclusively than is possible with human races. A yarrow plant can be cut in two or several parts; the parts may be replanted in soil, where they continue to grow and eventually flower. The parts have the same genotype; they are members of a clone. The differences which may appear among the plants growing from parts of the same individual replanted in different localities are due to the environments of these localities. In the experiments of Clausen, Keck, and Hiesey, individuals of the different races of yarrow were subdivided, each into three parts, and the parts were replanted in three experimental gardens. One of the gardens lies in the coastal region of California; the second, at a moderate elevation above the sea level in the forest zone of the Sierra Nevada; and the third high in the alpine zone of these mountains.

The coastal race of the yarrow planted in the forest zone of the mountains is forced into dormancy during the winters, grows slowly during the spring and the early summer, and flowers much later than the native race does. The coastal race is usually killed in the alpine zone during the first winter, and it never develops flowers; the genotype of the coastal race may be said to be lethal in the alpine zone. The race native in the forest zone of the mountains grows quite tall when planted in the coastal garden, but about two-thirds of the individuals become dormant during winter. In the alpine garden this race shows a variable behavior: some individuals die, others grow only slowly, and still others grow tall and come into flower, although too late in the season to ripen seed. Finally, the alpine race can grow and flower at both the coastal and the mountain gardens, but it is the only race which is able to cope successfully with the rigors of its native habitat. On the coast and in the forest zone the alpine race is, however, much weaker than indigenous plants.

There is no doubt, then, that the yarrow races have different hereditary endowments. On the other hand, both the external appearance

Figure 7.8.   Races of yarrow (Achillea) from California.   The upper, middle, and lower horizontal rows represent plants native in the alpine zone in the mountains, at mid-altitudes in the mountains, and in the valley respectively.   The vertical row on the left shows these plants as they appear when grown in an experimental garden at the sea level; in the middle, the plants grown in an experimental garden at a moderate altitude (4800 feet above sea level); on the right, the plants grown in the alpine zone (10,000 feet above sea level).   These pictures show, then, the norms of reaction of three races as manifested in three different environments.
(Courtesy of Dr. W. M. Hiesey.)

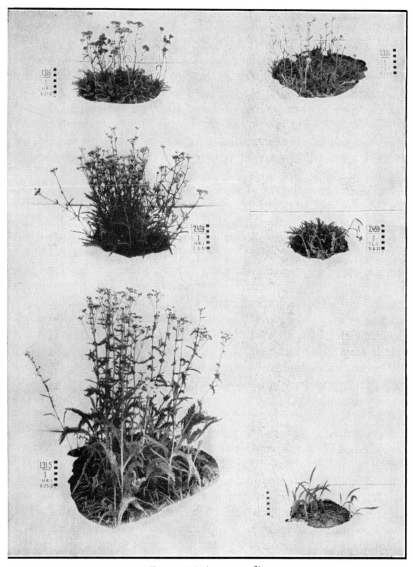

Figure 7.8 (*continued*)

and the physiological functions of individuals of each race are pro-foundly modified by transplantation to foreign environments, as Figure 7.8 clearly shows. It is neither heredity alone, nor the environment alone, which makes a yarrow race what it is. It is the developmental pattern engendered by a certain heredity in a certain environment.

Some Rules of Racial Variation. If we examine races of several more or less related species inhabiting the same country, some re-semblances between them are often noticed. For example, many species of beetles are represented in Arizona and in California by races which are colored more lightly than the races of the same species in the humid Pacific Northwest and in western Canada. It is as though the inhabitants of a given country followed a common "style." The existence of such styles or trends was noticed by zoologists and bot-anists of the past century. They interpreted these observations in a way which is not acceptable at the present time: they assumed that the geographic environment directly alters in some mysterious way the genotypes of diverse organisms. The problem has been re-exam-ined more recently by Rensch, Mayr, and others. These investigators concluded that some, and probably all, rules of racial variation result from parallel development by natural selection of analogous adapta-tions in different species of organisms.

It is easy to see that natural selection in cold climates will favor in diverse animals adaptations which minimize the heat loss; in hot cli-mates arrangements will be favored which facilitate the cooling of the body. Accordingly, the races of many mammals that live in cold countries have longer but finer fur than races of the same species in hot countries. Thus for the mountain lion (puma) in the relatively cool climate of the mountains of Mexico the mean length of the hair in the pelage is about 31 millimeters, whereas for the race of the same species in the equatorial climate of the Amazon valley the mean hair length in the comparable part of the pelage is only 12 millimeters. The European fox has fur 46 millimeters long in eastern Germany, and in subtropical Algeria only 39 millimeters. The otter fur in eastern Germany is 23 millimeters long, and in tropical Ceylon only 15 milli-meters long.

Races of many animals (warm-blooded as well as cold-blooded ones) which inhabit cold climates tend to be larger in body size than races which live in warm countries. Moreover, races of warm-blooded animals in cold countries have relatively shorter tails, legs, ears, and beaks than the inhabitants of warmer climates. The biological sig-nificance of these rules is understandable if we consider that a larger body has a relatively smaller body surface than a smaller body of the same shape. The body surface loses heat by radiation and by convection; accordingly, a relatively small body surface will be favored in cold climates, and a large body surface in hot climates. We need only to recall the discomfort felt in our ears in very cold weather to understand that relative reductions in size of such protruding body parts as ears, legs, and tails will be favored by natural selection in cold climates. In hot climates, on the contrary, these protruding body parts will facilitate the cooling of the body.

Major and Minor Races. Authorities in anthropology often disagree on just how many races compose mankind. Two to more than two hundred races have been distinguished by different specialists in race studies. So wide a divergence of opinion arose because race differences are quantitative rather than qualitative. Some races differ very slightly, others are quite distinct (see Chapter 13).

We have seen that the populations of *Drosophila pseudoobscura* which live at different elevations in the Sierra Nevada of California differ in the incidence of certain chromosomal structures (Figure 7.5). The same kinds of chromosomal structures occur at all elevations, although in different proportions. Much greater differences have been found between populations of this species of fly in California and in central Mexico. Most chromosomal structures which occur in California do not occur in Mexico, and vice versa; those which do occur in both regions have different frequencies. It can be stated that populations which live at different elevations in the California mountains are racially distinct from each other. Populations of California are racially distinct from populations of Mexico, but the differences between the California populations are much smaller than those between California and Mexico populations.

In man, the native populations of Europe (white), of central Africa (Negro), and of central Asia (Mongoloids) are obviously different, even to a superficial observer. The populations of different European countries are also different, but much less strikingly so. All these populations are racially distinct. Should we conclude that there exist "major" and "minor" races? In a way this is a correct description of the situation, but we must emphasize that there are also all possible transitions between very slightly and very strongly marked racial distinctions. Race differences of all magnitudes may be encountered. To a classifier of races this fact creates great difficulties, since it makes agreement on the number of races to be recognized virtually unattainable. To an evolutionist, however, the same fact is most significant.

It shows that race formation is a gradual process, which leads to a progressive divergence of populations in response to the environmental differences encountered in the territories which those populations inhabit.

Are Races "Real" or "Man-Made"? The abuse of the race concept by politicians has made many people skeptical of the usefulness of distinguishing any races at all. Indeed, do races actually exist as biological entities? Or are races arbitrary subdivisions which anthropologists and biologists have made for their own convenience? A proposal has also been made to abolish the term "race" altogether, and to distinguish instead "ethnic groups" in the human species. The argument in favor of this course is that the word "race" has become charged with too much emotion and prejudice.

It may well be doubted whether race prejudice can be effectively combated by calling races ethnic groups or by some other names. A better way would seem to be to explain to people the elementary biological facts underlying the scientific race concept. It is a plain fact, obvious to any reasonable observer, that mankind consists of populations, chiefly allopatric ones, which differ in the incidence of various genetic characters. The genetic differences between human populations are of the same kind as can be observed between races or subspecies of domestic and wild species of animals and plants.

How Many Races? Much of the misunderstanding surrounding the concept of race is due to people's confusing two logically and methodologically separate problems. The first problem is a biological one, and it may be presented as a question: "Are the populations which inhabit certain countries genetically, and hence racially, distinct?" The second problem is a question of classification and nomenclature: "Do certain populations differ sufficiently to deserve being given different names?" The first problem can, with adequate study, be solved quite objectively. If the populations in question do differ in the incidence of some genetic variants in their gene pools, they are racially distinct. Race differences are manifestly real and ascertainable facts. But the differences between the fly populations of adjacent sections of a forest, or between human populations of neighboring towns or districts, are very small; the differences between remote populations are large. It would be most inconvenient to give a separate racial name to every local population, and would merely burden the scientific literature. It is, then, up to the investigator to decide how great should the racial differences be to justify giving them names. It is arbitrary how many races we distinguish in a species, or rather it is a matter of convenience and common sense. For some purposes, for example for an elementary course of anthropology, it is better to recognize only a small number of "major" races. For a detailed study of the inhabitants of a country a finer subdivision may be called for. The human species, and other species, contain as many races as we see fit to distinguish (see Chapter 13).

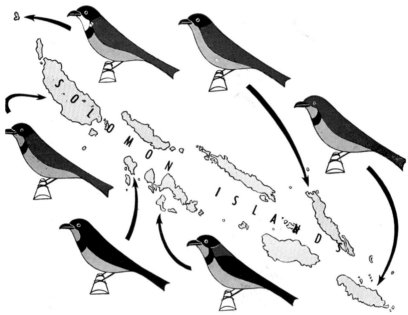

Figure 7.9. Races of the golden whistler (*Pachycephala pectoralis*) which live on different islands of the Solomon Archipelago, in tropical Pacific. (After Mayr.)

However, there is a biological phenomenon which may be made use of in order to make the racial groups more objective than they would otherwise be. One of the major difficulties with race classifications has been that, although the geographically remote populations are clearly distinct, the intermediate populations connect the extremes by insensible gradations. As we have seen, these gradations are due to the existence of gene gradients or clines. It frequently happens, however, that the gradients are not even; they do not consist of so much percentage increase, or decrease, of gene frequencies per every mile, or every hundred miles, traveled. Instead, in some geographic regions the gradients are more abrupt, in others they are less steep. For example, the human populations which reside on the two sides of the Himalaya Mountains or those living north and south of the Sahara Desert are fairly distinct. The reasons for this are not far to seek. Not only is the environment likely to be rather different on the two sides of a major geographic barrier, but such a barrier impedes the travel and migration between the populations which it separates. The racial divergence, then, is accelerated by geographic barriers. The race classifier turns this situation to his advantage by making his dividing lines between races or subspecies coincide with the zones of the steep gene gradients. The Himalayas separate the Hindu branch of the white race (or the Hindu race) from the yellow race; the Sahara separates the white and the Negro races.

Genetic Differences and Adaptation. To some people uniformity has a considerable emotional appeal, especially where man is involved. To gratify this emotion, J. J. Rousseau (1712–1778) invented his theory of "tabula rasa," according to which a newborn infant is a "blank page" on which environment and education write this or that story of the individual's life. Somewhat similar views have more recently been espoused by the behaviorist school of psychologists, as well as by certain fashionable exponents of psychoanalysis and cultural anthropology.

In part, the appeal of all these variants of the "tabula rasa" theory is due to the confusion of biological uniformity with social, legal, and religious equality. The idea of equality is certainly precious, since it is the basis of democracy and of humanitarian thinking in general. But this idea is derived not from biology but from the Christian tradition, which is the basis of Western civilization. People are most certainly not biologically alike, but they need not be so in order to be equal before the Law and before God. In fact, democracy may be regarded as an arrangement which permits unlike and yet equal persons to live together and to collaborate for the good of society and of mankind (see Chapter 14).

It is an ascertainable fact that the human species, as well as probably all other sexually reproducing species, show a greater or lesser amount of genetic diversity. This diversity is expressed within a Mendelian population in genetic differences among individual members of a breeding community. It is expressed in space by formation of allopatric or geographic races or subspecies, and it is expressed in time in changes which Mendelian populations undergo from generation to generation in the process of evolution.

There can be no doubt that most of the organic diversity in the sympatric, allopatric, and temporal levels has an important biological function to perform in making the populations adapted to live in different environments. No genotype is perfect, in the sense of making its carriers ideally adapted to live in all possible environments. A genotype may be superior to others in a certain environment but inferior in other environments. A genetically uniform species would be able to exploit successfully only a few ecological niches available in the territory where it lives. A polymorphic species can occupy a greater number of habitats. A species differentiated into races, other things being equal, may occupy a greater territory than a single race could. And a species which alters its genetic constitution when the environment changes, again other things being equal, is more likely to endure than a rigidly fixed species. It is most probable that, on the human level, the polymorphism within, and the race differences between, the populations have furnished the creative leaven for the cultural development of mankind.

Suggestions for Further Reading

Mayr, E. 1942. *Systematics and the Origin of Species.* Columbia University Press, New York.

This work has played an important role in achieving a synthesis of zoological systematics with the modern theory of evolution, which was originally based chiefly on the findings of genetics. A parallel, but more inclusive, work dealing with botanical systematics is Stebbins' book, quoted among the suggested readings in Chapter 6. The books by Andrewartha and Birch and by Dobzhansky, also quoted in Chapter 6, may also be useful for understanding the race and species concepts as used in modern biology.

Clausen, J. 1951. *Stages in the Evolution of Plant Species.* Cornell University Press, Ithaca.

Clausen, J., Keck, D. D., and Hiesey, W. M. 1948. *Experimental studies on the nature of species. III. Environmental responses of climatic races of Achillea. Carnegie Institution of Washington Publication 581.*

Dobzhansky, Th., and Epling, C. 1944. *Contributions to the genetics, taxonomy and ecology of Drosophila pseudoobscura and its relatives. Carnegie Institution of Washington Publication 554.*

Lack, D. L. 1947. *Darwin's Finches.* Cambridge University Press, London.

Patterson, J. T., and Stone, W. S. 1952. *Evolution of the Genus Drosophila.* Macmillan, New York.

These five books (Clausen to Patterson and Stone) describe experimental and observational studies on races and species of organisms which are particularly favorable for such studies.

Count, E. W. (Editor). 1950. *This Is Race.* Schumann, New York.

This is an anthology of anthropological writings concerned with the race concept as applied to man. With some exceptions, the writings included belong to the pregenetical period.

Boyd, W. C. 1950. *Genetics and the Races of Man.* Little, Brown, Boston.

Application of the genetical concept of race to man.

Coon, C. S., Garn, S. M., and Birdsell, J. B. 1950. *Races: a Study of the Problems of Race Formation in Man.* Ch. Thomas, Springfield, Ill.

A classification of human races and a discussion of the possible adaptive significance of human racial characteristics.

Origin and evolution of man. 1950. *Cold Spring Harbor Symposia on Quantitative Biology,* Volume 15.

The volume contains articles by thirty-seven authors, dealing with the problems of human polymorphism, race formation, and other aspects of human evolution.

Species

Darwin's great book was entitled *The Origin of Species* (the full title was rather more ponderous: *On the Origin of Species by Means of Natural Selection, or the Preservation of Favoured Races in the Struggle for Life*). Darwin knew as well as anybody that formation of races and species is only a part of the grand story of evolution. The origin of species, however, was of crucial importance in Darwin's day, because of the current view that species were created entities which could not be produced by natural processes.

In a different way, species formation is also regarded as a critical stage of the evolutionary process in modern theories. Races of a species are populations which can, and often do, cross and exchange genes. Hybridization of races may, and sometimes does, lead to their fusion in a single population. This has actually happened, for example, to some human races, the members of which intermarried so frequently that the races disappeared as separate Mendelian populations. Races are genetically open systems, and the divergence of races is a reversible process; it can be undone by hybridization. Species, on the other hand, are genetically closed systems, since they exchange genes rarely, or not at all. Evolutionary divergence of Mendelian populations tends to become irreversible once the species level is reached. For example, man and chimpanzee are most unlikely ever to exchange genes or to form a hybrid population.

A minority of modern evolutionists, among whom Goldschmidt is most prominent, believe that the known factors of evolution—mutation, gene recombination, selection, and genetic drift—account only for "microevolution," which is usually equated with race formation. Other, and as yet unknown, processes should explain *"macroevolution"*—the origin of species and species groups.

Hypothesis of Constancy of Species. Living beings seem infinitely variable; no two individuals are completely alike. But the variation is not entirely haphazard, since on closer acquaintance living creatures are seen to fall into discrete groups. Everyday language recognizes the existence of these discrete groups, refers to them as "kinds" of animals or of plants, and gives to each "kind" a vernacular name—cat, lion, tiger, jaguar, and puma (mountain lion), etc. Linnaeus (1707–1778), the father of systematic biology, called the "kinds" species, and gave to each species known to him a name in Latin. The species referred to above are *Felis maniculata, Felis leo, Felis tigris, Felis onca,* and *Felis concolor,* respectively.

The belief in constancy of species was not accepted by everybody before Darwin. Weirdest transformations of species were often credited. Greek and other mythologies are full of stories of gods transforming themselves or men into animals and back into men or gods. Theophrastos in ancient Greece, Pliny in ancient Rome, Albertus Magnus in the thirteenth century, Paracelsus in the sixteenth, Telliamed in the seventeenth, and Lysenko in the twentieth, all believed in transformation of one species into another. They thought that wheat occasionally produces rye or barley, that fishes turn into birds, etc. Oppian (third century Rome) reached the peak of absurdity: he believed that the ostrich arose from a cross between a camel and a sparrow.

Linnaeus faced the enormous task of classifying the organisms and making the immense variety of living forms intelligible. To him, the species was the elementary unit of classification, and supposing that this unit was fixed and unchangeable was a tenable opinion. He stated this opinion in his famous dictum: "Species tot sunt, quot diversas formas ab initio produxit Infinitum Ens" (Species are as many as were produced at the beginning by The Infinite). It is important to realize that in Linnaeus's day such a view did not appear contrary to facts, as it so clearly does now.

Development of the Species Concept from Linnaeus to Darwin. In 1758 Linnaeus knew 4235 species of animals. At present approximately 1,000,000 animal and about 265,000 plant species have been described. Furthermore, Linnaeus worked mostly in Sweden and in other countries of northwestern Europe, and his collections came naturally from that part of the world, with only a scattering of specimens from other countries. In other words, Linnaeus worked chiefly with sympatric (page 137) species. It happens that, for reasons explained below, sympatric species are usually quite discrete, no individuals intermediate between the species being found. If we collect animals or plants, for example. in the vicinity of New York, we usually find little difficulty in classifying the specimens into clear-cut species. The gaps between the species appear to be absolute and unbridgeable. To such species the hypothesis of constancy seems to apply reasonably well.

The late eighteenth and the nineteenth centuries were the times of rapid geographical exploration of the world. Collections of animals and plants were made in near and remote lands, and were deposited in the museums of Europe and of America. Zoologists and botanists had more and more allopatric (page 137) forms of life to classify. Here difficulties began to arise and to multiply, until the successors of Linnaeus saw themselves forced to abandon the idea that species are fixed.

We have seen, in Chapter 7, that populations of the same species which live in neighboring territories usually differ only slightly in the incidence of some genes and of bodily traits which these genes determine. Races found in remote territories, or in territories which are separated by barriers making migration difficult, may be more sharply distinct. If we knew only the native inhabitants of Europe and of central Africa, they would appear to us very different. But if we study people in all parts of the world, we find all kinds of races intermediate between those of Europe and central Africa. Remote races of many species differ even more than remote human races. In fact, remote races of a species may appear about as distinct as separate species.

Lamarck, whose long life was spent in classifying species of plants and animals, was perhaps the first to see clearly that a new working hypothesis was demanded by the new evidence. This hypothesis was that species evolve from races. Races and species are stages in the evolutionary divergence, produced by the adaptation of the organisms to their environments. Lamarck's contemporaries were not convinced that so radical a hypothesis was necessary, but some thirty years later Darwin came to the same conclusion: "In all these several respects the species of large genera present a strong analogy with varieties. And we can clearly understand these analogies if species have once existed as varieties, and have thus originated; whereas, these analogies are utterly inexplicable if each species has been independently created."

It is at this point immaterial that Lamarck and Darwin had different views concerning the processes which bring about the formation of new races and species. Lamarck thought that new races and species were formed chiefly through inheritance of the results of use and disuse of organs, whereas Darwin considered natural selection to be the most effective agent. They agreed that the absence of any dividing lines between races and species shows that races are incipient species. Thus the difficulty of making clear-cut classifications, which systematists found so annoying in their work, became the foundation of probably the greatest discovery which biological science has yet made.

Theory of Geographic Speciation. Although Darwin was quite familiar with species composed of geographic races, it remained for his successors to develop a theory of geographic species formation (speciation). This theory was stated by M. Wagner (1868 and later), Jordan (1905), and in our day by Rensch (1929) and by Mayr (1942). Any species tends to spread over the surface of the earth into all territories where it can live. Populations of a species may thus be exposed to different climatic or soil conditions, to different predators, parasites, and diseases, and generally to varying environments. Through natural selection, populations respond adaptively to the environmental differences, by becoming genotypically and phenotypically differentiated into races or subspecies. It stands to reason that geographically remote territories are likely to have more sharply different environments than adjacent territories. Accordingly, remote territories are likely to be inhabited by most distinct races. Some of the allopatric races may gradually become very different in genetic structure and in external appearance from other races. If and when this happens, the single ancestral species breaks up into two or several derived species. When the new species are fully formed, they may invade each other's territories, come to live side by side, and thus become sympatric species.

Most biologists are now agreed that the usual method by which one species may split up into two or more species is by way of divergence of geographic races. Whether this is the only method is questionable. Some investigators believe that populations may differentiate and become species by becoming specialized to eat different foods or to grow on different soils in the same territory, sympatrically. It is, indeed, probable that such sympatric species formation occurs in organisms which are able to reproduce asexually or by self-fertilization. Species formation by allopolyploidy (Chapter 9) is necessarily sympatric.

Geographic and Reproductive Isolation. Different races of man and different breeds of domesticated animals and plants often live sympatrically, in the same territory. Biologically, this is an unusual situation, since races of sexual and cross-breeding organisms are normally allopatric, but it is easy to see how it happens. In man the biological urge to mate is channeled by social custom. The regulation of marriage by custom has the biological result of slowing down the exchange of genes between different mating groups, such as social or economic classes and sympatric or allopatric races. In domesticated animals and plants the control of reproduction is exercised by man. Consider the races (breeds) of dogs, many of which live sympatrically. The gene exchange between them is restricted or prevented by man. When this restriction is weakened, the once separate sympatric races fuse into a single variable race—the mongrel.

In the state of nature the gene exchange between races of sexual organisms is limited by distance, by separation in space, by *geographic isolation*. This is why most races are allopatric. Neighboring allopatric populations usually interbreed more or less frequently, but the diffusion of genes from one race to other remote races is slow enough, so that the races remain distinct. Migration or diffusion of genes tends to make populations or races converge; natural selection and genetic drift tend to make them diverge. Actual convergence or divergence depends upon which of these factors get the upper hand.

Different, even closely related, species are often sympatric. For example, Patterson and Stone found that about forty species of Drosophila live together in one locality near Austin, Texas. Nevertheless, hybrids between these species are rare or absent. Why do races hybridize and exchange genes wherever possible, whereas species do not? The answer is that gene exchange between species is prevented by a variety of causes, known collectively as reproductive isolating mechanisms, in addition to geographic isolation which may or may not be present.

Distinct species may live either in the same or in different territories; both sympatric and allopatric species are common. The exchange of genes between sympatric species is limited or prevented by reproductive isolation; that between allopatric species, by geographic as well as by reproductive isolating mechanisms. For example, the wild ancestors of the domestic horse and of the domestic ass may have been in part sympatric. Under domestication, hybrids between them, mules, can be obtained, but mules are almost invariably sterile. Gene exchange between the populations of horses and asses is absent. The species are reproductively isolated. On the other hand, wild horses and zebras were allopatric species, since the former occurred, in historical times, in Europe and Asia and the latter in Africa (Chapter 9). Hybrids between domestic horses and zebras are known, but they are sterile. Horses and zebras could live in the same territory as sympatric species, although they did not actually do so, as far as known.

Figure 8.1.   Geographic distribution of two closely related species of flies, *Drosophila pseudoobscura* and *Drosophila persimilis*.

Reproductive Isolation between Two Species of Drosophila. *Drosophila pseudoobscura* and *Drosophila persimilis* are very closely related species. They live together, sympatrically, over a large territory from British Columbia to the mountains of California. *D. pseudoobscura* occurs alone in a much larger territory, extending to the Rocky Mountains, Texas, Mexico, and Guatemala (Figure 8.1).

Where the species are sympatric, they show some *ecological or habitat isolation,* that is, preference for different habitats. *D. pseudo-*

obscura is more frequent in warmer and drier locations, and at lower elevations in the mountains, than *D. persimilis*. The habitat isolation, however, is incomplete, and in many places the two species occur side by side. Their hybridization is impeded, however, by *sexual isolation*, that is, by preference for mating within, rather than between, the species, as can be demonstrated by a simple experiment. A mixture of virgin females of both species is exposed to males of one of them. The males inseminate a greater proportion of females of their own than of the foreign species (Table 8.1). If females of either species

TABLE 8.1

SEXUAL ISOLATION BETWEEN *Drosophila pseudoobscura* AND *Drosophila persimilis*

(Equal numbers of females of the two species were exposed to males of one of them. The numbers show the percentages of the females inseminated and left virgin in such experiments.)

Males \ Females	pseudoobscura		persimilis	
	Inseminated	Virgin	Inseminated	Virgin
pseudoobscura	84.3	15.7	7.0	93.0
persimilis	22.5	77.5	79.2	20.8

are offered a "choice" of mating with males of both species, they mate with conspecific males much more frequently than with foreign males.

Observations in nature have shown that under natural conditions the sexual isolation between the species is even stronger than the experimental data in Table 8.1 might suggest. Females inseminated by males of foreign species are exceedingly rare. This fact may be due in part to an *ethological isolation*, the two species being somewhat different in behavior: *D. pseudoobscura* is relatively more active during the afternoon and *D. persimilis* during the morning hours. Yet, the ethological isolation (of which sexual isolation is a part) is also incomplete, since some individuals of both species fly both in the morning and in the afternoon.

Hybrids between *D. pseudoobscura* and *D. persimilis* can be rather easily obtained in laboratory cultures, if females of one species are confined with males of the other. The hybrid flies of both sexes are as vigorous as the pure species, just as mules are not inferior in vigor either to horses or to donkeys. Again, like mules, the hybrid male flies show a complete *hybrid sterility*. They fail to produce any functional spermatozoa, on account of gross disturbances in their reproductive cells (see page 206). The female hybrids, on the contrary, are fully fertile; they deposit numerous eggs, which, when fertilized by males of either parental species, may produce viable larvae. However, the backcross hybrid progenies so obtained suffer a *hybrid breakdown;* they are so deficient in vigor and vitality that they survive only under favorable conditions in laboratory cultures.

To summarize: The gene exchange between *D. pseudoobscura* and *D. persimilis* is impeded by cooperation of at least five reproductive isolating mechanisms. None of these mechanisms is by itself sufficient to prevent completely all the gene exchange between the species; yet the combination of them does accomplish this function in nature. In laboratory experiments some gene exchange can be obtained, however. It is not an uncommon situation that species which never cross in nature can sometimes be crossed in experiments.

Reproductive Isolation between Species of Animals. Detailed studies of the reproductive isolation between various species of Drosophila have been made, especially by Patterson, Stone, and Spieth. They have revealed two significant facts. First, the gene exchange between species is apparently always prevented not by one but by a combination of several isolating mechanisms. Second, different pairs of species are kept apart by different combinations of isolating mechanisms. By and large, sexual isolation is most widespread. Spieth found that almost every species which he studied has its own characteristic methods of courtship and copulation. And yet, some undoubtedly distinct species, especially allopatric ones which never meet each other in the state of nature, show little or no sexual isolation. As a rule, males are less discriminating than females: whereas males may court females of their own and of a foreign species, females accept males of their own species more easily than they do other males.

Some pairs of species show *gametic isolation,* which seems to be absent between *Drosophila pseudoobscura* and *D. persimilis,* discussed above. The sperm delivered by a male into the genital ducts of a female is stored in a special organ, the seminal receptacle. When the male and the female belong to the same species, the sperm in the seminal receptacle remains alive for days and even weeks. But when a male of *Drosophila virilis* impregnates a female of *D. americana* (or male *D. americana,* female *D. virilis*) the sperm loses its fertilizing ability a day or two later. Some species of Drosophila have the so-called insemination reaction: the copulation is followed by a swelling of certain parts of the genital ducts of the female, which temporarily prevents the deposition of eggs and new copulations. The insemination reaction produced by an insemination by the sperm of a foreign species may be so violent that the females become permanently sterile; yet other species of Drosophila show no trace of insemination reaction.

A very common isolating mechanism is *hybrid inviability*. Fertilization of eggs of one species by spermatozoa of another may be accomplished, but the hybrid zygote may fail to develop normally. Thus a belief was long current that domestic goats occasionally produce hybrids with domestic sheep. Controlled experiments, with both natural and artificial insemination, showed, however, that cross-fertilization between these species does take place, but the hybrid embryos are aborted at a very early stage of pregnancy. It is virtually certain that a similar fate overtakes the hybrids between rabbits and hares, although alleged viable hybrids of this kind have been repeatedly claimed since 1780, and were even given a name—"leporids." In many marine animals no copulation occurs; eggs and spermatozoa are simply released into ambient water, and fertilization occurs outside the bodies of the parents. This external fertilization makes possible experimental hybridization of some very unlike organisms. In the classical experiments of Godlewsky (1906) and Baltzer (1910), several different genera of sea urchins were intercrossed, and sea urchin eggs were fertilized with the sperm of a sea lily. Sea urchins and sea lilies belong to different classes of the phylum of echinoderms. Such remote hybridization never yields normally developing hybrid embryos. Either the chromosomes of the father, brought in by the spermatozoon, are thrown out of the egg nucleus and disintegrate, in which case the embryo develops as that of the species of the mother. Or else, if the parental chromosomes divide and are included in the cleavage nuclei, the embryos show gross abnormalities and soon die off.

Isolating mechanisms which operate between species of higher animals are pretty much the same as those found between species of Drosophila and other invertebrates. As in Drosophila, the precise situation varies endlessly from species to species. Sexual isolation is often important, since the courtship behavior is generally unlike even in closely related species of birds and mammals. This sexual isolation may account for the fact that species hybrids are on the whole quite rare in the state of nature, although they are often obtained fairly easily in experiments. Thus, in captivity, many species and even genera of ducks produce hybrids, some of them quite viable and fertile, and yet very few hybrid ducks have ever been found in natural habitats. Dice and Blair found the same to be true for some species of deer mice (Peromyscus).

Various crosses have been made in captivity between domestic cattle (*Bos taurus*), American buffalo (*Bos americanus*), European buffalo (*Bos bonasus*), Asiatic yak (*Pheophagus grunnieus*), and Indonesian banteng (*Bibos banteng*). The hybrids are fully viable, although difficulties occur at parturition when a relatively small mother (domestic cow) gives birth to calves sired by large fathers (European buffalo). The F_1 hybrid bulls are completely sterile, but the cows are fertile even when intergeneric hybridization is involved, as in the case of cattle $\times$ yak. The hybrid cows, then, can be backcrossed to either parental species; among the resulting progenies, the females as well as some of the males may be fertile. Indeed, some introgression (see page 127) of genes from the yak into populations of cattle has taken place in some parts of central Asia, where the two species are kept together as domestic animals.

Reproductive Isolation in Plants. Among plant species we again meet a variety of isolating mechanisms. Hybrid inviability and hybrid sterility occur in plants as well as in animals. An interesting example of the former is hybrids between certain species of flax described by Laibach (1925). The hybrid embryos are so weak that they are unable to break the outer seed coat, and they die within the seed. Yet when they are artificially freed from the seed coat they give healthy seedlings and mature and fertile plants. Blakeslee and Satina (1944) found an even more extreme situation among hybrids between certain species of Jimson weed (Datura), where the hybrid embryos have to be cultivated on artificial media supplied with certain chemical substances, but may eventually grow normally. Some sterile plant hybrids will be discussed in the next chapter.

Some plant species are able, in experiments, to produce viable and fertile hybrids, but do not do so, or do only rarely, in nature. Their success may depend upon *habitat isolation,* as for two species of violets, V*iola arvensis* and V*iola tricolor.* The former species grows chiefly on calcareous soils; the latter occurs mostly on acid soils. The two species seldom meet (Clausen 1922). In the Yosemite region of the Sierra Nevada of California, the manzanita bush, *Arctostaphylos mariposa*, grows at lower elevations in the mountains than the related species, *Arctostaphylos patula.* In some places, however, the altitudinal ranges of the two species overlap, and there some hybrid bushes can be found.

The isolation of some species is due wholly or in part to the fact that their flowers attract different animals to transport their pollen. Grant (1951) found that the columbine *Aquilegia formosa* in the mountains of the Sierra Nevada is pollinated chiefly by humming birds, whereas the related *Aquilegia pubescens* attracts chiefly hawk moths. But bumblebees visit both species, and as a consequence some hybrids are produced in natural habitats. An extreme case of insect specificity has been discovered among certain orchids in North Africa. These species have a part of the flower resembling in shape and in color the females of species of wasps or bees; the male insects are attracted to these flowers and engage in copulatory movements, during which they receive and deposit the pollen of the plant. But different orchids resemble different species of wasps, making hybridization unlikely.

If flowers of one species receive the pollen of another species, hybrids are by no means always produced. In some plants the pollen of one species grows poorly in the style of a different species, and fails to reach the ovules in time to accomplish the fertilization. This, in addition to the inviability of the hybrid seeds, prevents the gene exchange between some species which grow in close proximity and are pollinated by unselective agents, such as wind.

Single Genes and Gene Systems. For the sake of simplicity, we have so far considered only the simplest microevolutionary changes, which involved substitution of one or of few genes. The transformation of colon bacteria susceptible to bacteriophage attack into resistant ones requires apparently a single gene change (Chapter 5). The same is probably true of the resistance of these bacteria to streptomycin, and of the resistance of the red scale to cyanide gas. When, as in the development of the resistance to penicillin in Staphylococcus bacteria, the modification occurs gradually, the process is due to accumulation of several mutations, each of which increases the resistance by a small amount (Chapter 5). Such mutations are said to be *additive.*

But evolution often involves more complex situations, some of which must be considered to gain an understanding of the biological meaning of species formation. The development of a living body, especially in higher organisms, involves joint action of all the genes which the body possesses. In evolution, the gene system as a whole undergoes changes, although the changes of the gene system are compounded of changes in individual genes. A gene system may be likened to a mosaic picture, and the genes to the component stones. The nature and quality of a mosaic picture are determined obviously by the pattern in which the stones are placed, as well as by the characters of the separate stones.

In Chapter 2 we have considered as an example of interaction of genes the determination of the coat color in horses. Here many genes are involved, the color being the result of co-action of all of them. Particularly interesting is the gene I, which in the presence of the gene B transforms the black coat color into bay, but in the absence of B has no known effects. The bi and bI horses are both chestnut (sorrel) in color. Suppose, for the sake of argument, that having the bay color is adaptively advantageous to the horse; should the gene I then be considered favorable or neutral? Obviously, this would depend upon the other genes which the organism has, particularly on the gene B.

Another example of gene interaction with which we are familiar is the chromosomal variants in natural populations of *Drosophila pseudoobscura* (Chapter 7). These chromosomes differ, it may be recalled, by inversions of blocks of genes in certain chromosomes. The heterozygotes which carry the two chromosomes of a pair with different gene arrangements are heterotic, that is, have a higher fitness than do the inversion homozygotes. Now this heterosis is produced by complexes of genes carried in the respective chromosomes. By using letters as symbols for genes, the matter may be represented thus: one chromosome has the genes $A_1B_1C_1D_1E_1$ and the other $A_2D_2C_2B_2E_2$. The heterosis is produced by the interaction of all these genes in the heterozygotes $A_1B_1C_1D_1E_1/A_2D_2C_2B_2E_2$, whereas the homozygotes which have two chromosomes with $A_1B_1C_1D_1E_1$, or two chromosomes $A_2D_2C_2B_2E_2$, have inferior fitness. The importance of the inversion of a segment of the chromosome is that the inversion prevents or greatly reduces the crossing over between the chromosomes (see page 144), and consequently the recombination of genes and the breakup of the gene complexes which produce the hybrid vigor.

Species as Systems of Genes. Heterosis found in inversion heterozygotes in populations of Drosophila sheds some light on a far more general problem, that of structure of the gene pool in many or all organisms which reproduce sexually and by cross-fertilization. Let us recall (Table 7.1) that a high proportion of the chromosomes in Drosophila populations produce low fitness when present in double dose (in homozygous condition), yet natural populations of Drosophila consist of individuals most of which are healthy and vigorous. Human populations behave like those of Drosophila flies: most "normal" human beings probably carry in heterozygous condition genes which would produce more or less serious disabilities if they were allowed to become homozygous. The chances of their becoming homozygous are increased when relatives marry; this is why the incidence of hereditary diseases is high in small populations in which inbreeding is common. For most natural populations, at least in common and successful species, inbreeding, however, is rather rare. Most of the genes in such populations are represented by numerous different alleles, any one of which is seldom homozygous. The fitness of the homozygotes, then, is of relatively little importance to the species. Far more important for the adaptedness of the population is the fitness of the heterozygous combinations, since most individuals in sexual populations are heterozygotes.

The situation just described has an interesting and important consequence: natural selection retains in natural populations those gene alleles which yield vigorous heterozygotes with other alleles present in the same populations. The gene pool of a sexual population comes, therefore, to consist of genes that are *coadapted*, that is, that fit well together when present in heterozygous individuals. To use a simile, natural selection in sexual organisms encourages genes that are "good mixers" rather than "rugged individualists."

The process of coadaptation makes a species something more than a collection of individuals. A sexual population (Mendelian population) is a system of genes which fit together, and yield highly fit individuals in the environments in which the population lives.

Hybrid Breakdown. Natural selection eliminates from populations of a species the genes which do not have the property of being "good mixers" with other genes in the same populations. But genes in different species, or even in remote races of the same species, need not be "good mixers." Thus at least some of the genes of the horse are not coadapted with the genes of the ass. The hybrids between these species, mules, show a disharmony—they are sterile. Even though mules may be vigorous and resistant animals as individuals, their adaptive value in the genetic sense is zero; they do not pass their genes to any progeny. Species of cottons produce vigorous and sometimes fertile F_1 hybrids. The F_2 hybrids, or the progenies obtained by backcrosses to the parental species, however, suffer a breakdown of fitness. Such hybrids are mostly weak and stunted "rogues" which cannot compete with their parents either as wild or as agricultural plants (see more about cotton hybrids in Chapter 9).

Not only hybrids between species but even those between remote races may suffer genetic breakdown. Wallace, Vetukhov, and Brncic have recently found that when populations of *Drosophila pseudoobscura* which live in the states of California, Nevada, Utah, and Colorado are intercrossed there is a perceptible loss of fitness among the F_2 hybrid progenies. Moore has shown (1946 and later) that when leopard frogs (*Rana pipiens*) from the northern part of the United States (for example, from New England) are crossed to frogs of the same species from Florida or from Texas the hybrid embryos die before completing their development. The northern and the southern leopard frogs behave as though they belonged to different species; they show in Moore's experiments a complete reproductive isolation because of the inviability of their hybrids. These northern and southern races are nevertheless capable of exchanging genes through the connecting populations which live in geographically intermediate areas. Thus the leopard frogs from New Jersey or from Oklahoma produce normally viable, or only slightly abnormal hybrids, when crossed to Vermont frogs. It is, then, perfectly conceivable that a useful gene, or gene combination, arising in Texas may eventually reach the Vermont populations, and vice versa.

Different species have different genes because they are adapted to live in different environments. Each species occupies a certain *ecological niche* in the economy of nature. Thus *Drosophila pseudoobscura* lives in warmer and drier habitats than *Drosophila persimilis* (see above). The genetic system of every species makes it fit to occupy its ecological niche and to lead a certain mode of life. The low fitness of interspecific hybrids, therefore, is a by-product of the parental species' becoming adapted to different environments. Gene exchanges between populations of distinct species are likely to produce genotypes which are adapted to neither of the environments to which their parents are adapted. As the popular saying goes, they are likely "to fall between two stools."

The harmful results of gene exchange between species, however, should not be exaggerated. *Some* of the combinations of genes which arise owing to hybridization of species may actually be valuable, since they may be adapted to environments to which neither parent is adapted. In the state of nature the adaptive value of mules would be zero, on account of their sterility; but this limitation does not prevent mules from being very useful as farm animals. Some of the most important cultivated plants are descendants of species hybrids (Chapter 9). Cultivated plants and animals live in man-created environments, which are often greatly different from natural environments. To fit his crops and his herds to the new environments, man had to provide them with new genotypes adapted to these environments. Such genotypes were produced in most instances by unrelenting artificial selection within a single species, but in some instances also by selection among hybrids between species. In doing so, man merely followed the methods of nature, which occasionally makes use of introgressive hybridization (page 127) to contrive adaptations to certain environments.

Origin of Reproductive Isolation between Species. Hybridization of the northern and the southern races of the leopard frog resulted, in Moore's experiments, in the production of inviable hybrids (see above). Such hybrids, however, are not produced in nature since the frog races involved are allopatric; the Vermont frogs have no chance to meet Florida frogs except in the laboratory of a biologist. The diffusion of genes between these races takes place only through the geographically intermediate races, which yield viable hybrids with their neighbors.

Compare with this the situation of the two Drosophila species— *Drosophila pseudoobscura* and *Drosophila persimilis* (see pages 170– 171). They live side by side in a territory extending from British Columbia to California (Figure 8.1), and in this whole territory they can meet, mate, and beget hybrid offspring. The hybrid males are sterile, and the backcross progenies suffer a hybrid breakdown, and are weaklings if they survive at all. The hybrids may be said to be adaptively worthless, at least in the state of nature. Yet when hybrids are produced, they consume food and occupy the place in the sun which can otherwise be exploited by the parental species. Building up reproductive isolating mechanisms that would prevent the hybridization of the species and the production of the hybrids should, then, be promoted by natural selection.

An experimental demonstration that selection can, indeed, build up reproductive isolation of species has been given by Koopman (1950). We have seen (Table 8.1) that one of the mechanisms which keep the species *Drosophila pseudoobscura* and *Drosophila persimilis* apart is sexual isolation. The flies show a preference for mating within the species and an aversion for mating between species. For reasons that are obscure, this sexual isolation is more nearly complete in the natural habitats of the flies than it is under laboratory conditions. In particular, the sexual isolation is weakened in the laboratory at low temperatures. If a mixture of equal proportions of the two species is kept at 15°C (59°F), the copulations between species are only slightly less frequent than those within the species.

Koopman made mixed populations of the two species, and maintained them for several generations. The experiment was so arranged that the hybrid flies that were produced were, in every generation, picked out and discarded. The non-hybrid flies, which were produced evidently by intraspecific matings, served to propagate the populations further. The result of the experiment was that the proportions of the hybrids produced in the populations waned from generation to generation; the proportions of the matings within the species gradually increased, and the proportions of interspecific copulations dwindled. The interpretation of these experimental results is simple. The original populations of one or of both species were evidently not uniform with respect to their sexual preferences. Some flies in experimental environments were more prone to mate with individuals of the foreign species than were other flies. Since the hybrids were eliminated from the populations, the flies which mated only with those of their own species contributed more offspring to the following generations than the more promiscuous individuals. This situation caused a process of selection of the more discriminating variants, and the outcome was an intensification of the sexual isolation. It is a reasonable working hypothesis that some of the isolating mechanisms between species are perfected also in nature by a process of natural selection.

Static and Dynamic Approaches to the Study of Species. The concept of species was developed in biology with a practical end in view. Linnaeus and his successors described and named species of animals and plants and built a classification of living beings. This work of systematization and classification is obviously the foundation of scientific biology. We must know, and be able to tell others, with just what creatures we are working. Linnaeus's work is being continued now by numerous investigators on the staffs of zoological and botanical museums in all civilized countries, as well as by individual specialists. When an insect pest is found to injure the crops, or an organism is suspected of being involved in the distribution of a disease, or simply when anyone finds an interesting creature, it is first of all sent to a specialist to be "determined," that is, to have its species name attached to it. Living and fossil species and races are so numerous that nobody knows all or even a large part of them; the work of systematics has necessarily to be done by specialists.

It is not surprising that for the practical work of naming and labeling species of animals and plants it is convenient to treat these species, so far as possible, as completely discrete pigeonholes in which to place museum specimens. When subspecies or races are described, it is expedient to treat them also as discrete pigeonholes. This is why Linnaeus espoused the view that species are created entities (page 166). But the knowledge of species as biological phenomena has not stood still since Linnaeus. Lamarck and Darwin, and since Darwin a great majority of biologists, regard species as branches of the stream of evolution. These branches become subdivided further and further when populations of a species living in different countries differentiate genetically and become different races. Diverging geographic races become incipient species when they begin to develop reproductive isolation. The speciation becomes consummated and irreversible when the reproductive isolation is complete.

Of course modern systematists not only accept the evolutionary view of species but also contribute greatly to the study and the understanding of the process of speciation. There is, nevertheless, some dualism in the usage of the species concept in biology. To a practical systematist whose task is to label species and races, intermediate specimens transitional between these species and races are obviously a nuisance. It is hard to assign names to intermediates. By contrast, a biologist who studies the process of speciation will look for just such transitions, for races which are about to become species or for incipient species which have not yet completed the development of the reproductive barriers between them. As a result, an investigator who gives names to species and races is likely to prefer a more static species concept, whereas one who studies the process of evolution will incline towards a more dynamic view. This explains the fact which seems otherwise very odd: nobody has yet proposed a definition of what constitutes a species that would be satisfactory to all biologists.

Rigid Definition of Species Is Impossible. In the history of biology attempts have been made again and again to give a definition of species with the aid of which we could always decide whether certain groups of organisms are races of the same species or are distinct species. For example, it has repeatedly been suggested that forms which produce inviable or sterile hybrids when crossed belong to different species, whereas those which produce fertile hybrids belong to the same species. Such a definition of species is unsatisfactory on two counts. First, the sterility and inviability of hybrids are matters of degree. Some fairly well-authenticated instances of fertility of female mules are on record, but it would be entirely unreasonable to say that horse and ass belong to the same species because one female mule per thousand is fertile. On the other hand, the Vermont and Florida races of the leopard frog are races of a single species, despite the fact that the hybrids between them are inviable. These races are able to exchange genes by way of geographically intervening populations. Second, as pointed out above, some very distinct species produce fertile hybrids in laboratory experiments but do not cross at all or only rarely in nature. Species may be kept apart by various reproductive isolating mechanisms, not only by hybrid inviability and sterility.

An even more fundamental reason why species cannot be rigidly defined is that the process of evolution and of species formation is in general a slow and gradual one. When we observe the animals and plants which live in the world around us, we see a single cross-section in time of the evolutionary family tree, as shown schematically in Figure 8.2. The branches of this family tree are like cables consisting of many strands—Mendelian populations which inhabit various localities. At the time level *A* strands form a single cable—a species not differentiated into clear-cut races. At another time level *B*, the strands are already segregated into two or more bundles and a few intermediate strands. This is a species broken up into races or incipient new species. At the time level *C*, we find separate cables of fully formed species. At the time levels at which we happen to live, some species are in the state *A*, others in the state *B*, and still others are groups of species, as in *C*.

When we observe the situation *A*, or one intermediate between *A* and *B*, there is no doubt at all that we are dealing with a single species. Thus mankind is a single biological species, *Homo sapiens*, subdivided into genetically not very sharply demarcated races which have not begun to evolve reproductive isolation. The situation *C* is equally clear. Nobody doubts that man, chimpanzee, gorilla, and orangutan are distinct species. So are the domestic cat, lion, tiger, jaguar, and puma. The situation *B*, however, is the difficult one. Here the populations are caught in transition, at the borderline between races and species. Here Darwin's famous advice is applicable: "In determining whether a form should be ranked as a species or a variety, the opinion of naturalists having sound judgment and wide experience seems the only guide to follow." This is, for example, the case with the "rings of races" discussed below (page 185).

It may be recalled at this point that the impossibility of drawing an absolute distinction between races and species was perhaps the principal argument which convinced Lamarck and Darwin that species are not fixed entities and that evolution does occur. It is, then, not a paradox to say that if some one should succeed in inventing a univer-

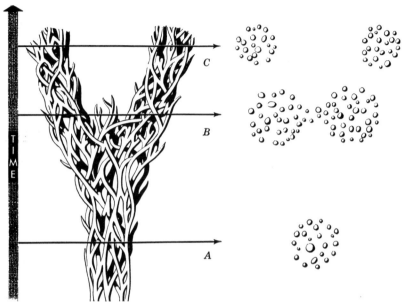

Figure 8.2.   Diagrammatic representation of the process of splitting of a single species (time level *A*) into two derived species (time level *C*). The species consist of populations or races, symbolized in the diagram as strands composing a bundle. Some of these strands branch (a population becoming divided into two or more populations), fuse together (races merging into single populations), or end blindly (populations becoming extinct). The cross sections shown on the right indicate the situations as seen on three successive time levels, *A*, *B*, and *C*.

sally applicable, static definition of species, he would cast serious doubts on the validity of the theory of evolution.

Species in Sexual Cross-fertilizing Organisms.   A majority of living beings, and certainly most of the higher organisms, reproduce sexually and by cross-fertilization; we may, then, concentrate our attention on the nature of species in sexual forms. As a starting point in the argument, let us recall that in sexual species races are usually allopatric— confined to different territories. It is the geographic separation of races which prevents them from crossing and exchanging genes at rates which would result in fusion of these races into a single variable population. Until civilization had developed, human races were also allopatric (see Chapter 13). At present some human races exist also sympatrically, as do also races (breeds) of domestic animals and plants. This became possible because of the rise of social isolating forces (in man) and of the regulation of the reproduction by human conscious or unconscious effort (in domesticated forms).

Yet as races diverge more and more, they become adapted to different environments in their respective territories or to different modes of life. Suppose, for example, that two races of an insect species became adapted to feed on different plants, on pine and on fir trees. In many places pine trees and fir trees grow together, in mixed stands. So long as the races are allopatric they cannot fully exploit the available resources of food. They cannot exist together for long in the same territory, because when they meet, they mate and produce hybrid offspring; soon the hybrids would far outnumber the parental races. What is the escape from this biological dilemma? It is, clearly, the development of reproductive isolation between the races. A reproductively isolated species specialized to feed on pines, and one specialized to live on fir trees, can live together wherever both food plants are available, and separately where only pines or only firs are present. Species may be either allopatric or sympatric.

The essential feature of the process of speciation, of transformation of races into species, is, then, the development of reproductive isolation between Mendelian populations. Species are the outcome of this process; species of sexual and cross-fertilizing organisms may accordingly be defined as reproductively isolated populations or groups of populations. Man is a single species, because the races of which it is composed show no reproductive isolation, and are in fact exchanging genes at increasing rates in many parts of the world, the social and cultural barriers notwithstanding. Horse and ass are different species, because they are reproductively almost completely isolated, and the gene exchange between them, if any, is of negligible importance for the species as wholes.

Borderlines between Species and Race. The above definitions of speciation and of species do not permit drawing an absolute distinction between race and species, even in sexually reproducing organisms. When a situation like that represented as the level *B* in Figure 8.2 is encountered, it would be arbitrary to say whether certain populations are to be considered races or species. Such situations do occur in nature. We have considered above the races of the leopard frog studied by Moore. The races in Vermont and in Florida are reproductively isolated, since the hybrids between them are inviable. They happen to live in different places, and gene exchange between them can occur only via the geographically intervening populations. But suppose that the Vermont and the Florida races should occur in the same territory; they would then behave as though they were different

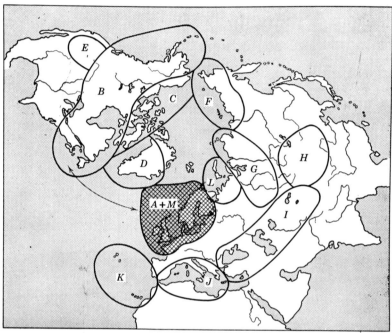

Figure 8.3. Races of herring gulls. In northwestern Europe, two populations, *Larus argentatus* and *Larus fuscus* (shown in the figure as A and M), share the same territory without hybridization, and consequently behave as different species. Nevertheless, they are connected by a circle of races (B, C, D, F, G, and L) living in North America and northern Asia. (After Mayr.)

species, since gene exchange between them is excluded by reproductive isolation.

Such conditions are actually known. In northwestern Europe (British Isles, Scandanavia) live two species of herring gulls (*Larus argentatus* and *fuscus*) which do not mix, form no intermediate populations, and in general behave as reproductively isolated species usually do. According to Mayr, these two European "good species" of gulls are, however, connected by an unbroken chain of intergrading races (Figure 8.3). These races live around the Polar Ocean, in Labrador,

Canada, northeastern Siberia, northwestern Siberia, and northern Russia. The *argentatus* and *fuscus* populations of gulls may, it would
seem, exchange genes, but not by forming hybrids in western Europe
where they live together. Instead, the gene exchange must take the
circuitous route through Asia and North America. *Argentatus* and

Figure 8.4. The two species of towhees which intercross in certain localities in
central Mexico. Above is *Pipilo ocai*, and below *Pipilo erythrocephalus*. (After
R. Stebbins and Ch. G. Sibley.)

fuscus appear to be races of the same species. The biological situation
being what it is, these gulls may be called races or species, whichever
may seem most convenient to those who study them.

Sibley has recently described the intergradations between the
spotted towhee (*Pipilo erythrophthalmus*) and the collared towhee
(*Pipilo ocai*). The first of these very distinctive-looking birds occurs
in the mountains of northern Mexico and in the United States (Figure
8.4). The second occurs only in some localities in southern Mexico.
In at least one of these localities the spotted and the collared towhees

live together, apparently without mixing. But elsewhere in southern Mexico the populations are variable mixtures of the two "pure" forms. If the locality, or localities, where the two towhees live together did not exist or were not discovered, we would be justified in placing all these birds in a single species with several races. The existence of the sympatric and evidently reproductively isolated populations makes this interpretation inadequate. We may think that this is a case of relatively recent hybridization of species which until then were behaving like good species ecologically isolated in different habitats. The burning of the forests, the cultivation of land, and other man-made changes in the environment have created new habitats, in which both towhees can live and in which they are no longer isolated.

Biological Species and Species of Systematics. We have chosen to regard the development of reproductive isolation between diverging races as the touchstone of species formation. This is not an arbitrary choice. As pointed out above, the attainment of reproductive isolation is a very significant stage in the evolutionary path of a population. It transforms genetically open systems (races) into genetically closed systems (species); it makes the evolutionary divergence of populations irreversible; it puts, so to speak, a seal of finality on the populations being committed to different ways of life.

To discover directly whether certain populations are or are not reproductively isolated, experiments must be made to test whether or not various isolating mechanisms discussed above are present or absent. Zoological and botanical systematists who describe species and races of animals and plants are, however, very seldom in a position to make such experiments. Indeed, systematists work mostly with dead and preserved specimens stored in museums and herbaria. Most species are described by people who never had a chance either to see them alive or to visit the territories where these species occur. How can systematists find out whether the organisms which they study are or are not reproductively isolated? Fortunately, this can be done in many instances. The methods of study used by modern systematists yield indirect but usually reliable evidence on this score.

Systematists regard as species groups of creatures which are clearly different in body structure, and among which transitional or intermediate specimens are absent. Domestic cat, lion, tiger, jaguar, and puma have always been considered species and not races, because no specimen has ever been found which could not be assigned to one of these species with certainty. The absence of intermediates between populations is a presumptive evidence that these populations are reproductively isolated. If they were not isolated and exchanged genes, intermediates probably would appear. Thus intermediates between even the most distinctive human races are known. If the populations live in the same country, sympatrically, and yet intermediates between them do not occur, they are almost certainly isolated reproductively. We must, of course, beware of mistaking the clear-cut variants within a polymorphic population for distinct species (see Chapter 7). Intermediates between the different blood groups in man are absent, but this does not make the carriers of these blood groups belong to different species. Mistakes of this sort have been made from time to time, and this is why Darwin considered "sound judgment and wide experience" necessary in those who study species.

A more serious source of difficulty in recognizing species is the existence of distinctive allopatric forms. Sympatric species produce no intermediates because they are reproductively isolated. But when populations live in different countries, allopatrically, and testing them experimentally is not practicable, the decision is often hard to reach. Most often the systematist resorts to studying the populations of geographically intervening territories; if these populations are intermediate between those found in remote places, there is probably some gene exchange between all the populations, and they belong to a single species. This is why we could, for example, infer that man is a single species even if we did not know directly that there is no reproductive isolation between any human populations. But what to do with the sycamore, *Platanus occidentalis* and the plane tree, *Platanus orientalis*, which are native respectively to eastern United States and to southeastern Europe and western Asia? They are quite distinctive in appearance, but they can be crossed artificially and produce vigorous and fertile hybrids. No intermediates between them occur in nature, but such intermediates have little chance of being formed since the geographic distributions of the two kinds of trees are widely separated, and the intervening countries have no native plane trees at all. Botanists regard them as distinct species because they look so different, and the geneticist Stebbins agrees because they would probably be kept apart by ecological isolation if they were brought together in the same territory.

Sibling Species and Species in Asexual Organisms. The reproductive isolation between *Drosophila pseudoobscura* and *Drosophila persimilis* has been discussed above (pages 170–171). There can be no doubt that biologically they are distinct species, yet these flies are so similar in external appearance that a zoologist who studies them under a small magnification of a microscope cannot distinguish them at all (they do differ in a more recondite way—the genitalic armatures of the males show a slight but constant difference). Species which are clearly distinct biologically but are very similar or identical in appearance are referred to as *sibling species*. Their existence may be troublesome to systematists working with insects preserved on pins in museum drawers, but it is very enlightening to the science of biology as a whole.

When we observe that two organisms are different in appearance, it should be kept in mind that externally visible differences are only the outward signs of physiological differences, which are in turn based on genetic differences. It happens that in most living creatures genetic differences are reflected in externally visible distinctions. This fact validates the methods of study of species used by systematists. Their species and biological species are usually the same things. But in some organisms, such as the two Drosophila species discussed above, genetic differences great enough to give rise to reproductive isolation have not produced visible changes in external body structures. Considered biologically, these species deserve being recognized as such no less than the tiger and the lion, which happen to be easily distinguishable in external appearance. To say that insect species must necessarily be distinguishable in museum specimens, pinned and dried out as has been customary with insect collectors for two centuries, is like asking modern physicians to use only the instruments and drugs which physicians used two hundred years ago.

The definition of species as reproductively isolated populations has, however, no meaning where sexuality is lost or where self-fertilization is the usual or exclusive method of begetting progeny. Yet bacteriologists have to describe bacteria which reproduce chiefly asexually and form clones, and botanists have to deal with plants like wheats most of which reproduce chiefly by self-pollination and form pure lines. Since Linnaeus, it has been customary to give species names to all organisms, regardless of the methods by which they reproduce (and these methods of reproduction have become understood only recently anyway). The clones of bacteria and the pure lines of wheats do form assemblages of similar forms adapted to live in similar ways; these assemblages are called species. This is a reasonable procedure; we should only keep in mind that the "species" in asexual and in self-fertilizing organisms are not the same biological phenomena as species of insects, birds, mammals, or of cross-fertilizing higher plants.

Are Species Arbitrary Groupings or Natural Entities? The world around us is infinitely variable. We never encounter twice the same situation, and objects which we observe, whether living or inanimate, change with time. To make this infinite variety intelligible and manageable, the human mind combines the situations and objects which it regards as similar in some respects into groups, and gives to each grouping a name. Thus there is a class of objects called furniture; within this class we may distinguish tables, chairs, shelves, etc.; among tables, office tables, dining-room tables, kitchen tables, etc., can be distinguished. Living organisms are a part of our environment; they are enormously diversified, and they have to be classified in order to be comprehensible. The species has served, and is serving, as a convenient category of classification.

However, sexual reproduction makes species of sexual organisms something more than a tool for classification. Individuals of sexual species are interdependent in a way analogous to cells in a multicellular body. Cells are physiologically, and individuals of sexual species are reproductively, interrelated. The reproductive interdependence of members of sexual species is necessary for continued existence of their kind, generation after generation. Thus mankind is more than a name for a class of objects. It is a biological reality, not only because all men are kin to each other by virtue of common descent, but even more so because all human beings are, at least potentially, part and parcel of the gene pool from which the genetic endowments of their posterity will arise. A sexual species is the ultimate extension of the ancestral family; it is also the family of the future.

Suggestions for Further Reading

The references given at the end of Chapter 7 will be useful for a study of the problem of species. The problems of race and species are closely interrelated.

9

Evolution under Domestication and Evolution by Polyploidy

When *The Origin of Species* was published in 1859, neither Darwin nor any one else claimed to have witnessed one species giving rise to another. Darwin's theory was a scientifically legitimate inference from indirect evidence. Numerous facts in biology made sense on the hypothesis that species evolve by gradual change and differentiation from races. Nevertheless, Darwin collected with great care the observed facts which showed that organisms undergo genetic changes and may become altered in the course of time. He found many such facts recorded by the breeders of domesticated animals and plants. The breeders produce new varieties of animals and plants to suit their needs or fancies. Moreover, they do so by means of artificial selection, often following hybridization of diverse varieties or races. Darwin's natural selection was a counterpart of artificial selection which had been known to be effective in domesticated forms. In 1868, Darwin summarized the evidence concerning evolution under domestication in a book entitled *The Variation of Animals and Plants under Domestication.*

Experimental evidence of the occurrence of evolution is at present much greater than it was in Darwin's time. Among microorganisms, evolutionary changes due to interaction of mutation and selection can be observed under controlled experimental conditions (see Chapter 5). To be sure, these changes involve alterations of single genes or, at most, of small numbers of genes. They are called microevolutionary changes, to distinguish them from macroevolution, which results in production of new genera, families, and classes. Macroevolution entails changes in many, perhaps in all, genes composing the genotype. Evolution under domestication continues to be interesting to modern

191

evolutionists; it involves genetic changes of a magnitude intermediate between microevolution, which is easily observable in a test tube, and macroevolution which requires time on a geological scale.

A special kind of experimentally observable evolutionary change is caused by the doubling of the chromosome complement—by polyploidy (see pages 201–208). The polyploids often behave with respect to their progenitors as full-fledged new species. Here we have, then, experimental origination of new species—a feat which was beyond reach of biologists in Darwin's time. Moreover, the production of new species by polyploidy is known to occur not only in experiments but in nature as well. Experimental demonstration of the origin of species was completed when some naturally occurring polyploid species were resynthesized from other species in experiments.

Degree and Antiquity of Domestication. There is no generally accepted definition of what a "domesticated" animal or plant is. For our purposes it will be satisfactory to regard as domesticated those forms which regularly reproduce in captivity and whose populations are controlled by man. It is man who determines how much wheat or corn is to be sown, and which kittens or puppies are to be kept and which disposed of. Even with this definition it is hard to tell how many animal and plant species have been domesticated. Some forms have been so thoroughly domesticated that they are utterly unable to exist except with man's help. In corn (maize), the seeds are firmly anchored in the cob, and the whole ear is enclosed in a protective cover (the husks) which prevents the seeds' reaching the soil. No wild plant with such an arrangement of seeds could possibly survive, and, as will be shown below, the problem of the origin of corn is not an easy one. On the other hand, the rubber tree (*Hevea brasiliensis*) grows wild in the jungles of equatorial Brazil, as well as on plantations in tropical Asia. The wild and the planted populations of the rubber trees are only beginning to diverge genetically. The domestication of the dog took place 10,000 to 12,000 years ago, in the Middle Stone Age (Mesolithic); that of the maral deer in Asia, and of the little Australian parrot budgerigar only a century ago. Domesticated forms of some species were obtained and then lost. Thus in ancient Egypt, about 3000 to 1000 B.C., there were domesticated varieties of the Nilotic goose and of at least two species of antelopes, which now exist only as wild species. Some authorities believe that the inhabitants of southern Chile had, in pre-Columbian days, domesticated the giant sloth, a huge animal at present known only as a fossil; its bones as well as remains of its skin, hair, and dung have been found.

TABLE 9.1

PLACE AND APPROXIMATE DATE OF DOMESTICATION OF PRINCIPAL
DOMESTIC ANIMALS

(After Krumbiegel, modified.)

Common Name	Scientific Name	Place of Domestication	Date of Domestication	Number of Domestic Varieties
Dog	*Canis familiaris*	Northern Hemisphere	10,000–8000 B.C.	200
Cat	*Felis maniculata*	Egypt	2000 B.C.	25
Cattle	*Bos taurus*	Europe, western Asia	Neolithic, 6000–2000 B.C.	60
Water buffalo	*Bos bubalus*	India	Prehistoric	?
Bali cattle	*Bibos sondaicus*	Indonesia	Prehistoric	?
Yak	*Poephagus grunniens*	Tibet, Turkestan	Prehistoric	?
Sheep	*Ovis aries*	Europe, middle Asia	Mesolithic and Neolithic	50
Goat	*Capra hircus*	Europe, middle Asia	Mesolithic and Neolithic	20
Maral	*Cervus maral*	Southern Siberia	A.D. 1850	1
Pig	*Sus scrofa*	Europe, western Asia	Neolithic, 5000–2000 B.C.	35
Horse	*Equus caballus*	Europe, Asia	Neolithic and Bronze, 3000–2000 B.C.	60
Ass	*Equus asinus*	North Africa	Prehistoric	15
Camel	*Camelus bactrianus*	Middle Asia	Prehistoric	?
Dromedary	*Camelus dromedarius*	Africa	Prehistoric	?
Llama	*Lama huanacus*	Peru, Chile	Prehistoric	?
Rabbit	*Oryctolagus cuniculus*	Mediterranean	1000 B.C.	20
Guinea pig	*Cavia porcellus*	Peru, Chile	Prehistoric	25
Tame mouse	*Mus musculus*	China, Europe(?)	?	?
Goose	*Anser anser*	Western Asia, Europe	Bronze Age(?)	20
Duck	*Anas platyrhynchos*	China, Europe	1000 B.C.(?)	30
Chicken	*Gallus domesticus*	India, Indochina	3000 B.C.(?)	125
Turkey	*Meleagris gallopavo*	Mexico, Eastern U.S.A.	Pre-Columbian	6
Guinea hen	*Numida numida*	West Africa	Prehistoric and A.D. 1500	1
Peacock	*Pavo cristatus*	India	Early Historic	4
Pigeon	*Columba livia*	Asia Minor(?) India(?)	Prehistoric	140
Canary	*Serinus canaria*	Canary Islands	A.D. 1500	20
Budgerigar	*Melopsittacus undulatus*	Australia	A.D. 1840	5

Table 9.1 is a brief summary of the available information concerning the time and the place of the domestication of the chief domestic
animals. Much of this information is very inexact and subject to
doubt; often all that can be said is that the domestication took place
in prehistoric times, that is, before the light of history had dawned
in the part of the world where the domestication of a given species
had occurred. Two things, nevertheless, are clear. First, different
peoples in all parts of the world realized the value of having domestic
animals, and were able to carry out the difficult process of domestication. Second, the longer a species has been domesticated the more
numerous and more diversified are its domestic varieties. Thus the
dog is the most ancient domestic animal, and has produced the largest
number of breeds. Furthermore, some dog breeds differ so much in
appearance, as well as in temperament and behavior, that it is hard

to believe that they all belong to the same species. Compare the little Chihuahua with a Great Dane; or an ebullient Fox Terrier with a stolid Saint Bernard. Nevertheless, all these breeds do belong to one species, since they are capable of exchanging genes, and often do so, either directly by occasional hybridization, or via the intermediate breeds where crossing is impossible because of an extreme difference in size. The dog species has a common gene pool, subdivided, to be sure, into the gene pools of the various breeds. Domestic chickens and pigeons are the most ancient domesticated birds, and they also form numerous breeds. The domestic goose is an exception to the rule: its domestication is undoubtedly ancient, but it has given rise to relatively few distinct breeds.

Centers of Origin of Domesticated Plants. The number of plant species in various stages of domestication is conservatively estimated at three hundred, which is many times greater than the number of species of domestic animals. Pioneer studies concerning the origins of cultivated plants were made in the last century by A. de Candolle (1778–1841) and Darwin, and in the current century by Vavilov (1887–1942). Vavilov came to the conclusion that most species of cultivated plants were first domesticated in a relatively small number of countries. These countries are called the *centers of origin;* their location is shown on the map in Figure 9.1. It is not surprising that the centers of origin of cultivated plants largely coincide with the ancient centers of human civilization.

Vavilov has distinguished eight or nine such centers. (1) *Chinese,* including China, particularly its mountainous interior, and Korea. This center has given mankind many varieties of oats, barleys, millets, soya and other beans, bamboo, sugar cane, some cabbages, oranges and lemons, peaches, apricots, pears, prunes, cherries, tea, poppy, and many other useful plants less well known to our Western civilization. (2) and (3) *Indian* and *Indomalayan* centers, which may also be treated as a single one, embracing India (but not western Pakistan), Burma, Indochina, and western Indonesia. This is the land of the origin of rice, which is estimated to be the main staple to perhaps 60 per cent of humanity, sorghum (Indian), some beans, eggplant, cucumber, bamboos, sugar cane (Indomalayan), bananas (Indomalayan), mango (Indian), some oranges and lemons, breadfruit (Indomalayan), cocoanut palm (Indomalayan), diploid cotton, pepper (Indian) and many less widely known plants. (4) *Middle-Asiatic,* in northern Pakistan, Kashmir, Afghanistan, in the southern part of Rus-

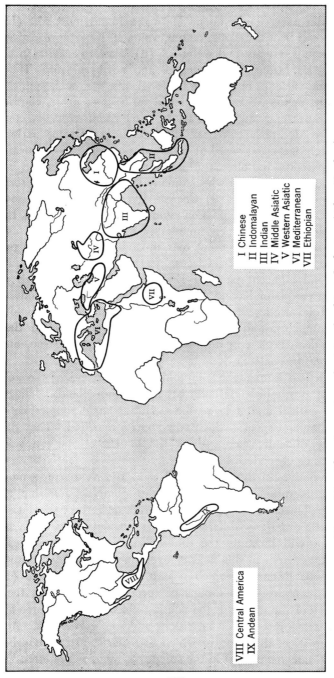

Figure 9.1. The nine centers of origin of cultivated plants. (After Vavilov.)

I Chinese
II Indomalayan
III Indian
IV Middle Asiatic
V Western Asiatic
VI Mediterranean
VII Ethiopian

VIII Central America
IX Andean

sian Middle Asia (Turkestan). Here are found most soft (bread) wheats, some beans, melons, onions, spinach, some apricots, apples, pears, almonds, grapes, and walnuts. (5) *Western Asiatic*, in the interior of Asia Minor, Transcaucasia, and northern Iran. Here are native some varieties of hard and soft wheats, rye, oats, lentils, peas, flax, poppy, melons, carrots, and some varieties of pears, cherries, almonds, grapes, figs, and other fruits. (6) *Mediterranean*, countries around the Mediterranean Sea. This center gave some varieties of wheats (relatively little used at present), peas, flax, sugar beets, cabbages, asparagus, and olives. (7) *Ethiopian*, in Ethiopia and Eritrea. This is the center of hard wheats, many varieties of barleys, sorghum, flax, sesame, and coffee. (8) *Central American*, embracing southern Mexico, Guatemala, and possibly some of the West Indian Islands. This is the source of such immensely important cultures as corn (maize), some beans, sweet potatoes, upland cottons, peppers, papaya, and many other tropical fruit trees. (9) *South American* or *Andean*, in Peru and adjacent parts of Equador and Bolivia. This region shares the credit for having given origin to corn and to some of the most useful varieties of cottons, and also to potatoes, tomatoes, tobacco, pumpkins, and the quinine tree. Somewhere to the east of the Andean center, in tropical Brazil, pineapples, cacao, and the rubber tree originated.

It is hard to estimate the importance to mankind of the achievements of the primitive agriculturists in the above lands. They managed the critical first steps of the evolution under domestication of most of the plant species which now nourish mankind. They did this immensely difficult work without the benefit of modern scientific knowledge or of modern technology.

Wild Relatives of the Domestic Horse. We choose for a more detailed consideration of evolution under domestication one animal species, the horse, and two plant species, cotton and corn. These three species will exemplify different kinds of evolutionary changes that occur, and will illustrate the different kinds of uncertainties with which the research in this field of evolutionary biology has to cope.

The genus Equus, to which belongs the domestic horse (*Equus caballus*), contains three groups of species now living in the wild state. One of the groups is the zebras, which comprise three species with numerous races living in eastern and southern Africa. Another group consists of the asses, of which two species are recognized—the onager (*Equus hemionus*) in the steppes of middle Asia, and the true wild ass (*Equus asinus*) in northeastern Africa. The latter is without doubt the wild progenitor of the domestic donkey.

Neither the zebras nor the asses have a part in the ancestry of the domestic horse. Domestic horses and domestic asses are crossed on a large scale to produce mules. In 1920 there were about 5,650,000, and in 1949 about 2,353,000 mules on farms in the United States alone. The practice of breeding mules is an ancient one, well known to Aristotle. But mules are interspecific hybrids which are almost invariably sterile; the few recorded fertile female mules certainly do not provide a channel for a regular gene exchange between the gene pools of these species (see Chapter 8). Zebras have been crossed to horses in zoological gardens, but the hybrids, called zebroids, are sterile. Zebras, asses, and horses are close relatives which arose rather recently, geologically speaking, from a common ancestor (see Chapter 12). But they have diverged genetically far enough to become reproductively completely isolated. Their evolutionary paths are separate.

The only true wild horse lives in a part of middle Asia, more precisely in the deserts of western Mongolia. It has been given a specific name of Przevalsky horse (*Equus przevalskii*)—which is even more difficult for English speakers to pronounce than is the name of the author of this book. The wild horse is only as tall as a small pony, 12 to 15 "hands" (48 to 52 inches) from the ground to the withers, and rather ungainly in appearance from the standpoint of a lover of horseflesh. It should be noted that it has a short erect mane, no forelock, and is a dun color (cf. page 38). It is wild and intractable even after a prolonged life in captivity. The wild and the domestic horses cross easily and produce fertile progeny.

The wild Przevalsky horse is the last survivor of a species which in historical times was much more widespread. A wild horse called tarpan was quite common in the steppes of southern and southeastern Russia as recently as the last century. Tarpans were a nuisance to the pioneer settlers, since they interfered with the crops and led away domestic mares. They were hunted and exterminated, the last tarpan having been killed around 1860 in the steppe north of the Black Sea. The ancient Romans encountered numerous "forest horses" when their empire spread to what are at present Spain, France, and Germany. How different the tarpans and the forest horses were from the Przevalsky horse is not exactly known. The tarpan was allegedly mouse colored instead of dun; this difference may be due to a single gene (see page 38). The forest horse was relatively tall (about 60 inches), with stout limbs and a long but narrow head. Its portrait, drawn by an artist of the Stone Age on a cave wall at Altamira, Spain, shows an erect mane, like that of the now living wild horse.

Is the Domestic Horse Monophyletic or Polyphyletic? Just when and where the first horses were domesticated is unknown. The first historical records of domestic horses appear at almost the opposite ends of Asia, in Mesopotamia (Iraq) and in China, about simultaneously, around 2000 B.C. Horses were brought to Mesopotamia from the north, possibly from the Russian steppe. It is, hence, conjectured that the tarpan was domesticated by the nomad inhabitants of the steppe a few centuries earlier, possibly around 2500 B.C. But the horses that came to China were most likely the descendants of the Przevalsky horse, domesticated in the wilds of Mongolia quite independently from the tarpan.

It is most likely, though obviously unprovable, that horses were domesticated many times and in many places in the steppes and deserts of eastern Europe and Asia, and in the forest zone of western Europe. The first record of a horse hitched to a chariot appears in Greece around 1700 B.C., in Egypt 1600 B.C., in India 1500 B.C. By 1000 B.C. horses were known and widely used in most parts of Europe, and in Asia and Africa outside the tropical forest zones. Mounted horsemen first participated in the Olympic games in 648 B.C.

The problem of whether the now living domestic horses are descended from a single wild ancestor (monophyletically) or from two or several ancestors (polyphyletically) has been long and inconclusively discussed by the students of the horse origins. Perhaps it does not really matter. If the gene pool of the domestic horse contained genes of two different species, such as horse and ass, every one would agree with the polyphyletic hypothesis. But the Przevalsky horse, the tarpan, and the forest horse were clearly geographic races of the same wild species, which at one time was distributed perhaps from the Atlantic coast of Europe to the Pacific coast of Asia. Most likely this species could be divided not into three but into more numerous races, and quite possibly most or all of these races contributed their genes to the gene pool of the modern horse. The recombination of the genes contributed by these races, plus the genes which arose by mutation since the domestication, gave rise to the variety of horse breeds.

The Domestic Horse Breeds. Regardless of how many wild ancestral races were domesticated, their descendants underwent considerable genetic changes. These changes took place because the horses were used for different purposes, and each purpose was best served by different genotypes in the horse populations. Natural and artificial selection perpetuated the suitable genotypes and eliminated the unsuitable ones. The existing diversity of horse breeds is the result.

Nomadic cultures most completely dependent on horses developed particularly in Mongolia and in Middle Asia. Here horses were, and still are, used as meat and milk animals, as well as for riding and for transportation of the tents in which the nomads live and their furnishings. Horse meat and fermented mare's milk still are important staples in some parts of Asia. The horse breeds suitable for these multiple uses must be before all else sturdy, tireless, able to subsist on scant food, and to resist inclement weather. This type required relatively little change from the wild horse condition, except development of some tameness. The horses of Mongolia are the most "primitive" existing breeds, clearly resembling the wild Przevalsky horse, including the possession of an erect mane and a high frequency of the dun coat color. The hordes of Genghis Khan, mounted on such horses, erupted from Asia into Europe in the thirteenth century. They swept all resistance before them; this "Scourge of God" could not have occurred except for a perfect balance between the cultural heredity of a human population and the biological heredity of a horse population.

Quite different types of horses appeared in western Europe, where horses were used and valued primarily for warfare. But here the mounted warrior tried to make himself less vulnerable by donning progressively heavier armor. The speed of the horse had to be sacrificed to its ability to carry great weights. Hence the Middle Ages saw the appearance in Europe of large, heavy, and powerful breeds of horses, perhaps having a strong dose of the genes of the forest horse which lived wild in these parts.

The invention of firearms, however, ended the usefulness of armor. The horses which used to carry knights in battle now began to serve a different purpose: transportation of heavy loads and heavy farm labor. Thus arose the powerful "cold-blooded" draft horses: Percherons in France, Belgians in Belgium, Clydesdales, Shires, and Suffolks in England. Stallions of these breeds are often enormous animals, 64 to 70 inches tall, weighing 1800, 2000, and even 2200 pounds. The American farm horses carry some genes derived from these breeds, together with those of miscellaneous "utility" horses of western European origin.

Still other horse breeds were developed in Mediterranean countries and in the Near East, also in response to war needs. Until the invention of saddles with stirrups, the cavalry either fought standing in a horse-drawn chariot or the men dismounted to begin combat. The Greeks and Romans did not have stirrups. The stirrups, invented somewhere in Asia, furnish fulcra which permit mounted combat. The speed, agility, and alertness of the cavalry horse now became vital. Accordingly, there appeared various breeds of "light" riding horses, among which the Barb in northern Africa and the Arabian were most important. Just when these breeds first appeared is uncertain, but by the time of Mohammed, in the seventh century A.D., Arabia possessed a highly valued variety of horses. The Arabian horse is regarded by many people as the most beautiful of all horse breeds, if, indeed, not the most beautiful of all animals. However that may be, it is certain that the Arabian and related Eastern breeds have been highly esteemed as riding animals for centuries. Their genes have become diffused the world over in many more recent breeds.

The Race Horse. If the origins of the breeds discussed above are lost in the mists of antiquity, that of the English thoroughbred breed is known in fair detail. After the passing of the heavily armored medieval knights mounted on slow horses, light but fast Eastern horses were imported into western Europe at increasingly frequent intervals. A population of progressively lighter riding horses gradually resulted from hybridization of the imported and local breeds. A new breed was started in England by mating several local mares with three stallions imported from the East between 1689 and 1730. These stallions were either pure Arabian, or at any rate carried many genes derived from the Arabian breed. The hybrid offspring were mated among themselves, and in the second generation three stallions were selected—Matchem, Eclipse, and Herod. Most thoroughbred horses are descended from these stallions and from their female siblings and relatives.

The pedigree of the thoroughbreds, carefully recorded in the so-called stud books, is a most complex network of descent relationships beginning with the horses named above. All individuals are multiply related to each other. It should be realized, however, that this pedigree involves also a most intense and careful selection of individuals possessing the desired properties, and of these the most desired has been speed. A modern thoroughbred horse is a strikingly different animal from its Arabian (or near-Arabian) ancestors. It is considerably taller (64 inches or higher), and capable of much greater speeds—the present record is a mile run in 1 minute and $33\frac{1}{2}$ seconds.

A thoroughbred is also an animal requiring the most elaborate care and feeding, and it is too nervous and high-strung to be used for any purposes other than running on a race track or crossing to other horse breeds to "improve" the breed.

To an evolutionist, the thoroughbred horse is an interesting example of a great change in the direction chosen by man which can be wrought in an organism by selection within a rather small number of generations. And if we compare the thoroughbred with the wild horse from Mongolia we find the two animals certainly as distinct as or more distinct than are "natural" species of the genus Equus. Why, then, have no reproductive isolating mechanisms developed to make them full-fledged species? The answer is necessarily speculative, but it is reasonable to think that it is because breeds of domesticated animals are isolated from each other and from their progenitors owing to the control of their reproduction by man.

Cultivated Cottons. Despite the recent invention of synthetic fibers (rayon, nylon, etc.), the cotton plant is, and will probably remain, the chief source of the textiles which clothe humanity. The most ancient cotton textiles known are dated about 3000 B.C. They have been found in the excavations of Mohenjo-Daro, among remains of the Indus civilization, which is one of the three most ancient civilizations in the world (the other two being Egyptian and Babylonian). Moreover, the Mohenjo-Daro textiles are obviously made by a skilled craftsman, indicating that cotton must have first been used at some time prior to 3000 B.C. Probably quite independently of the Indus Civilization, cotton was domesticated also in the Americas, since cotton textiles are found in the pre-Inca graves in Peru. Cotton was used extensively by many tribes in pre-Columbian days, including some of the tribes in the southwestern United States.

There is, however, an important difference between the Old World and the New World cultivated cottons. All cottons native to the Old World have 26 chromosomes (13 pairs) in their cells (Figure 9.2). All New World cultivated cottons have twice as many chromosomes (52 or 26 pairs); hence the New World cottons are polyploid or, to be more exact, tetraploid (see page 65).

How did this difference arise? One of the possibilities is that the New World cottons arose from a single ancestral species, having 26 chromosomes, simply by reduplication of the chromosome complement (by *autopolyploidy*). Another possibility is that two different species, each having 26 chromosomes, have crossed, and that the duplication of the chromosome complement took place in the hybrid. If so, the

52-chromosome cotton contains chromosome complements of two different ancestral species. Such a polyploid is called *allopolyploid*. To
find out which of these possibilities is the right one, certain observations and experiments have to be carried out, as described below.

Wild Cottons. All cottons belong to the botanical genus Gossypium,
which contains at least 20 different species. The technical differences

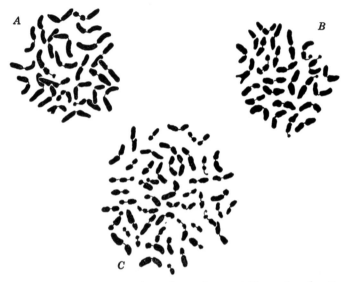

Figure 9.2. The chromosomes of a cultivated tetraploid species of cotton (*C*),
and an American (*A*), and an Old World (*B*) diploid species. The tetraploid
(*C*) arose presumably by hybridization of the two diploids (*A* and *B*), followed
by a duplication of the chromosome complement. (After Sikka, Ihsan-ur-Rahman
and Afzal.)

by which a botanist recognizes these species do not interest us here,
but the numbers of chromosomes in them do interest us. In the Old
World (in Africa, southern Asia, and Australia) 9 of the species exist.
Two of them (*Gossypium arboreum* and *Gossypium herbaceum*) have
spinnable lint on their seeds and are cultivated, and 7 of them are
lintless and grow as wild plants. All these species are diploid, with
26 chromosomes (Figure 9.2). In the New World (in Arizona, Mexico,
Peru, and the Galapagos Islands) 8 wild species exist which have no
lint. All these species are also diploid, with 26 chromosomes. The
two native American species cultivated for their lint (*G. hirsutum*, the
cotton of the Cotton Belt of the United States, and *G. barbadense*,

cultivated in tropical America) are, as we know, tetraploid, with 52 chromosomes. So is a wild and lintless species which lives on the Hawaiian Islands (*G. tomentosum*).

Hybrids between Species of Cotton. By artificial cross-pollination it is fairly easy to obtain hybrids between species of Gossypium. The progeny of an American wild diploid species (26 chromosomes), crossed to an American cultivated tetraploid species (52 chromosomes), will have 39 chromosomes, and will be triploid. Such triploid hybrids are largely sterile, but the behavior of the chromosomes at meiosis can be observed under the microscope. The cells at meiosis show about 13 bivalents (that is, 26 chromosomes that have come together in pairs) and 13 univalents. Next, let us cross an American cultivated tetraploid to an Old World diploid species. The progeny is again triploid, 39 chromosomes, largely sterile, and showing approximately 13 bivalents and 13 univalents at meiosis.

What do the above observations mean? The most reasonable interpretation is that the chromosomal complement of an American tetraploid cotton (26) contains a set of 13 chromosomes sufficiently like those of the American diploid cotton species, so that these chromosomes pair up and make 13 bivalents at meiosis in the hybrid. By the same token, the American tetraploid cotton must contain 13 chromosomes like those of the Old World species (see Figure 9.2).

The validity of this interpretation can be tested by more experiments. Let us obtain hybrids between diploid species. Hybrids between different American diploid species are, of course, diploid; they are fertile, and show 13 bivalents at meiosis. The same is true for hybrids between different Old World diploid species, but things go differently when an American diploid species is crossed to an Old World diploid. The hybrid is more or less sterile, and its 26 chromosomes form few or no bivalents at meiosis.* The chromosomes of different Old World species are still so nearly similar that they "recognize" each other and pair in hybrids. The same is true for chromosomes of different diploid American species. But the chromosomes of American diploids become in the process of evolution so different from the chromosomes of the Old World species that they pair no longer.

* The story as here presented is somewhat oversimplified. Actually the chromosomal pairing in hybrid meiosis is variable, and in some cells some chromosomes fail to pair which do pair in other cells of the same hybrid. This is due to the occurrence of structural changes in the chromosomes in the evolutionary process (see pages 65, 148). The chromosomal similarity or dissimilarity is not an all-or-none affair.

When Did the Tetraploid Cottons Appear? The tetraploid American cultivated cottons are allotetraploid, that is, they contain a set of chromosomes like those still existing in American diploid species, and one set like those in Old World diploid species. An ancestor of the cotton plants now growing on a field in Alabama must have been an F_1 hybrid between two different species of cottons, one of which must have resembled cottons now growing wild in America and the other growing in the Old World. All students of the problem of origin of cottons now agree that such hybridization must have occurred. They do not agree nearly so well about the place and the time of the hybridization.

Indeed, in order to produce hybrids, the cotton species which now live on different continents on the opposite sides of the globe had to meet somewhere. Wild cottons now grow only in tropical and subtropical lands; intense and prolonged selection was necessary to obtain cotton varieties capable of being cultivated in warm-temperate climates, like that of the southern United States. The only place where the American continent meets the Old World continental mass is the vicinity of the Bering Strait, in the Arctic. The climate of the Bering Strait region is far too cold for any cotton to survive. The alternative is to suppose that seeds of the Old World cottons were somehow transported to tropical America either from Asia across the whole wide Pacific Ocean, or from Africa across the Atlantic. Cotton seeds, however, are rapidly killed by sea water, so that they could not be transported by ocean currents. They are too heavy to be transported by wind.

Harland (1939) sought to escape the above dilemma by supposing that the crossing of the diploid species which gave rise to the American tetraploid cottons took place in Cretaceous or in Eocene times, many millions of years ago (Table 12.1). Geologists believe that in those remote times the climates of the whole earth, including the present arctic regions, were much warmer than at present. Some also believed that there may have existed a continent in the place of the present Pacific Ocean, but most geologists now definitely oppose this idea. Be that as it may, Harland surmised that the tetraploid cottons arose very long ago.

On the contrary, Hutchinson, Silow, and Stephens (1947) assume that the American tetraploids are of relatively very recent origin. The inhabitants of the South Sea Islands have made many journeys across the uncharted ocean. Suppose, then, that some of these seafarers came to the West Coast of South America and brought with them seeds of an Asiatic diploid cotton with spinnable lint. The plants which grew from these seeds then crossed to a native American diploid species which grew near by, and gave an allotetraploid with superior lint quality, which was picked up and cultivated by the Indians.

Neither hypothesis can be considered proven, although recent cytological and distributional data make Harland's hypothesis, or some modification of it, more probable. Anyway, the evolution of cotton under domestication went remarkably fast. As we know, the wild species of cotton have no spinnable lint, but only useless fuzz on their seeds. Before cotton textiles were made at Mohenjo-Daro in 3000 B.C. (see above), a considerable amount of selection work must have been done. Egypt, the economic welfare of which depends at present largely on its cotton crop, received cotton much later, about 500 B.C. Ancient Egyptian and Babylonian textiles were made of flax or of wool. The development of the cotton crop in China and in Middle Asia is even more recent—between A.D. 700 and 1300. This is probably because cotton is originally a tropical plant which is perennial in habit, that is, grows for several years. Before it could be grown successfully in temperate lands, annual races (which complete their development, from seed to seed, within a year) had to be developed. Such races were developed both in the Old and in the New World. If the Hutchinson-Silow-Stephens hypothesis is correct, the American cultivated cottons arose, possibly somewhere in Peru on the Pacific Coast of South America, perhaps some two thousand years ago. Yet by the time Columbus landed, there were two distinct cultivated species, *Gossypium hirsutum* and *G. barbadense*, with numerous varieties. Some of these varieties were of such high quality that they were introduced in the Old World and largely displaced there the native diploid cottons. The commercial cotton crop the world over consists at present predominantly of tetraploids, which are native in tropical America.

Raphanobrassica, an Experimental New Species. The hypothesis of allopolyploid origin of cultivated American cottons is made necessary by much experimental and observational evidence. The event postulated by this hypothesis occurred, however, in the dim past, but a quite analogous process has actually been observed in experiments on other plants. The classical example is the new allotetraploid species obtained by Karpechenko (1926) by crossing the common cabbage (*Brassica oleracea*) and radish (*Raphanus sativus*). These plants, as their names show, belong to different botanical genera, but they have similar chromosome numbers—18 (9 pairs). Karpechenko obtained diploid cabbage × radish hybrids, which had, as expected, 18 chromosomes, 9 from cabbage and 9 from radish. The cabbage and radish chromosomes fail to pair at meiosis in this hybrid, and the hybrid is sterile.

This is a situation observed also in many other, in fact in most, sterile interspecific hybrids. It was first seen by the Finnish geneticist, Federley, in 1913 in hybrids between certain species of moths. Owing to the occurrence in evolution of inversions, translocations, and other chromosomal changes, the gene arrangement in the chromosomes of different species becomes so thoroughly "scrambled" that these chromosomes no longer "recognize" each other as homologues. The difference in the chromosome structure becomes manifest particularly at meiosis in the hybrids, when the chromosomes of the parents should normally come together in pairs (Chapter 3). Their failure to do so initiates grave disturbances in the processes of sex cell formation. The result is that the hybrid, although it may be quite normal and vigorous, fails to produce normal sex cells and is sterile.

The cabbage × radish hybrid, however, was not completely sterile. Karpechenko obtained from it several seeds and grew a small F_2 generation. These F_2 plants proved to be tetraploid; they had 36 chromosomes in their cells, 18 chromosomes of cabbage and 18 of radish. Such seeds arose from ovules and pollen grains in which the meiosis failed altogether, and came to possess the entire chromosome complement of the hybrid—9 cabbage and 9 radish chromosomes.

The tetraploid hybrids grew to be tall and vigorous plants, called Raphanobrassica. Agriculturally this new plant is, alas, useless, since it happens to have a root like cabbage and foliage like radish. But it is a very important plant for a biologist, being the first new species (or genus) produced in experiment. Indeed, the allotetraploid Raphanobrassica is quite fertile, its meiosis being quite normal with 18 bivalents normally formed. Since it has 18 cabbage and 18 radish chromosomes in its cells, there is no difficulty in pairing, and 9 cabbage and 9 radish bivalents arise. Despite its hybrid origin, Raphanobrassica breeds true. Moreover, it is reproductively isolated from its own ancestors—the cabbage and the radish. The Raphanobrassica × cabbage and Raphanobrassica × radish hybrids are formed with difficulty; they are triploid (27 chromosomes), and largely sterile. In short, Raphanobrassica is a new plant species by any reasonable definition of species.

The experimental production of new species is an important achievement of evolutionary biology. Some still surviving anti-evolutionists cling to the forlorn hope that all changes observed in experimental organisms are intraspecific changes. Indeed, a mutant of *Drosophila melanogaster* is still a fly and belongs to the same species as its ancestors. A thoroughbred horse is still a horse. But Raphanobrassica is evidently neither a cabbage nor a radish; it is a new and hitherto unknown organism—Raphanobrassica.

Natural Allopolyploids. During the thirty years since Karpechenko's pioneer experiments, several new species have been synthesized by allopolyploidy. These experiments merely copy a method of species formation which nature has used on a fairly large scale, at least in the plant kingdom. As we have seen above, there is strong evidence that the cultivated American species of cotton arose by this method. Other species of cultivated and wild plants, among them most wheats, oats, sugar cane, tobacco, potato, coffee, most cultivated roses, raspberries, and many other useful plants, are allopolyploids. Allopolyploidy was probably the method of species formation in plant genera in which the chromosome numbers of the known species form a series of multiples of some low "basic" number. Thus wheats and related grasses have species with 14, 28, and 42 chromosomes (the "basic" number is, then, 7).

Particularly interesting are the experiments in which experimentally synthesized allopolyploid species are similar to or identical with naturally occurring ones. Here the evolutionary process which has at some time in the past produced certain "natural" species is repeated in experiments. Beasley (1942) came close to resynthesizing an American tetraploid cotton from hybrids of a wild American diploid (*Gossypium thurberi*) from Arizona and an African cultivated diploid (*Gossypium arboreum*). He obtained a tetraploid hybrid which was sterile as a male (that is, failed to produce functional pollen grains). Its meiosis, however, was normal and it set seed freely when pollinated by ordinary American tetraploid cotton. The meiosis in these backcross hybrids was also nearly normal. It is likely that the Arizona wild cotton is not the American diploid species which is the ancestor of the tetraploids, but it is close to the true ancestor.

A full success was gained for the first time by the Swedish geneticist Muntzing (1930). The species *Galeopsis tetrahit*, of the mint family, has twice as many chromosomes (32) as the related species, *G. speciosa* and *G. pubescens* (16). Muntzing crossed the latter two species, and among the offspring of their hybrids selected plants with doubled chromosome complements. These plants he called "artificial *tetrahit*," since they reproduced the natural species of that name, freely crossed to the latter, and gave fertile hybrids with normal chromosome pairing. In short, Muntzing has recreated *G. tetrahit,* a natural species which arose by a similar process of crossing two other species and doubling the chromosome complement in the hybrid. Since 1930 several other natural species have been so recreated.

Origin of new species by polyploidy is, of course, not the most usual method of emergence of species in evolution, although polyploidy has played an important role in certain groups of organisms, especially in the plant kingdom. The doubling of the chromosome number is a process which, when it occurs in a species hybrid, may create a new species almost instantaneously. This is why species which have arisen by polyploidy may sometimes be reproduced in experiments. The emergence of new species from races is, as discussed in Chapter 8, a slow process which takes quasi-geological time to be completed. Species which arise in that way may have similar or different chromosome numbers, but they seldom have chromosome numbers which are multiples of each other. More important than changes in the numbers are the internal reconstructions which take place in the chromosomes by mutation, inversion, translocation, duplication, and deletion of genes.

Corn and Its Relatives. Except in very cold countries and in wet tropical lowlands, maize or Indian corn (*Zea mays*) is one of the principal crops which nourish mankind. The land area annually planted to corn is estimated at 221 million acres. The origin of this highly important plant, however, is far from completely known. As will be shown below, the uncertainties encountered in studies of corn origins are of a quite different nature from those to be contended with in the domestic horse and in cotton evolution.

As pointed out above, corn has been so profoundly modified in the process of adapting it to man's needs that it is utterly unable to propagate itself without human help and to live as a wild plant. Its wild progenitor must necessarily have been a rather different-looking plant. Botanists place corn among the Maydeae, a subdivision of the grass family. Sugar cane and sorghum belong to the same family, but they are not closely related to corn. A much closer relative is teosinte, *Zea mexicana* (or *Euchlaena mexicana,* since it is considered by some to belong to a different genus), which grows in parts of southern Mexico and of Guatemala, mostly as a weed in or near fields of cultivated corn. Teosinte is a tall grass with rather broad leaves, though not as broad as corn leaves. It resembles corn also in having male flowers (producing pollen) concentrated in a "tassel" at the top of the main stalk. Another resemblance to corn is that the female flowers (which produce ovules and seeds) are borne on spikes which, like the ears of corn, are produced on the sides of the main stalk. The seed spike of teosinte, however, is quite unlike that of corn, since it easily breaks up when the seeds are ripe and lets the seeds fall out. Teosinte seeds are also very different from corn seeds. They are enclosed in horny shells, which are made up of parts of the rachis or stem and modified glumes, protective covers on the seeds of most grasses (Figure 9.3). In modern corn the glumes are reduced to mere scales imbedded in the cob.

Another relative of corn is the genus Tripsacum (gama grass), of which several species are known native to Central, South, and North America. Tripsacum are perennial grasses, with narrow leaves and numerous "tillers," that is, stalks coming out of the same root system. In contrast both to maize and to teosinte, it has male and female flowers on the same spike at the top of the stalk. The seeds have horny glumes, and the spike disarticulates when the seeds are ripe. Although the spike is partially enclosed in husks (protective covers made by modified leaves), the seeds easily fall out (Figure 9.2). Finally, whereas

Figure 9.3. The two presumed parents and their progeny. On the left are shown an inflorescence and some seeds of a gamma grass (Tripsacum), of a teosinte in the middle, and of cultivated corn on the right. Teosinte arose probably from a hybrid between Tripsacum and primitive corn. (Courtesy of Professor P. C. Mangelsdorf.)

corn and most teosintes are diploids with 20 chromosomes (10 pairs), gama grass is either diploid with 36 or tetraploid with 72 chromosomes.

Is Teosinte the Parent or Offspring of Corn? A hypothesis of the origin of corn put forward by Ascherson (1875), and supported by Vavilov and most other authorities until 1939, was that teosinte is the progenitor from which maize developed by a series of mutations favored by artificial selection. This would mean that corn arose somewhere in Central America, where teosinte is now still growing in semiwild condition. To be sure, teosinte is not at present used as food; but its seeds can be "popped" by heat, thus shattering the horny cover and exposing the more palatable grain.

It now appears, however, that the teosinte hypothesis was a false clue to the riddle of maize origin. Mangelsdorf and Reeves suggested in 1939 that teosinte, far from being the ancestor of corn, is derived from corn by means of hybridization of primitive corn with a species of Tripsacum. According to this view, teosinte is in fact genetically a corn with some sections of Tripsacum chromosomes included in its genotype.

The evidence that this extraordinary situation actually obtains in reality comes chiefly from experiments of crossing teosinte with modern cultivated corn. The hybrids are fertile, and the segregation in F_2 and later generations shows that the genes which determine the visible differences between corn and teosinte are concentrated mainly in four chromosome segments in as many chromosome pairs. Both maize and teosinte have 10 pairs of chromosomes, and it is most unusual for species of either plants or animals to have most chromosomes remain similar in the process of evolution, the changes being confined to only a few segments of chromosomes. These blocks of genes are supposed to be acquired from Tripsacum through hybridization which took place at some unknown time in the past, presumably in Central America where corn, Tripsacum, and teosinte often occur together. Despite the striking differences in appearance between corn and teosinte, Mangelsdorf and Reeves propose to consider the latter not a separate genus, but only a species or even a variety of corn.

Primitive Corn. If teosinte is not the wild ancestor of corn, then what was this ancestor like and where did it live? This problem must be regarded as still unsolved, but Mangelsdorf and his collaborators have obtained interesting data which suggest a probable solution. More than a century ago, Saint-Hilaire (1829) surmised that corn might have developed from the so-called pod corn (Figure 9.4). The chief characteristics of the pod corn are produced by alleles of a single dominant gene, called tunicate, the presence of which causes rather drastic changes in the body of the plant. The seeds of pod corn are each enclosed in a papery cover consisting of enlarged glumes (the same structures which give the horny covers of the teosinte and gama grass seeds, see above). The ears on the sides of the main stalk of the plant are suppressed, or are elongated, branched, and protrud-

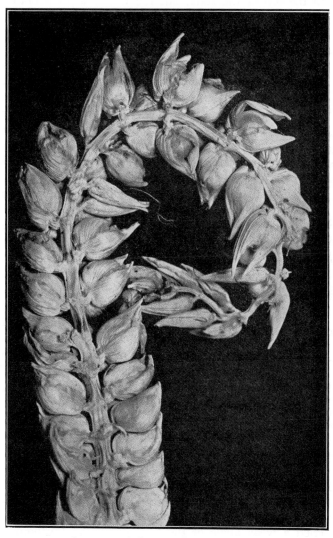

Figure 9.4. Terminal portion of the ear of a primitive Guarany pod corn from South America. Slightly enlarged. (After Mangelsdorf.)

ing from the husks. Much of the plant's energy is diverted to massive tassels on the top of the stalk, but the tassels contain both female and male flowers. Pod corn is not cultivated as such, but it does occur as an admixture in the fields of indigenous maize raised by some Indians, particularly in South America.

Mangelsdorf has pointed out that pod corn has some of the characteristics which were most likely present in the wild corn progenitor. This does not mean that pod corn as it exists now is that progenitor; wild corn unmodified by culture is probably extinct. But an important event in the evolution of corn from a wild to a cultivated plant might well have been a mutation of the tunicate gene, which transformed a pod corn into something more like the modern corn. Just where and when this mutation was first observed and utilized by man is quite unknown.

Again, we should not think that the transformation of wild into cultivated corn was due to a single mutation. On the contrary, the process involved numerous gene substitutions. Some idea of what these were may be gained by studying the primitive corn raised by prehistoric Indians and discovered by archeologists. The most interesting of such discoveries has been made in a cave in New Mexico, and described by Mangelsdorf and Smith. The oldest corn remains in this cave are estimated by radio-carbon dating of associated charcoal to be about 5930 years old (with an experimental error of about 310 years). A reconstruction of an ear of this ancient corn is shown in Figure 9.5. This is already a developed, cultivated, not a wild, plant; but it is a dwarf compared to the ear in modern corn. More important still, the kernels are partially enclosed in glumes, leading to the inference that this corn carried a weak allele of the tunicate gene. Furthermore, the miniature ear was not tightly enclosed in husks as in modern corn, but merely had its base surrounded by a loose cover of leaf sheaths, which surrounded the young inflorescence when the silks first appeared but spread open when the grains were mature.

Figure 9.5. Reconstruction of an ear of a primitive variety of corn cultivated by Indian agriculturists in the American Southwest some 5900 years ago. (From Mangelsdorf and Smith.)

It is fair to say that the most primitive corn from the New Mexico cave is closer to the probable wild ancestor than to the modern corn.

This does not mean, of course, that corn was domesticated in New Mexico. Even in the very early times Indian tribes had trade relations with their neighbors, so that a useful plant or a useful technique could gradually spread throughout the Americas. One of the guesses is that the wild ancestor of corn was a rather rare plant growing in a limited territory somewhere in the interior of the continent of South America, but this is only a guess. Archeologists may discover in South America remains of maize as old as or older than that found in New Mexico, and such a find may make the story of corn much clearer than it is now.

Cultivated Corn. The spike of the primitive corn found in the New Mexico cave (Figure 9.5) is a dwarf compared to modern corn. Surely, the yields which prehistoric farmers obtained from their plantings would be regarded as pitifully small by farmers in our day. The tremendous increase in yields is one measure of the progress accomplished through persistent and long-continued selection since corn became a cultivated plant. We should keep in mind that selection had to produce not just one high-yielding variety but many varieties, adapted to different climatic and agricultural conditions in the lands where corn is cultivated. Some of these varieties are illustrated in Figure 9.6. A variety that is good in Iowa may be worthless in Peru, and vice versa. The tropical varieties are genetically adapted to the short days, and the temperate land varieties to the long summer days which occur when the fields are normally planted. They simply fail to flower when exposed to days and nights of a duration abnormal for them. As a matter of fact, corn is so sensitive to the environmental conditions that for optimal yields we have to breed genotypes "tailored" to each particular region in which they are to be grown. This is why separate corn-breeding programs are pursued not only in different countries but also in every state of the United States where corn culture is economically important.

Mangelsdorf, Anderson, and others suppose that some of the genetic building blocks for the creation of the varieties adapted to so many different local conditions may have been furnished by hybridization of the domestic corn with wild species of Tripsacum. Although Tripsacum is a grass very sharply different from corn in almost every character, they can be crossed. The hybrids are largely sterile, but some seeds can be obtained by pollinating the hybrid ovules with corn pollen. There may occur an introgression (page 127) of Tripsacum genes into corn populations. As we have seen above, teosinte may

be one of the products resulting from such introgression. It may
serve as a bridge for further transfusion of Tripsacum genes into corn.
Whether the hypothesis of Tripsacum introgression is justified, only

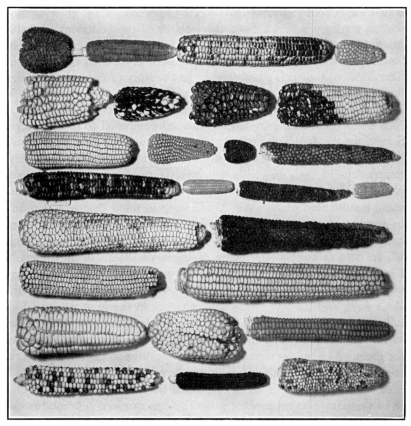

Figure 9.6.   Diversity of varieties of corn cultivated at the present time in different parts of the world.   (Courtesy of Professor P. C. Mangelsdorf.)

the future can tell; it is certainly useful because it inspires many
interesting experiments.

Hybrid Corn.   Within the last two or three decades a spectacular
improvement of the yield of corn plantings in the United States and
elsewhere has been obtained by the introduction of hybrid corn. The
success of hybrid corn may be regarded as the most important contribution of evolutionary biology to human welfare yet produced.
The essentials of the story are as follows.   Darwin showed long ago

(1877) that plant progenies obtained by self-pollination within a flower, by cross-pollination of different flowers of the same plant, or of different individuals of the same strain, are deficient in vigor. They suffer *inbreeding degeneration.* Conversely, the progenies obtained by crossing different strains exhibit *hybrid vigor* (or *heterosis,* as it is now called).

In 1908 and 1909 the geneticist G. H. Shull published his studies on inbreeding and crossing in corn. A corn plant can be "selfed" by transferring the pollen from the tassel to the stigmas (silks) of the same individual. In a cornfield most seeds come, however, from cross-pollination of silks of one individual by pollen grains of other individuals. The "normal" vigor of the field "variety" is maintained by the cross-pollination. Shull found that inbred lines, obtained by systematic selfing, rapidly dwindle in vigor, size, and yield of the plants. Intercrossing *different* inbred lines gives progenies in which the vigor is restored up to the average level of the variety from which the inbred lines were obtained. But hybrids between some inbred lines may even exceed the original variety in productiveness.

Here, then, was a "theoretical" investigation which resulted in a first-rate "practical" discovery. Before this discovery could be exploited in practical farming, however, another problem had to be solved. The hybrid seed must be obtained from inbred lines which consist of weak plants giving poor yields. Getting enough seed from them to plant large fields is prohibitively expensive. Jones (1917) solved the problem by means of the so-called double-cross method (Figure 9.7). Instead of two inbred lines, four inbred ones are used. They are first intercrossed in pairs, $A \times B$ and $C \times D$. The two hybrids obtained are vigorous and high-yielding. They are interplanted in parallel rows, and the tassels are removed from one of the hybrids, so that its silks can receive pollen only from the other hybrid ($A \times B) \times (C \times D$). The resulting seeds are planted on ordinary farms and grow into high-yielding plants. However, the very high yields occur in only one generation, and the fields have to be replanted every year with fresh hybrid seeds.

Corn-breeding programs based on hybrid corn were started soon after 1917, and by 1933 hybrid corn acquired a considerable importance in commercial plantings. The average yield of corn on farms in the United States in the early nineteen-thirties was estimated at about 22 bushels per acre; by 1950 it was about 33 bushels per acre, and colossal yields of more than 100, and even above 200 bushels per acre, are reported under exceptionally favorable conditions. Most, though not

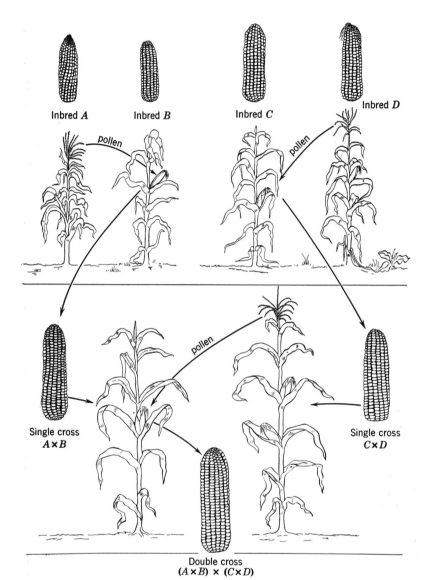

Inbred *A*   Inbred *B*   Inbred *C*   Inbred *D*

pollen   pollen

Single cross
A × B

pollen

Single cross
C × D

Double cross
(A × B) × (C × D)

Figure 9.7. A diagram showing the method of production of *hybrid corn*. Four inbred lines, denoted *A*, *B*, *C*, and *D*, are intercrossed in pairs, giving vigorous *single-cross* hybrids; these are in turn intercrossed, giving the *double-cross* seeds, which are used for commercial plantings.

all, of this phenomenal improvement is ascribable to the introduction of the hybrid corn. It is not surprising, then, that by 1950 more than 75 per cent of the corn-producing fields in the United States, estimated at about 65 million acres, was planted to hybrid corn. In the chief corn-producing states, such as Iowa, the hybrid corn plantings occupy close to 100 per cent of the corn acreage. It became urgently necessary to save the original field "varieties" of corn from total extinction. Their persistence is important because they carry the gene pool from which new inbred lines can be isolated, which may yield hybrids even superior to the now available ones.

Heterosis in Different Organisms. The spectacular success of hybrid corn has inspired attempts to exploit hybrid vigor in other cultivated plants and domestic animals. These attempts are mostly in the experimental stage, but at least some of them are yielding encouraging results. Heterosis is a phenomenon of obvious practical, as well as theoretical, importance. The understanding of its biological nature is, nevertheless, far from satisfactory.

Darwin concluded on the basis of his experiments (see above) that hybrid vigor arises from the union of diverse heredities serving as a stimulus inducing powerful growth and general well-being of the organism. In modern terms, this would mean that heterozygosis for many genes is *per se* a viability stimulus. But this cannot be the whole story. The loss of vigor produced by inbreeding and the luxuriant development induced by crossing of different strains are much more pronounced in some organisms than in others. Thus heterosis in corn is very important, whereas in wheat it is absent or barely detectable. According to Mangelsdorf, even the best inbred lines of corn yield no more than half as much as do the open-pollinated varieties from which the inbred lines are isolated. Many of the inbred lines are so weak that they can be maintained at all only with difficulty. In contrast, self-fertilization is the rule in many wheats, oats, barleys, beans, etc. A field of wheat consists, then, of a single or of several inbred lines which have been selected because they are vigorous and high-yielding. In general, the inbreeding depression is most pronounced in species which normally live in large cross-fertilizing populations, such as corn or rye. In normally self-fertilizing forms there is little inbreeding depression and little heterosis upon crossing. Man stands somewhere in the middle of this heterosis range. History records that some royal dynasties practiced brother-sister marriage, which is a very close inbreeding, for many generations without known adverse effects. On the other hand, recessive hereditary diseases occur most frequently in families with much consanguinity, that is, where parents are relatives. **Genetic Mechanisms Which Bring about Heterosis.** As pointed out in Chapter 7, "heterosis" is a common name for several different phenomena. Perhaps the simplest of these is *mutational heterosis.* We have seen (pages 139–142) that recessive mutants accumulate in populations of species which reproduce sexually and by cross-fertilization. No matter how deleterious, or even lethal, may be a mutant when homozygous, it is "sheltered" in heterozygotes with normal dominant alleles. A heterozygous carrier of a serious recessive hereditary disease may enjoy robust health. Thus it happens that in wild populations of Drosophila, and doubtless of many other organisms as well, most individuals are carriers of one or more deleterious recessives. The frequency of any one deleterious mutant in the gene pool, however, is usually so low that, when individuals who mate are not very closely related, the probability that both parents would by chance carry the same deleterious recessive mutants is not very great. The defective homozygotes are, consequently, rare in the populations so long as consanguinity is avoided.

Suppose that a recessive gene which is deleterious when homozygous has a frequency $q = 0.01$ in the gene pool of a population. Assume that this population reproduces sexually, that it consists of a large number of individuals, and that it is panmictic (the matings occur at random). The frequency of homozygotes who will suffer from the harmful effects of this gene in this population will, then, be $q^2 = 0.01^2$, or one per 10,000 individuals (see Chapter 6, and particularly page 120). The hereditary disease or malformation produced by the homozygosis for this gene will be a rare one in the population. But suppose now that we are dealing with a population in which matings of brothers and sisters occasionally take place. Brothers and sisters have a fifty-fifty chance of having both inherited a given gene from their parents. The probability that the siblings who mate will both carry a recessive which one of their parents carried in heterozygous condition is $0.5 \times 0.5 = 0.25$, or one-quarter. A quarter of their progeny is likely to be homozygous for the recessive. Thus one-sixteenth of the progeny of a brother-sister mating will be homozygous for any one gene inherited from the grandparents. Self-fertilization is, of course, a form of inbreeding even more extreme than brother-sister mating. If a self-fertilizing individual of, for example, wheat is heterozygous for a recessive mutant gene, a quarter of its progeny will be homozygous for that gene.

There is no doubt that a part of the degeneration of the progeny resulting from consanguinity and inbreeding in such species as man or corn results from homozygosis for recessive deleterious genes. There is also no doubt that the absence of deleterious effects of consanguinity in normally self-fertilizing species is due in part to the rapid elimination of the deleterious recessive mutants. In wheat a deleterious recessive mutant is not sheltered for long in heterozygotes, and is eliminated by natural selection far more rapidly than it would be in corn or in man. Nevertheless, mutational heterosis is only a part of the whole heterosis phenomenon, and at present it is not certain how large or how small a part.

Another mechanism which causes hybrid vigor is *balanced heterosis*, which we have discussed in another connection (Chapter 7, pages 142–147). In Drosophila natural populations of some species consist mostly of individuals heterozygous for certain chromosomal inversions, and such individuals possess high fitness. But chromosomal homozygotes are also produced in the populations, and these homozygotes are less fit than are the heterozygotes. Natural selection maintains a balanced polymorphism, with a certain optimal proportion of hetero- and homozygotes arising in each generation. It is certain that balanced polymorphism is widespread in sexual species in which inbreeding is normally rare, but just how widespread we are not certain.

Populations of many species consist of two or more "phases" which differ in color, in shape of some body parts, or in other traits. Although the phases may appear very strikingly different to the human eye (Figure 9.8), they interbreed freely both in nature and in experiments. In a number of cases it has been shown (by Ford in some butterflies, by da Cunha in a species of Drosophila, etc.) that the phases differ in a single gene or in a few genes, and that their maintenance in nature is due to the heterozygotes being adaptively superior to the homozygotes. Allison (1954) found that at least one hereditary disease is maintained in human populations by a similar mechanism. Heterozygous carriers of the gene for the sickle-cell anemia are more resistant to malaria than are "normal" homozygotes which do not carry this gene at all. Yet the sickle-cell homozygotes die of an acute anemia (see page 141).

Balanced heterosis is likely to be most important in sexual species which are so well adapted and successful in their environments that they build large, variable, and panmictic populations. Crow (1948, 1952) came to the conclusion that at least 95 per cent of the hybrid vigor in corn is due to balanced heterosis, and 5 per cent or less to mutational heterosis. In large populations the effects of a rare ge*t*e on the fitness of homozygotes are relatively unimportant compared to its effects in heterozygotes. This is because the homozygotes for rare

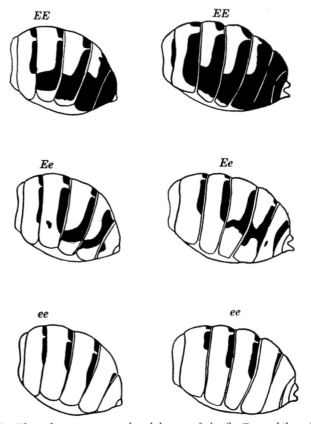

Figure 9.8. The color patterns on the abdomen of the fly *Drosophila polymorpha* living in many parts of Brazil. These patterns are produced by homozygosis and heterozygosis for two alleles of a single gene, denoted *E* and *e*. Female and male abdomens of each genotype are shown. (From da Cunha.)

genes occur much less frequently relative to the heterozygotes (see page 121). Wallace (1951) has shown that balanced heterosis develops in laboratory populations of Drosophila subjected to continuous treatment with radium rays, although this treatment induces numerous deleterious mutants. How important is the balanced heterosis in maintaining the "normal" fitness in populations of domestic animals and in man himself? Is it possible that the existence in man of several blood groups and of taste blindness is due to balanced polymorphism? May the excessively fat and excessively lean persons which occur in human populations represent the homozygotes, the existence of which in the species is a necessary by-product of the "normal" well-proportioned heterozygotes being in a majority in these populations? Only more research can answer these and other fundamental questions of basic population biology of man.

Suggestions for Further Reading

Darwin, Ch. 1868. *Variations of Plants and Animals under Domestication.*

Though the evidence which Darwin had at his disposal concerning the origins of domesticated animals and plants was much less than is available at present, his book remains a classic which is well worth reading. It is available in several editions.

Simpson, G. G. 1951. *Horses.* Oxford University Press, New York.

A delightfully written as well as scholarly discussion of the evolution of fossil and living horses.

Hutchinson, J. B., Silow, R. A., and Stephens, S. G. 1947. *The Evolution of Gossypium and the Cultivated Cottons.* Oxford University Press, London.

A study of the wild and cultivated cottons and their origins.

Mangelsdorf, P. C. 1947. *The origin and evolution of maize. Advances in Genetics,* Volume 1, pages 161–207.

Mangelsdorf, P. C., and Smith, C. E., Jr. 1949. *New archeological evidence on evolution in maize. Harvard University Botanical Museum Leaflets,* Volume 13, pages 213–247.

Stebbins, G. L. 1950. *Variation and Evolution in Plants.* Columbia University Press, New York.

Chapters VIII and IX contain an excellent discussion of the origin of species by polyploidy.

Gowen, J. W. (Editor). 1952. *Heterosis.*

A symposium on heterosis and its applications in agriculture. The articles written by J. F. Crow and P. C. Mangelsdorf are particularly interesting.

Lerner, I. M. 1954. *Genetic homeostasis.* John Wiley, New York.

The most modern discussion of the genetic basis of heterosis and of its evolutionary significance.

10

Evolution of the Organic Form and Function

Preformation and Epigenesis. Having retired early from a profitable business, Antony van Leeuwenhoek of Delft, Holland, became an amateur microscopist eager to examine anything under his microscope. In 1675 he examined the seminal fluids of several animals, including man. He saw swimming in these fluids the "animalcules," or the spermatozoa as we would say now. This was a discovery enough to make anybody famous, but a few years later another countryman of Leeuwenhoek "improved" on it by publishing a picture of a human spermatozoon in the head of which he saw a "homunculus," a tiny figure of a man (1694). This seemed a really magnificent discovery, for it appeared to solve at one stroke the difficult problems of heredity and development. The human body is all ready, *preformed,* in the male sex cell; all it needs to become an adult man is to increase in size.

To be sure, some of the authorities of that time did not feel convinced that the homunculus resides in spermatozoa, and preferred to look for him in the female sex cell, the egg. But whether they belonged to the school of "animalculists" or to that of "ovists," they believed the idea of preformation to be an excellent one. Especially so when Jan Swammerdam, of Leyden, Holland, developed the idea by supposing that the homunculi in the sex cells contain within them still smaller homunculi; those have more minute homunculi, and so ad infinitum. The reproductive organs of Adam—or of Eve—contained within them the entire mankind to come, packed like boxes within boxes. The utter absurdity of this notion was not obvious at the time, since it was not realized that within a few generations the homunculi would have to be smaller than atoms.

The preformation theory, and its extreme version the "box theory,"

222

appealed strongly to many people. To the Calvinists it gave a scientific confirmation of the doctrine of predestination. The philosopher Leibniz (1648–1716) saw that the theory explained very simply the whole creation, as well as the immortality of the soul and the dogma of original sin. The whole world was preformed all at once, for all ages to come. All that has happened in the universe since then is a gradual unfolding of something that was there from the beginning.

The homunculus variety of the preformation theory was disproved by Malpighi (1628–1694) and Kaspar Wolff (1733–1794), who showed that the hen's egg contains at the beginning nothing whatever resembling a miniature chick. The chick embryo develops gradually, passing through a succession of stages which are by no means just larger or smaller copies of one another. The development is *epigenetic;* it is a succession of qualitatively different processes following each other in a definite sequence. Wolff regarded this epigenesis to be a product of a vital force, and it remained for Karl von Baer (1792–1876) to give a

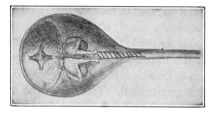

Figure 10.1. A *homunculus* imagined to exist in a human spermatozoon by an early microscopist. (After Hartsoeker, 1694, from Curtis and Guthrie.)

scientific version of the epigenetic theory of embryonic development.

Do not imagine, however, that the preformist way of thinking in biology is dead. As we shall see, in one form or another it always existed, and probably always will exist. The same is true of the epigenetic way of thinking. The idea that things are preformed, predestined, just waiting around the corner for their turn to appear, is pleasing and comforting to many people. Everything is destiny, fate. But to other people predestination is a denial of freedom and novelty. They prefer to think that the flow of events in the world may be changed creatively, and that new things do arise. The influence of these two types of thinking is very clear in the development of biological theories.

Progression of Living Beings. The living things which we observe in the world around us are tremendously diversified. What sense, if any, is there in their diversity? A possible answer is that we see in nature a progression of things from a less perfect to a more perfect state, and that the living creatures occupy different steps in this single ladder of progress. To Aristotle (384–322 B.C.), "The nature advances by small steps from inanimate things to animate. . . . . After the realm of lifeless things, there follows the realm of plants. . . . The plants appear to be animate compared to other things, but inanimate compared to the animals. . . ." Among marine life we find, according to Aristotle, creatures which occupy steps, intermediate between plants and animals. Thus sponges are almost exactly like plants, whereas oysters and mussels are somewhat more animal-like. Then follow "bloodless" animals (which we now call invertebrates), and those which have blood (vertebrates). Among the last, we have the different steps of perfection represented by fishes, birds, oviparous quadrupeds (reptiles), and viviparous quadrupeds (mammals). The top rung of the ladder is occupied by man. Just below man are the monkeys, which share some human and some quadruped properties.

To Aristotle the ladder of progress did not mean that the occupants of the upper rungs have arisen by an evolutionary process from those lower down on the ladder (see Chapter 14). The ladder is just there; it is preformed. This idea was tremendously popular right down to the nineteenth century. To Leibniz, the "force of the principle of continuity" is so great that he ventures to predict that whenever some rungs of the ladder seem to be unoccupied (that is, when intermediates between some groups of living beings are unknown), their occupants will be discovered by further studies. This sounds almost like the assurance of an evolutionist that "missing links" between existing groups of organisms have existed in the past and become extinct. To Leibniz it meant only that the preformed order of nature cannot be incomplete. The Swiss zoologist Bonnet (1720–1793) worked out the ladder of nature in greatest detail. It begins (starting at the top) with man–orangutan–monkey–quadruped–flying squirrel–bat–ostrich–bird–etc. The steps between animals and plants are occupied by polyps–sea anemones–sensitive plant (Mimosa)–plants; and the steps between the living and non-living by truffles–corals–fossils–asbestos–talcum. The bottom is "pure earth"–water–air–fire–"finer matters."

Lamarck (1744–1829), the pioneer of evolutionism, took the leap into the future by asserting that the more complex organisms have actually evolved from the simpler ones. The diversity of living creatures is not preformed, it has arisen in the course of time. But Lamarck still clung to the notion of a single ladder of progress, although he had it branch in some places. This mistake cost him dearly. His adversary Cuvier (1768–1833), the great anatomist and paleontologist, had little difficulty in showing that no single ladder of progress exists in the biological world. The contemporaries thought that Cuvier had invalidated the idea of evolution as well.

Types. Living creatures are obviously too diverse to be arranged in a single file from the highest to the lowest. A slight acquaintance with the anatomy of a bat will show that, contrary to Bonnet, it is in no way intermediate between a mammal and a bird. Another notion can be tried instead—the notion of type, which has already been mentioned in another connection (page 134). According to Plato (427–347 B.C.), the world as we see it consists of mere shadows of the real but invisible world of eternal, unchangeable, and perfect ideas of things. Men as we see them are variable, and many are miserable specimens; but there exists in some heaven the Idea of Man of inconceivable purity, beauty, and perfection. Animals and plants are also variable, but an acquaintance with them shows that many organisms resemble each other, as though they were variations on a limited number of basic themes. These basic themes were called types or ground plans.

In 1790 the great poet Goethe (1749–1832) published a biological work, *The Metamorphoses of Plants*, in which he devised the "Primeval Plant" (Urpflanze, in German). According to Goethe, "Everything is a leaf." What he means is that various organs of the plant, such as the cotyledons of seeds, petals and sepals of flowers, stamens and pistils, which are the male and the female organs, are all modifications of a single structure—the leaf (Figure 10.2). "Through this simplicity," says Goethe, "becomes possible the greatest diversity" of forms among plants, which he has carefully observed himself and studied in the works of others. Goethe is quite explicit in saying that the Primeval Plant which he describes and figures does not actually exist now, and presumably never existed as an ancestor of all other plants. Although some historians are eager to make Goethe an evolutionist, he was not one. The Primeval Plant is the ideal type of a plant, and the plants that actually grow are varying manifestations of this type. Goethe, and his younger countryman Oken (1779–1851), tried also to devise a ground plan of the vertebrate animals, or rather of skulls. The skull bones are modifications of six vertebrae. Again, this did not mean a reconstruction of an actual ancestor with six extra vertebrae in place of a head; it meant only "the concept, the Idea of the animal."

We have already mentioned Cuvier as an opponent of Lamarck. To Cuvier, all animals were variations of four great types or ground plans: those of the vertebrates, mollusks, segmented animals (arthropods and worms), and radially symmetrical animals. Having extensively studied

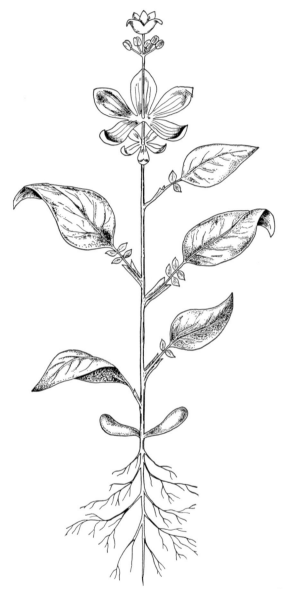

Figure 10.2.   Goethe's theoretical prototype of flowering plants.

the fossils found in the vicinity of Paris, Cuvier knew well that his four types are represented in the different strata by different animals. Had he studied fossils also in other countries, he might have seen that the changes of the inhabitants from stratum to stratum meant evolution. But it so happens that near Paris there are six sharply different geological formations, the intermediates between which are not represented. To Cuvier, this meant that life on earth was repeatedly destroyed by some catastrophes, and repeatedly created anew, and always according to the same ground plans!

Homology. The idealistic philosophy of Plato, leading to construction of ideal "types" or "ground plans," proved to be a wrong guide to the understanding of organic form. Nevertheless, the work of the typologists yielded many facts that are of enduring value. In comparing different animals or plants, we readily notice that some of their organs and body parts have the same fundamental structure, although they may be different in appearance and in use. The English anatomist Owen proposed in 1843 to call such organs or body parts *homologous*. But the phenomenon to which this name applies was known to Aristotle, who saw quite clearly that human arms are the homologues of the forelegs of quadruped mammals. In 1555 the Frenchman Belon compared the skeletons of a bird and a man and identified the homologous bones, which he indicated by similar letters in the two drawings in Figure 10.3. Belon's drawings are perfectly acceptable in a manual of comparative anatomy today.

In modern terms Goethe's Primeval Plant embodies his correct recognition of the homology between corresponding parts of the same plant, such as leaves and flower petals (this is called *serial homology*), as well as between parts of different plants (*special homology*). Cuvier's four types of animal structure were also based on his ability to perceive the homologies of the corresponding parts in different animals. The great problem is this: how does homology arise? The solution of this problem was supplied by Darwin: different organisms possess homologous organs because they are descended from a common ancestor. By and large, the greater the similarity in the body structure, the closer is the common ancestry; the less the similarity, the more remote is the descent relationship.

Homology does not prove evolution, in the sense that nobody has actually witnessed the gradual changes in the millions of consecutive generations which led from a common ancestor to a bird on the one hand and to man on the other. But homology suggests evolution; the facts of homology make sense if they are supposed to be due to evolution of now different organisms from a common stock. They do not make sense otherwise. To be sure, some die-hard anti-evolutionists still insist that homology means only that the Creator gratuitously chose to make homologous organs in quite unrelated organisms. This opinion may be said to be implicitly blasphemous: it actually ac-

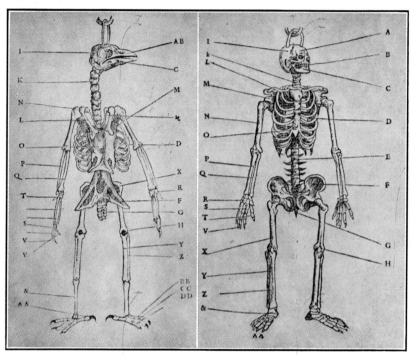

Figure 10.3.   Homologous bones in the skeleton of a bird and a man, as drawn by Belon in 1555.   (After Zimmermann.)

cuses the Creator of arranging things so that they suggest evolution merely to mislead honest students of His works.

The phenomena of homology explained by evolution are, of course, innumerable. Descriptive zoology and botany may be said to be concerned chiefly with detecting homologies. Belon's homologizing the skeletons of man and bird was, of course, followed by similar successful comparisons of the skeletons of all vertebrates, from fish to man. The science of comparative anatomy of vertebrates deals with identification and description of homologous organs in the different vertebrate animals.

Homologies of the Mouth Parts in Insects. Figure 10.4 shows the homologies of the mouth parts in some insects. The homologous parts are shown similarly labeled. At first sight, the mouth parts of the

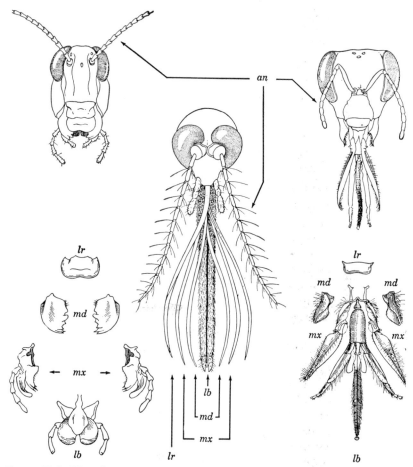

Figure 10.4. Homologous mouth parts in a grasshopper, a honey bee, and a mosquito. *lb*, labium with its palpi; *lr*, labrum; *md*, mandibles; *mx*, maxilla with its palpi; *an*, antenna.

biting type, like those of a cockroach or of a grasshopper, are different from those of a sucking type, found in a bee, a mosquito, or in a fly. But a patient study not only of the extreme kinds of mouth parts shown in Figure 10.4 but also of many other kinds of insects, some of which seem to "bridge the gaps," gradually sheds light on the situation. The student begins to perceive what pieces of the mouth machinery of a mosquito correspond to the different parts of the cockroach mouth. Finally it becomes evident that all the innumerable insects really have their mouth apparatus built out of homologous pieces, but these pieces can be vastly different in form. Pre-Darwinian biologists would have said that all insects have their mouth parts built as variants of the same ground plan. We must add that the only reasonable interpretation of the generality of the ground plan yet proposed is that it indicates common descent. All insects have evolved in the course of time from similar progenitors.

Next, we should ask ourselves this question: what has caused the mosquito mouth to appear so different from the cockroach mouth? The reasonable hypothesis is that these insects have different mouth parts because they feed on different foods. A cockroach bites off pieces of solid or semi-solid foods with its mandibles, then masticates the food with its mandibles and maxillae, and finally pushes it down the mouth opening located at the base of the labium. It has organs of chemical sense on the palpi of the maxillae and the labium, which test the quality of the food. The delicate parts of the mouth are protected by the shield of the labium. A female mosquito gets its food in an entirely different way, by drawing blood from animals much larger than itself. With the mouth parts of a cockroach it might never bite through the skin, or if it did would cause the animal much pain and a defense reaction. Instead, a mosquito pierces the skin with the aid of its mandibles and maxillae transformed into finest and sharpest needles. The operation is often so nearly painless that the animal frequently does not perceive the presence of the bloodthirsty insect and does not drive it away. The mosquito sucks the blood up into its mouth through a fine tube formed by its labium. The mouth parts of a cockroach would be far less efficient for this purpose, and a mosquito would be quite unable to feed on the kind of food which a cockroach eats.

However, we must beware of thinking that the nature of an organ is explained by finding out the function which this organ performs. Animals and plants do not get organs just because they need them or can conveniently use them. To think so would mean ascribing purposes to nature. This is *teleological* reasoning, which has no place in science because it explains nothing. But the fear of teleology can be carried too far. Some biologists go to the extreme of saying that the function of an organ has nothing to do with its being there. Yet nobody can deny that man has eyes to see with, and a mosquito has its mouth parts to get blood with. It is pedantic to quibble even about the statement that the purpose of the eyes is seeing. There is really nothing objectionable about such a statement, which simply describes what the organ does, provided that one always keeps in mind that the presence of an organ and its function are at the opposite ends of a long and complex chain of cause-and-effect relationships. Some of the connecting links in this causal chain are the processes of mutation, sexual recombination, and natural selection over a long series of generations. Darwin has done away with teleology, by giving a rational explanation of the evolutionary processes which mold an organ so that it becomes fit for the performance of a given function. (For further discussion of this problem, see Chapter 14.)

Analogy. Different functions make homologous organs dissimilar in form. Similar functions may make different, non-homologous organs come to resemble each other. Owen (1843) proposed to call such organs *analogous*. A classical example of analogy is the wings of a bird, a bat, and a butterfly. These organs are unquestionably similar in function—they are, indeed, wings. But they are very different in organization. A bat wing is a skin fold between the four fingers of a hand, the bones of the fingers being lengthened to perform a supporting function, like the ribs of an umbrella. A fifth finger, the thumb, is short and has a strong claw, by means of which the animal suspends itself while at rest from a branch of a tree or a ceiling of a cave. In a bird the supporting surface of the wing is composed of feathers, not of a skin fold. The skeletal framework of a bird wing corresponds to that of the whole human arm; but the finger bones (phalanges) are elongated in only one finger, other fingers being rudimentary. Now, although the bones of a bat wing and a bird wing are homologous, the wings themselves are quite differently constructed. The wings of a butterfly consist of a membrane formed by two layers of cells, supported by "wing veins" which are thickenings of the membrane. Parts of a butterfly wing are not homologous to parts of either bat or bird wings. These are analogous organs.

As stated above, early zoologists regarded bats to be intermediate between mammals and birds (Bonnet, in the eighteenth century; still earlier Gesner, in the sixteenth, and others). We can see that the resemblance of bats to birds is due chiefly to analogy, to the presence of organs of dissimilar structure which, however, serve similar functions—wings for flying. Otherwise the bodies of bats are built like those of mammals; bats, indeed, are mammals. Whales were considered gigantic fishes, until John Ray (1627–1705) pointed out that they breathe with lungs instead of with gills, have a heart with two ventricles like mammals instead of a single ventricle like fishes, and resemble mammals in everything except in the almost complete absence of hair. And yet whales and porpoises certainly resemble fishes in body shape more than they do any other mammals. The reason for this is not far to seek: the streamlined body shape and the presence of fins instead of legs are greatly advantageous for living in water. Natural selection has favored in water-dwelling animals, whether in fish or in mammals, those characteristics which fit them for the water life. As far as the body shape is concerned, the ancestors of a fish and a whale were presumably less similar than these animals are today. The evolution was in this case *convergent*. But note that the convergence has affected only some traits which have a direct bearing on the way of life as a water inhabitant. The body structures as a whole have not converged.

Natural and Artificial Classification. "Without classification—only chaos," such was the admonition of Linnaeus (1707–1778) to the young science of biology. Animals and plants must be classified for the same reason that books must be classified in any large library or stamps in any large collection. Anybody who has tried to find a book misplaced in library stacks knows this by experience. But how should the classification be made? The difficulty arises because different systems of classification are possible. Stamps are classified usually by country, then by time of issue, by denomination, and by variations in the shade of color and of perforation. But books may be classified according to the name of the author, or by language, or according to the subject matter, or the date of publication. Living beings vary in many more ways than either stamps or books; hence the choice of their classification system is even more complex.

None of the methods of classifying books are intrinsically better than the others; and each method is more convenient, and is therefore used in some libraries. The convenience of a classification when it is being used is, then, the criterion of its validity. The Book of Leviticus divides the water-dwelling animals into those which have fins and scales and those which do not. This division separates, for example, the eels from fishes and combines them with a lot of most diverse invertebrate animals. The Roman Pliny divided the animals into those living on earth, in water, and in the air. This system combines bats with birds, whales and porpoises with fishes, and places the amphibians athwart the dividing line. Biologists find these classifications inconvenient because, it is said, they are artificial instead of natural.

A *natural classification* must take into account the greatest possible number of characteristics of the organisms classified. Thus saying that an animal is a fish tells a zoologist at once that it respires with gills, has a heart with a single ventricle, a certain structure of the brain, of the kidneys, and many other things. A mammal respires with lungs, has a heart with two ventricles, different brain and kidney structures, feeds its young with milk, usually has hair, etc. Pliny's classification does not do so well for the purposes of a zoologist, because it tells him at most whether he should look for the animal in water or out, and next to nothing about the body structure of that animal. This is, of course, not a valid objection against an artificial classification, such as that of the Book of Leviticus, inasmuch as its author had in mind purposes quite different from those of a zoologist.

In making the natural classification we must, then, distinguish between homology and analogy. To do this requires a great deal of study and insight, and it took centuries to erect what we reasonably believe to be the natural system of the animal and plant kingdoms. As a matter of fact, Aristotle made a classification which we consider much superior to Pliny's. For example, he did distinguish mammals, birds, reptiles, and fishes, although he did not perceive that a cuttle-fish (a cephalopod mollusk) is an animal really very different from an ordinary fish. Linnaeus keenly appreciated the advantages of natural classification, and yet his division of the plant kingdom into twenty-four classes is pretty artificial by modern standards. The Linnaean classes were based entirely on the structure of the reproductive organs (flowers), and fifteen of the classes differ merely in the numbers of the stamens which a flower possesses. Cuvier did much better classifying animals, but his group Radiata, combining forms as diverse as corals, sponges, and sea urchins, is an artificial one.

Phylogenetic System. Quite a new understanding of the meaning of natural classification was given by Darwin. Before Darwin, zoologists and botanists had to strive for classifications which expressed the fundamental, rather than only superficial, similarities and dissimilarities of the animals and plants. But the classification so arrived at was completely static; it was just there, preformed in the order of things. To Darwin the fundamental similarities (homologies) meant evidence of descent from common ancestors. A classification which expressed these similarities became, then, a description of the evolutionary development, of the phylogeny, of the organisms so classified. A natural system is one which puts together the near kin, and separates the distant relatives.

To some of Darwin's successors, especially to Haeckel (1834–1919), this idea became the cornerstone and the inspiration of their work. Building the natural system of animals and plants is now more than construction of a catalogue of organisms for the convenience of fellow biologists. It is also a study of the pedigree of the living world, of the history of its evolutionary development. It is fair to say that the last decades of the nineteenth century were dominated in biology by the building of the system of organisms under the guise of studying their phylogeny. The modern classification of animals and plants was achieved thanks to the labors of a multitude of zoologists and botanists chiefly of that century.

This immense work may now be regarded as finished in the main, although, of course, numerous special problems still await solution. For example, there is no reasonable doubt that mammals, birds, and reptiles are natural classes. But the Australian monotremes (the duckbill and the spiny anteater) are a curious group, the evaluation of which is still in doubt. They have hair and nurse their young like mammals, and yet lay eggs in reptilian fashion and have some other odd structural features. Some authorities consider them intermediate between reptiles and mammals, and related to the ancestral stock by means of which a group of reptiles gave rise to the mammals. Other authorities believe the monotremes to be rather an independent off-shoot from the reptiles, the mammals having arisen from something quite unlike the monotremes.

In 1894–1896 Haeckel published his great work *Systematic Phylogeny; a Sketch of a Natural System of Organisms Based on their Descent*, in which he presented what he believed to have been a genealogic tree of the living world. Many biologists are at present rather less optimistic about the reliability of such genealogies than were biologists in Haeckel's day. After all, the modern natural classification of organisms is still based on the same kind of data which were used by Linnaeus and by Cuvier. To be sure, these data are at present incomparably more complete and detailed than they were a century or two centuries ago, but the phylogenetic interpretation of the natural system has not changed the classification to any appreciable extent. There is no reason to doubt that similarities between organisms usually indicate common descent, except when the similarities are due to analogy rather than to homology. However, if we desire to learn something about the actual history of life on earth, the study of the now living organisms, no matter how detailed. is no safe substitute for the study of fossils.

Biogenetic Law. The end of the nineteenth and the beginning of the present century saw most biologists busily constructing phylogenies of the animal and plant kingdoms. As we have seen, the chief method used for this purpose was careful comparative study of the body structures of diverse organisms, which usually permitted homologies to be distinguished from analogies. Another and almost equally potent method was the study of the development of the organisms, especially of the embryonic development.

The bodies of animals and plants are often most intricately and wonderfully built. Yet these bodies arise from very obscure beginnings, single egg cells fertilized by single sperms, and by means of developmental processes which have seemed utterly mysterious. The preformation and box theories (see above) tried to solve the problem by pushing it back to the act of original creation, but this proved a wrong lead. Examination of the embryos of different organisms showed at once that these theories lacked foundation. Nehemiah Grew (1682) found that an apple seed contains a structure which in no way resembles a miniature apple tree. Animal embryos were studied beginning with Fabricius of Aquapendente in Padua (1537–1619) and his great English pupil, William Harvey (1578–1657). Malpighi (1628–1694) was apparently the first to apply to this study the then novel instrument—the microscope. Wolff, von Baer (see page 223), Purkinje (1787–1869), and their successors built the science of embryology, which progressively unraveled the developmental stages of all classes of living beings. Everywhere the development proved to be epigenetic rather than preformistic.

Embryologists were impressed by a rather different aspect of the matter. In 1821 Meckel concluded: "Embryos of higher animals pass, before they complete their development, through a succession of stages. . . . The embryos of higher animals, of mammals and especially of man, pass through stages resembling more or less completely, in the appearance of separate organs as well as of the whole body . . . the lower animals." Indeed, the body starts by being a single cell, and is to that extent like the unicellular organisms. Then it becomes composed of two layers of cells, the ectoderm and the endoderm, like a hydra or a coral. Especially impressive was the discovery that mammalian and human embryos at a certain stage have in the neck region gill pouches and gill bars. In these embryos these structures never function in respiration, but in the fishes they do. A mammalian embryo, then, passes a "fish stage." The embryonic development of higher organisms seems to retrace a sequence of body structures corresponding first to the lower and then to progressively higher forms. Darwin pointed out that the above observations are most easily understood if the higher organisms are the evolutionary descendants of the lower ones. Haeckel, who had a talent for making pithy formulae, expressed the idea thus: "Ontogeny (the development of an individual) is a brief and rapid recapitulation of the phylogeny," and he gave to this formula the ambitious name of the "basic biogenetic law" (1866). If the embryo of an organism is an archive which contains a telescoped evolutionary history, the study of the embryonic development becomes a method of unraveling the phylogeny of the group. Haeckel and his many followers eagerly proceeded to do just that. The result was accumulation of accurate and detailed data on the embryology of all kinds of organisms. However, most biologists are at present inclined to believe that the "basic biogenetic law" rather overstated the extent to which the embryonic development is an accurate record of the past evolutionary history. The situation may be understood best by considering two examples of the evidence relevant to the issue.

Development of the Urogenital Organs in Vertebrates. Three kinds of kidneys occur among the vertebrates, known as pronephros, mesonephros, and metanephros. A pronephros is a series of tubules, which draw waste products not from the blood stream but directly from the liquid filling the spaces between the organs in the body cavity. These waste products are conducted to the outside of the body by means of a pair of tubes—the pronephric ducts. The pronephros functions as a kidney only in the most primitive vertebrates, such as young lampreys (Cyclostomata); but a pronephros is nevertheless formed in the embryos of all other vertebrates. In the mammalian embryo it never functions as an organ of excretion, but it is there just the same (Figure 10.5).

Next, there appears in the embryos of all vertebrates a pair of kidneys of quite different structure—the mesonephros. These kidneys have an abundant supply of blood vessels from which the renal tubules draw the waste products. The mesonephros communicates with the outside by means of a duct called the Wolffian duct, which develops by modification of the pronephric duct. This is the functional kidney of most fishes and of amphibians, but it is formed, next to the pronephros, also in the embryos of the reptiles, birds, and mammals. In these embryos, however, it is only a temporary arrangement, which soon disappears, leaving behind the Wolffian duct which is put to other uses (Figure 10.5).

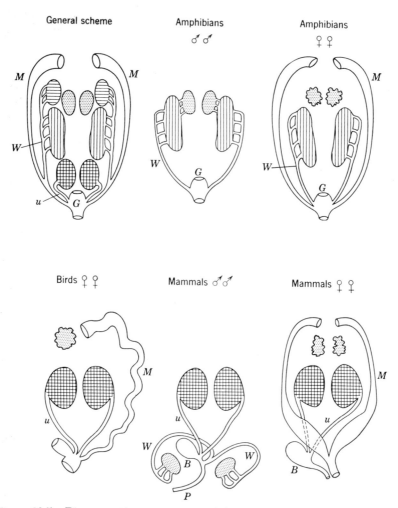

Figure 10.5. Diagrammatic representation of the urogenital organ system in various vertebrate animals. The sex gland is shown stippled, primary kidney (pronephros) by horizontal shading, secondary kidney (mesonephros) by vertical shading, and tertiary kidney (metanephros) by cross-shading. *B*, urinary bladder; *G* gut; *M*, Müllerian duct (oviduct); *P*, penis; *U*, ureter; *W*, Wolffian duct.

In the higher vertebrates there arises a third kidney, the metanephros, which is the urine secretor in the adult animals. It has a duct of its own, called the ureter. The metanephros and its ureters are wholly absent in fishes and amphibians.

The development of the excretory organs, the kidneys, is intimately connected with the development of the reproductive organs. In the frog and other amphibians the sperm produced by the testes is conducted to the outside through the mesonephric, Wolffian, ducts. The eggs from the ovary are picked up by another pair of ducts, the Müllerian ducts. These two pairs of ducts, the Wolffian and the Müllerian, are formed in the embryos of most vertebrates. Thus the human embryo about six weeks old has both of them. In the male embryo the Wolffian ducts persist and become the sperm ducts, losing all relation to the adult kidneys in the reptiles, birds, and mammals. The Müllerian ducts disappear, except for small vestiges. In the female, the Müllerian ducts develop into the oviducts, and in mammals also into the uterus and a part of the vagina. The Wolffian ducts disappear, leaving behind two rudiments in the ovary (Figure 10.5).

Why should pronephros and mesonephros, which are the kidneys of the lower vertebrates, be formed and then disappear in the embryos of the higher vertebrates? This would certainly be inexplicable if the higher vertebrates were not the descendants of the lower. Again, an anti-evolutionist would have to blame God for having arranged things just to mislead the zoologist. The biogenetic law does contain an important kernel of truth. But it does not follow that a human embryo is in a lamprey stage when it has the pronephros, and in a frog stage when it has a mesonephros. At these or at any other stages the human embryo has no far-reaching resemblance to any adult animal. Von Baer stated the facts clearly as early as 1828, when he wrote: "An embryo of a higher animal is never basically like any other animal, only like the embryo of the latter." In other words, the development of the embryo does not reproduce for our benefit the portraits of the near or remote ancestors. But the evolutionary descent is manifest in embryos forming certain organs homologous to those found in the adults of quite different, but phylogenetically related, organisms.

Larvae of Some Crustaceans. Just as with the embryos, remarkable similarities are often found between the larvae of animals which are quite dissimilar as adults. Many lower crustaceans, such as the little copepod Cyclops, produce eggs from which hatches a very tiny but characteristic free-swimming larva, called the nauplius (Figure 10.6). The nauplius, with its three pairs of legs, eventually meta-

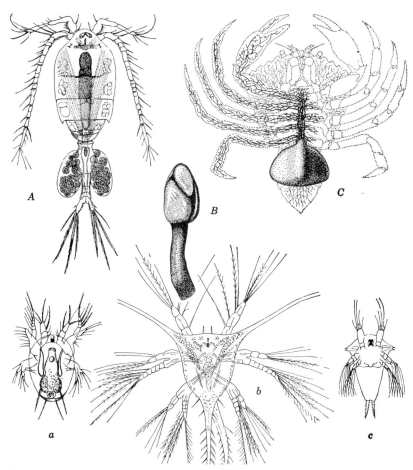

Figure 10.6. Similarity of the larval stages (below) in crustaceans which are very different as adults (above). From left to right: (*A*, *a*) The free-swimming copepod Cyclops; (*B*, *b*) the gooseneck barnacle Lepas, which lives attached to rocks by a peduncle; and (*C*, *c*) Sacculina, which in adult condition lives as a parasite on crabs. Sacculina's body gives off root-like outgrowths which penetrate inside of the body of the victim and envelop its internal organs (shown only on the left side in *C*). The different animals are not drawn to same scale.

morphoses into an adult Cyclops, having several pairs of legs and leg-like appendages, a complex nerve system and sense organs, as well as organs of reproduction. The barnacles look in the adult condition about as unlike a Cyclops as can be imagined. Instead of swimming freely in water (in the plankton), a barnacle is attached to rocks or to the surface of other organisms on the sea bottom or in the tidal zone. It usually has a hard shell consisting of several calcareous pieces, inside of which is found an animal glued to its support by its head.

The classification of barnacles was long in doubt. Even so perspicacious a zoologist as Lamarck placed them in his phylogenetic system between the segmented worms and the mollusks. It was not until it was discovered that the barnacles begin their existence as typical nauplius larvae that they were placed as an order, Cirripedia, among the crustaceans (Figure 10.6). Some other close relatives of the Cyclops and of the barnacles are in the adult condition unlike either. Thus the Sacculina is a parasite living on crabs. Its body is a shapeless sack containing chiefly the enormous reproductive organs; this sack is connected to a system of root-like processes, which penetrate inside the crab's body and envelop the digestive tube of the latter. Sacculina needs no digestive organs of its own because it absorbs the food digested by the gut of the crab! And yet the larval form of this parasite which has lost almost all semblance of animal form is still a free-swimming nauplius (Figure 10.6).

Taking the biogenetic law literally, we would have to conclude that the ancestor of Cyclops, of barnacles, and of Sacculina was a kind of nauplius which reached sexual maturity and reproduced in a state which in its descendants is a passing larval phase. But no such animal actually exists, and it is regarded unlikely that it ever existed. The nauplius phase is there not for the enlightenment of zoologists but because having it is useful to the creatures. Barnacles and Sacculina do not move freely when mature, the nauplius larva being the stage in which they become dispersed and find places to live. The developmental and embryonic stages, like the adult condition, are subject to evolutionary changes. Mutations occur which alter the embryo, and natural selection perpetuates the genotypes which yield developmental patterns most advantageous not only in the adult stage but also during the whole lifetime.

The common ancestor of the Cyclops and of the Cirripedia was not a nauplius, but it probably did pass a nauplius-like larval stage. Having this kind of larva proved selectively advantageous for many of its descendants, although the adult forms became adapted to quite dif

ferent ways of life and became very strikingly unlike. An embryo or
a larva is not simply an archive of the evolutionary records. It is a
living organism, a dynamic biological system, which is maintained or
modified by natural selection in accordance with the demands of the
environment in which the organism lives. It is only fair to add that
Haeckel realized all this, but he nevertheless created for his phylogenies a lot of theoretical intermediate links between the now-
existing organisms. These intermediates have lived only on the pages
of books in which they were described.

Vestigial Organs. Another line of evidence bearing on the evolutionary history is found in the presence in many organisms of vestigial

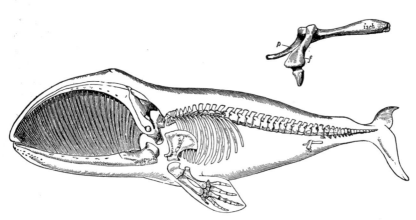

Figure 10.7. Skeleton of a whale, including a vestigial pelvis which seems to
perform no useful function in this animal. (After Romanes, from Newman.)

organs. Thus the spinal column in man ends in several small vertebrae
which form the bone called coccyx. The coccyx is buried among
muscles instead of projecting to the outside, but it is obvious that the
coccyx is the homologue of the tail vertebrae of other vertebrates.
Indeed, the human embryo develops a tail which to begin with is
about as prominent as the tails of embryonic mammals which have
tails when adults. However, in the human embryo the tail does not
grow as fast as the body does, and by the sixth week of pregnancy it
may already be classed as a vestige. To give another example, the
whale has under the skin in the belly region some relatively small
bones which are the remains of the pelvis and of the hind legs.

Why should man possess a token of a tail and a whale have a trace of the pelvis? Why should mammalian embryos develop pronephros kidneys which they never use? There was a time when the zoologist Severino (1586–1656) and the botanist de Candolle (1778–1841) regarded vestigial organs simply as souvenirs left by nature to indicate the type, or ground plan, which it followed in constructing a given creature. With Darwin and his followers the vestigial organs became the show pieces of evolutionism. Man's coccyx testifies that our ancestors possessed a waggable tail; whale's pelvis is there because whale's ancestors had four legs and made use of their pelves. Human embryos have a pronephros because our fish-like ancestors had one.

There is, indeed, no doubt that vestigial rudimentary organs silently proclaim the fact of evolution. But evolution does not explain their presence completely. After all, some organs may be lost in evolution without leaving a trace. The vermiform appendix of the caecum intestine is a vestigial organ in man, but the intestine of the cat has no vermiform appendix. If the human coccyx, the vermiform appendix, or the breasts in male mammals are really useless to their possessors, why did they not disappear entirely?

To understand this, we must remember that heredity, development, and evolution are essentially epigenetic and not preformistic. We do not inherit from our ancestors, close or remote, separate characters or organs, functional or vestigial. What we do inherit is, instead, genes which determine the pattern of developmental processes. The fertilized egg is a single cell which becomes many cells; these cells become compounded into various organs and acquire various physiological functions; the body grows, reaches a stage when it is capable of reproducing its like, and finally becomes old and dies. Embryonic recapitulations and vestigial organs are integral parts of the developmental patterns which the now living organisms have inherited from their evolutionary ancestry. The coccyx arises in the process of building the spinal column; the development of a whale embryo follows some of the paths which are common to all mammals and involve formation of a pelvis and of hind legs; the pronephros appears because the urogenital system arises by this method. When we talk or write about the anatomy of man or of some other organism, we are likely to represent the body as the sum of organs or tissues which develop independently in ontogeny and in phylogeny. But in reality it is the developmental system as a whole which is preserved or modified by natural selection in the process of evolution. Haeckel's biogenetic law, in the last analysis, is simply an expression of the unity and of a relative stability of the developmental system in evolution.

Biochemical Homology. Morphology, the study of the external and anatomical structure of the body, developed in the history of biological science before physiology, which investigates the processes which take place in the organisms. The theory of evolution was a great generalization derived chiefly from morphological evidence. We have, however, pointed out that a body structure is always an outcome of developmental processes which are basically physical and chemical. A "trait," such as color or shape of some body part, is an outward sign of physiological processes which have brought it about. The current century has seen rapid progress in physiology, and it is now becoming possible to trace physiological evolution just as classical evolutionists traced its morphological aspect. Some biologists even believe that "our final theory of evolution will see it largely as a biochemical process" (Haldane, 1937).

Almost two centuries ago Lavoisier, the father of chemistry, discovered that the process of respiration resembles in a general way that of combustion. A molecule of sugar combines with six molecules of oxygen to give carbon dioxide, water, and heat, thus.

$$C_6H_{12}O_6 + 6O_2 \rightarrow 6CO_2 + 6H_2O + Energy$$

But the work of the last quarter of a century has shown that the combustion in the living body is a vastly more intricate and interesting process, which occurs with the aid of many enzymes and involves many intermediate steps. A description of this process, which has been studied in most detail in the muscles of higher animals, can be found in any modern textbook of physiology or biochemistry. In a most general way, complex sugars (such as glycogens in animals or starches in plants) are first split to the simplest sugar, glucose. Glucose is combined with phosphoric acid ("phosphorylated") to a glucose phosphate, and, through some ten further reactions facilitated by a series of specific enzymes, turned into pyruvic acid ($C_3H_4O_3$). The phosphorylation occurs with the aid of a remarkable substance, adenosine triphosphate, abbreviated ATP. ATP has a high energy content, which it transfers to the phosphorylated glucose. The degradation of the glucose phosphate to pyruvic acid involves, however, liberation of much energy which is used up in the functioning of the living cell (such as contraction of the muscle). Pyruvic acid is then broken down to carbon dioxide and water by an even more complex system of enzymatic reactions, known as the "citric acid cycle." The important thing here is that the chemical reactions are reversible, so that the processes can go in either direction, depending on the presence in the cells of various substances involved and on the need for or the availability of excess energy. Such an arrangement, according to the principles of physical chemistry which we need not consider here, is most economical in that it does not waste energy on heat production, and in that the living cell can respond adaptively to changes in its environment.

It is most significant for our purposes that this elaborate chemical machinery is remarkably widespread in the living world. It is found not only in quite different kinds of cells in higher animals (muscles, liver, kidney, nerve cells), but also in quite different organisms, such as insects, mollusks, protozoans, plants, yeasts, and even bacteria. It is at present impossible to tell how great may be the differences between the processes of cellular respiration in different groups of organisms. But it is very clear that these processes have much more in common in most diverse organisms than any biologist would have ventured to speculate until these similarities were actually found. We are dealing here with most striking biochemical homologies which attest that the whole living world is really one large family adapted to subsist in different manners in different environments. An anti-evolutionist would have a hard time to account for the inexplicable caprice of a deity who chose to install exactly the same enzymatic mechanisms in a human body cell and in a yeast cell.

Biochemical Variations and Evolutionary Relationships. Here we may consider just one example of the kind of biochemical evidence which throws light on the evolutionary relationships of morphologically quite different organisms.

The evolutionary derivation of the phylum of vertebrates, to which belong the higher animals from fish to the gentle reader of this book, has been a happy hunting ground for speculation among zoologists. Every major animal phylum was at one time or another considered a possible ancestor or cousin of the vertebrates; there was even an attempt to derive the vertebrates from fossil relatives of modern spiders, the so-called water scorpions. The least strained of these speculations related the vertebrates to the echinoderm phylum (sea urchins, starfishes, brittle stars, sea cucumbers, etc.). The chief evidence in favor of this view is an obscure marine animal, the acorn worm (Balanoglossus, Figure 10.8). This animal has its nerve system located on the dorsal side from the gut, as in all vertebrates, and not on the belly (ventral) side, as in the invertebrates. It has gill slits like a fish (remember the presence of gill bars in mammalian embryos!), and a structure which some authorities considered to resemble the notochord of a vertebrate. None of the echinoderms has a trace of any of these features. But the larva of the acorn worm has a most un-vertebrate appearance, and an unmistakable resemblance to the larvae of the echinoderms. It may be, then, that the acorn worm is the last sur-

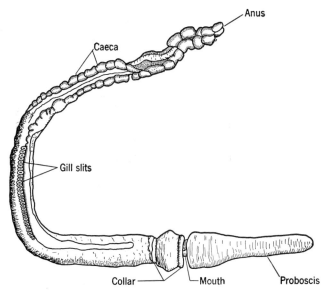

Figure 10.8. Balanoglossus, a representative of Hemichordata, a group which may contain greatly modified descendants of the common ancestors of vertebrates and echinoderms, as explained in the text. (After Derjugin.)

vivor of a kind of animals that were related to the ancestors of both vertebrates and echinoderms.

Recently a group of English biochemists (Needham, Baldwin, and Yudkin) produced strong supporting evidence in favor of the above hypothesis. Associated with the adenosine triphosphate (ATP, see above) in the muscle cells is another substance, phosphagen, which is involved in the resynthesis of the ATP after muscle contraction. But the phosphagens are not the same in the muscles of different animals. Muscles of vertebrates have a kind of phosphagen called creatine phosphate. The invertebrates use a related but different substance, arginine phosphate. But there are exceptions: the jaw muscles of some sea urchins contain both creatine phosphate and arginine phosphate, side by side; the brittle stars appear to have creatine phosphate, like the vertebrates. At least one species of star-fish has only arginine phosphate. The only other animal which is unorthodox in this respect is again the acorn worm. Some species of Balanoglossus have only creatine phosphate, but one species has been reported to have both creatine and arginine phosphates.

This does not mean, of course, that the vertebrate animals have descended from sea urchins or from acorn worms, any more than Darwin's theory meant that "man is descended from a monkey." The now living echinoderms are about as unlikely ancestors of the vertebrates as any animal can be. The biochemical machinery of the echinoderm muscles shows, however, a spectacular variability, such as could be expected in a group of animals the ancestors of which were also the ancestors of the acorn worms and of the vertebrates.

Serological Reactions. One of the most remarkable adaptive reactions in the higher animals is their ability to protect themselves against the invasions of pathogenic microorganisms by formation of antibodies (see page 13). When bacteria or viruses, alive or killed, are introduced into the blood stream, there appear in the blood serum (the liquid portion of the blood) chemical substances, antibodies, which can kill or neutralize the microorganisms of the same kind which induced the formation of the antibodies. This natural protective reaction, however, may be used experimentally to produce data bearing on the problems of biochemical similarities and dissimilarities between organisms.

Suppose that human blood, or minced tissue, is injected into a suitable animal, such as a rabbit. After a while the serum of the injected rabbit will contain antibodies to the human blood. This change can be detected by mixing in a test tube some serum of the immunized rabbit with human serum; the "immune reaction" will be manifested by the formation of a precipitate which will settle on the bottom of the test tube. Of course this immune reaction will develop with a serum of any human being, not only that of the individual who furnished the material injected into the rabbit. This fact means that all human beings are chemically similar enough so that a rabbit immunized against the serum of one is immunized to all human sera.

Next, the serum of a rabbit immunized against human serum may be mixed with the serum of a chimpanzee or other anthropoid apes. A precipitate is formed, showing that the chimpanzee blood proteins are much like the human ones. But the serum of a monkey, such as a baboon, gives a very much weaker immune reaction with less precipitate. Here the chemical similarities are evidently more limited but still perceptible. A dog serum gives little or no precipitate at all. Man and dog sera are chemically very different.

With proper technical refinements the serological tests are made to give quantitative data which may be used to evaluate the biochemical (or, more precisely, serological) resemblances and differences between organisms. Such serological comparisons have been made for a variety of animals and also for some plants. By and large, the serological differences go hand in hand with the differences in the body structure, and consequently with the position of the organisms involved in the modern natural classification system. This being so, some interesting attempts were made to use serological reactions as a criterion of relationship where the usual morphological data yield not wholly satisfactory results. Thus some zoologists consider rabbits and hares to be so different from mice, squirrels, guinea pigs, and beavers that they put the rabbits and hares in a separate order, Lagomorpha, and the latter group in the old order Rodentia (rodents). Other zoologists consider the lagomorphs and rodents to be members of a single order, Rodentia. Moody and his collaborators found that rabbits are serologically very unlike the rodents. In fact, their data show a closer similarity between a rabbit and cattle than between a rabbit and a guinea pig or a rat. This is, of course, evidence in favor of giving the lagomorphs the status of a separate order.

Gene Homology. The resemblance between the hearts of a whale and of other mammals is unquestionably due to homology, whereas the resemblance between the fins of a whale and of a fish is due to analogy. The whale is undoubtedly a mammal and not a fish, but the distinction between homology and analogy is not always so easy. The lagomorphs and the rodents have very similar gnawing incisor teeth. Should we give a greater weight to the morphological similarity of the teeth, or to the biochemical difference revealed by the serological tests? Have the lagomorphs and the rodents inherited their gnawing incisors from common ancestors or acquired them independently by convergent evolution? Because of the possibility of such doubts, it is interesting that the phenomenon of homology extends right down to the gene level of biological organization.

Suppose that half of the male progeny of a Drosophila female are red-eyed and the other half are white-eyed (cf. page 61). Ignoring the possibility of mutation, we can say that the red-eyed males carry the same gene for red eyes, or, more precisely, the division products of the red gene which their mother carried in its X-chromosome. Similarly, the white-eyed sons have white genes descended from the white gene in the other X-chromosome of their mother. We can take a long further step and say that the red and the white genes, which act as alleles, are both descendants of a gene which was present in a common ancestor of the flies crossed. Indeed, mutations which produce white alleles from red have been repeatedly observed. The white and the red alleles of the "white gene" in *Drosophila melanogaster* are certainly homologous.

Drosophila simulans, a species very similar to *Drosophila melanogaster*, also has red eyes, and also produces by mutation white-eyed strains. Does *Drosophila simulans* have a homologue of the "white gene" of *Drosophila melanogaster?* We can be sure that it does, because the two species can be crossed; and, although the offspring are sterile, they show that the eye color in the hybrids between the species is inherited exactly as it is within either parental species. Sturtevant has found by means of similar evidence that *Drosophila melanogaster* and *Drosophila simulans* carry a number of homologous genes. In fact, no gene has been found present in one species but lacking a homologue in the other. Gene homology was demonstrated by similar experiments also in some other pairs of species that can be crossed and produce hybrids. Harland, Stephens, and others have carried out particularly elegant investigations of this sort in several related species of cottons (concerning these species, see Chapter 9). The presence of homologous genes in different species is, of course, the strongest possible evidence of the descent of these species from a common ancestor, short of actual resynthesis of these species in experiments (cf. Chapter 9).

Many species cannot be crossed, or produce hybrids which fail to survive to the stage when certain body traits, such as coloration, develop. Such species may nevertheless produce strikingly similar mutants. For example, white-eyed mutants due to sex-linked recessive genes are known in about a dozen different species of Drosophila. Even more remarkable is that different species of rodents and lagomorphs (domestic mouse, rat, guinea pig, rabbit) and even representatives of other orders of mammals (cattle, sheep, horse, dog, cat, man) give rise to kindred mutants. Thus most of the species named have albino forms due to recessive gene alleles, genes which produce characteristic kinds of spotting, genes which give the "wild" (agouti) coloration of the pelage, etc. A not very rare dominant gene in man gives a light "forelock" of hair, as well as an albinotic condition of parts of the skin on the face, chest, and abdomen (the manifestation of this gene is particularly striking in normally dark-skinned races). It is tempting to compare this gene with genes which give a similar distribution of white parts in other animals, such as dogs and cats.

Different species, genera, and even different orders of mammals may still have some homologous genes, descended from the genes which were carried in their common ancestors. This is, indeed, most likely justified, at least for the parallel color mutants in the different rodents, but we must beware of placing too much reliance on inferences of this kind. When the gene homology in different species cannot be demonstrated by crossing these species and examining their hybrids, the phenotypically similar mutants may be analogous rather than homologous. That this danger is a very real one is shown by the existence within the same species of phenotypically similar mutants which are produced by non-homologous, and non-allelic, genes. For example, several eye-color mutants are known in *Drosophila melanogaster* which differ from the normal fly by having a bright red eye. It is hard to distinguish these mutants (called vermilion, cinnabar, scarlet, cardinal, etc.) by inspection, and yet the genes which produce them lie in different chromosomes, and the hybrid offspring of the different recessive mutants have a normal eye color. Human genetics has also several instances when similar traits are produced by different genes. For example, there are at least two different genes which give color blindness.

Are Genes Preformistic? The discovery that many fundamental biochemical processes are similar in most diverse organisms (see above) makes the problem of gene homology especially difficult. It is the more so since the important work of Beadle and his school has developed the idea that an intimate relationship exists between genes and enzymes. Working particularly with the fungus Neurospora, this school found, especially after 1940, that many mutations induced by ultraviolet treatments and other means have each just one step blocked in some metabolic reaction chain. It looks as though every gene is responsible for the production of just one enzyme which mediates some chemical reaction in the metabolic machinery of the cell, or at least that there is a "one gene–one function" relationship in the cell physiology.

Several enzymes performing apparently identical functions have been discovered in organisms as different as mammals and yeast or bacterial cells, and there is every likelihood that such discoveries will be multiplied in the years to come. Should we conclude on this basis that man and bacteria still possess some genes in common? Some biologists regard such a conclusion as likely and others as improbable.

The attitudes of different biologists towards this unsolved problem reflect in a most interesting manner the preformist and the epigenetic types of thinking which, as we have seen, are traceable in biological science almost from its inception.

As described in Chapter 4, the early ideas concerning the nature of heredity were clearly preformistic. Darwin's hypothesis of pangenesis assumed a two-way relationship between the organs of the body and the sex cells. The organs and tissues manufacture each their own vestiges called gemmules; the gemmules are transported to the reproductive glands through the blood stream or similar means; in the developing embryo each gemmule gives the organ of which it is the likeness. According to Weismann, whose views were influential around the turn of the century when genetics got its start, there existed a strictly one-way street between the sex cells and the body. The germ plasm in the sex cells consists of "determinants" which reproduce themselves by division. The development is essentially a sorting out the determinants present in the fertilized egg, until each organ and cell comes to contain only the determinant which makes that cell what it should be in the finished organism. Surely Weismann has not imagined a "homunculus" hidden in a sex cell or in a chromosome, but in effect his determinants amounted to a sort of a dismembered mosaic the stones of which could make a homunculus when put in the right order. And, incidentally, it was when Weismann attempted to figure out how this mosaic was put together in the embryonic development that his ingenious theory broke down.

The gene of the geneticists was, to begin with, uncommitted either to preformism or to epigenesis. Johannsen, who invented the word "gene" (1909), was especially anxious to keep it austerely pure of any such implications; to him the gene was just "something" in the sex cells which determines various "properties" of the organism. He wisely refrained from speculating about how the determination occurred. But the purity did not last long, partly because of the language which biologists were using. When one speaks of the gene for white eyes in Drosophila, a wrong impression is created that this gene is concerned with the development of the eye color and nothing else (see, however, the discussion of manifold effects of genes, page 35). The preformism put out by the front door returned by the back door. Every gene was named for something, an organ or a character, or a disease. A visible character, however, is a sign that some physiological reaction had taken place. When physiologists and biochemists began to decipher the chemical nature of these reactions, the gene became tied to an enzyme or to a "function." There the matter rests for the present. More knowledge about the nature of the gene action and of the embryonic development is needed to throw new light on the fundamental biological problems involved here. In conclusion, however, it should be stressed that similarity of the known end effects of genes does not prove that these genes are identical. Consider, for example, the fact that all classes of vertebrates have eyes of basically the same structure. Harland pointed out (1936) that it does not follow from this that the same genes make the eyes of a fish, of a bird, and of man. In fact, there may not be any particular genes which make the eye in any of these. The formation of the eye in the development is a part of the development of the embryo as a whole, which is governed not by any one gene but by the whole genotype. Of course changes (mutations) of some genes are known to strike at some parts of the developmental machinery (such as the development of the eye or of some of its parts) more than at other developmental processes. However, it is not only possible but, indeed, likely that different, non-homologous and non-allelic, genes may show such effects in different organisms. Muller (1939) has called this the change of the gene function: the role which a gene plays in the development of the organism does not remain constant in the evolutionary process, even though some organs (such as eyes) remain clearly homologous for long times during the evolutionary history. The presence of the same enzymes in human beings and in yeast cells means, then, that these enzymes play adaptively very important, and perhaps irreplaceable, functions in the cellular metabolism. But even if the specificity of each enzyme is impressed upon it by one and only one gene, it is probable that different genes do it in man and in the yeast.

Suggestions for Further Reading

Locy, W. A. 1925. *Growth of Biology.* Holt, New York.
Nordenskiold, E. 1928. *The History of Biology.* Knopf, New York.
Darlington, C. D. 1953. *The Facts of Life.* Allen & Unwin, London.

Darlington's book contains a very interestingly written, if partisan, account of the history of some basic ideas of genetics and evolution. The other two books furnish good factual descriptions, but their interpretations are not always in tune with modern biology.

Buchsbaum, R. 1948. *Animals without Backbones.* 2nd Edition. Chicago University Press, Chicago.

252 Evolution of the Organic Form and Function

De Beer, G. R. 1951. *Embryos and Ancestors.* 2nd Edition. Oxford University Press, New York.

Gregory, W. K. 1951. *Evolution Emerging.* Macmillan, New York.

Romer, A. S. 1949. *The Vertebrate Body.* Saunders, Philadelphia.

Simpson, G. G. 1944. *The principles of classification and a classification of mammals. Bulletin of the American Museum of Natural History,* Volume 85.

Young, J. Z. 1950. *The Life of Vertebrates.* Clarendon Press, Oxford.

These six books (Buchsbaum to Young) furnish excellent accounts of comparative anatomy and embryology viewed in evolutionary perspective.

Baldwin, E. 1948. *An Introduction to Comparative Biochemistry.* Cambridge University Press, New York.

Florkin, M., and Morgulis, S. 1949. *Biochemical Evolution.* Academic Press, New York.

Haldane, J. B. S. 1954. *The Biochemistry of Genetics.* Allen & Unwin, London.

Wald, G. 1946. *The chemical evolution of vision. The Harvey Lectures,* Series 41, pages 117–160.

Wald, G. 1952. *Biochemical evolution.* In *Modern Trends in Physiology and Biochemistry.* Academic Press, New York.

Physiology and biochemistry are the biological disciplines which have thus far been least influenced by evolutionary thought. The works cited above represent pioneering attempts in studies on the evolution of biochemical systems.

11 ————————

Evolution of Sex

According to Plato's romantic myth, the world was at some remote time populated by perfect beings who were female on one side of the body and male on the other. Then angry gods sundered the two sides, and made the detached halves, females and males, forever seek to restore the lost wholeness in love. Until the beginning of the current century, Plato's myth was about as good an elucidation of the origin and meaning of sex as could be had. Aristotle, Plato's more realistic-minded disciple and rival, declared that the female supplies the matter and the male the motion of the future life. He thought that the female was "cold" and the male "hot." Consequently, the conceptions which occur when warm winds are blowing give more males, and cold winds bring more females. The conjectures and speculations concerning sex which were being solemnly discussed in Darwin's day were not much above the level reached by Aristotle more than two thousand years earlier.

Two discoveries changed the situation at the turn of the twentieth century. First, the microscope revealed the existence of sex chromosomes (see Chapter 3). In organisms with separate sexes every cell of a female body differs in the chromosome complement from every male cell. The behavior of the sex chromosomes at meiosis explains very simply how the sex of an individual is decided at the moment when the egg is fertilized. Second, an insight into the biological meaning of sex was obtained by deduction from Mendel's discoveries. Mendel's work showed that gene recombination in sexually produced progenies creates an immense amount of genetic variability and of raw materials for evolution (Chapter 2). Sex arose in organic evolution as a master adaptation which makes all other evolutionary adaptations more readily accessible.

253

Since the importance of sex in evolution is so great, sex itself underwent a long and complex evolution. Perhaps no other biological
function appears in such a bewildering diversity of forms in different
organisms as does sexual reproduction. Yet, despite this diversity, sex
everywhere serves the same basic biological function—production of
genetic variability by gene segregation and recombination. The story

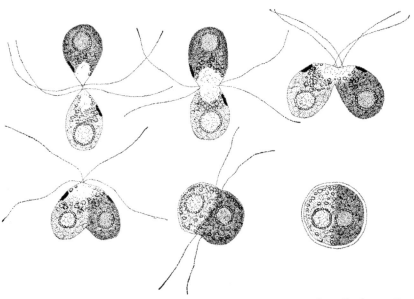

Figure 11.1. Sexual process in a primitive alga, Dunaliella. The cells that unite
are so similar that neither of them can be regarded as female or male. (After
Lerche.)

of the evolution of sex has an intrinsic interest, and moreover it reveals evolutionary principles of wide significance.

Sexuality in Unicellular Organisms. All the fundamental characteristics of sexual reproduction appear fully formed even in the simplest organisms. Figure 11.1 shows the sexual process in the one-
celled green alga, Dunaliella. The individual cells, propelled by their
flagella, lead independent lives in water, and propagate chiefly asexually, by simple fission. But under appropriate conditions of light and
nutrition they come together and unite in pairs; their bodies fuse completely, and their nuclei do likewise. The resulting cell (*zygote*) has,
of course, twice as many chromosomes in its nucleus as were present
in the cells which fused (*gametes*). The zygote may enter upon a

period of rest, or it may undergo at once two meiotic divisions. These divisions yield four cells, each with half as many chromosomes as were present in the zygote; the cells separate and start a new cycle of independent existence and asexual reproduction.

The critical events in any sexual process are two, fertilization and meiosis. Both are observed in the alga shown in Figure 11.1, but it may be noted that the cells which fuse are so much alike in appearance that neither of them can be regarded as female or as male. The two sexes in these primitive organisms are called simply plus and minus. That the plus sex is genetically different from the minus can be demonstrated by a simple experiment. Single cells are isolated, and their asexual progenies (clones) are kept in separate cultures. No sexual fusions take place within a clone, since all cells are of the same sex. But when cells from different clones are mixed, pairs may be formed. Clones which give rise to pairs are of different sex. The difference between the plus and minus sexes is inherited very simply; among the four cells which arise from a zygote as a result of meiosis, two cells give rise to plus and two to minus clones.

A situation, known as *relative sexuality,* which at first sight seems to be paradoxical, arises in some algae and some lower fungi which have not two but several "sexes." Figure 11.2 illustrates a case when eight "sexes" can be distinguished, beginning with "strong plus" ($+4$), "weak plus" ($+1$), "weak minus" (-1), and so on to "strong minus" (-4). Any plus strain gives sexual fusions with any minus strain; but a strong plus gives fusions also with a weak plus, and a strong minus with a weak minus. The extremes of each sexual group behave towards each other as representatives of different sexes. The inheritance of relative sexuality is rather complex and not completely worked out.

Female and Male Sex Cells. In unicellular organisms every cell may under proper environmental conditions act as a gamete, that is, participate in a sexual fusion. In multicellular creatures there is a division of labor between cells of different tissues; cells are specialized to perform different functions. An animal body consists of skin cells, muscle cells, bone cells, glandular cells, nerve cells, and finally sex cells which carry the function of reproduction. The sex cells which unite may be alike or they may be different. In some marine brown algae the sex cells are as much alike as the gametes shown in Figure 11.1. Here we cannot, therefore, speak of female and male sex cells. But in other brown algae one of the gametes that fuse is much larger than its partner. The larger gamete contains a supply of nutritive

Evolution of Sex

materials; it is the female cell. The smaller gamete contains little food supply but it is efficiently motile; it is the male gamete. The differences between female and male sex cells are the outcome

Sex	♀ 4	♀ 3	♀ 2	♀ 1	♂ 1	♂ 2	♂ 3	♂ 4
♀ 4	—	—	weak	medium	strong	strong	strong	strong
♀ 3	—	—	—	weak	strong	strong	strong	strong
♀ 2	weak	—	—	—	strong	strong	strong	strong
♀ 1	medium	weak	—	—	medium	strong	strong	strong
♂ 1	strong	strong	strong	medium	—	—	weak	medium
♂ 2	strong	strong	strong	strong	—	—	—	weak
♂ 3	strong	strong	strong	strong	—	—	—	—
♂ 4	strong	strong	strong	strong	medium	weak	—	—

Figure 11.2. Relative sexuality in the alga Chlamydomonas. Eight types of strains are distinguished which exhibit varying degrees of sexual affinity for each other. The dash — shows that no sexual unions occur in certain combinations. In other combinations a weak, medium, or strong sexual affinity is exhibited. (After Moewus.)

of division of labor. The female furnishes the nourishment for the future organism, whereas male cells are specialized for rapid mobility. In a way, Aristotle was right when he said that the female is the provider of matter and the male of motion. What Aristotle could not know was that the female and male sexual elements are alike in that both carry nuclei with similar chromosome complements, and consequently are equally potent and efficient in the transmission of heredity. In all higher organisms, animals as well as plants, female and male gametes are extremely different in size, appearance, and structure. An egg cell may have a mass millions of times greater than the spermatozoon, and yet the female and male cells are very much alike in their genetic contents.

Hermaphroditism. However striking are the differences between female and male gametes, eggs and spermatozoa, both kinds of sex cells may be produced in the body of the same individuals. An organism which gives rise to female as well as to male sex cells is called a *hermaphrodite*. Many invertebrate animals are hermaphrodites. A majority of flowering plants are also *monoecious* or hermaphroditic. A flower usually contains female parts which produce ovules, and male parts which give rise to pollen grains. Some plants, such as willows, however, are *dioecious* or bisexual. A willow tree produces either female or male flowers but not both.

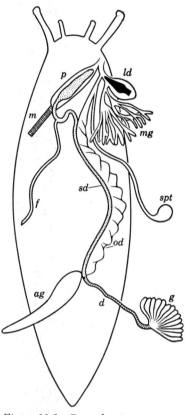

In snails and slugs (pulmonate mollusks), every individual has a single hermaphrodite gland which produces eggs and spermatozoa at the same time. The sexual ducts which carry these eggs and spermatozoa to the outside, however, are separate, and so are the female and male copulatory organs (Figure 11.3). Self-fertilization of the eggs by the spermatozoa of the same individual occurs only rarely. The usual situation is that two hermaphroditic snails mate, and the eggs of each are fertilized by the spermatozoa of the other. In earthworms the male and the female sex glands are separate, and so are the sexual ducts. The copulation leads usually to mutual insemination. Hermaphroditism is rare among insects and among vertebrate animals. Among the latter it occurs only in

Figure 11.3. Reproductive organs in a hermaphroditic snail. *g*, the *ovotestis* or hermaphrodite gland, in which both egg cells and spermatozoa are formed; *d*, hermaphrodite duct, through which both egg cells and spermatozoa pass; *ag*, accessory gland; *od*, oviduct, and *sd*, sperm duct, respectively; *spt*, spermatheca, in which the sperm of another individual is stored after copulation; *p*, penis, and *m*, the muscle retractor of penis; *f*, flagellum; *ld*, "love dart," used in the courtship process; *mg*, mucous glands.

some fishes, in which a young individual first develops and functions as one sex, for example, as a female, but then changes into a male. A vestigial hermaphroditism of a similar kind has been found by Witschi also in some species of frogs.

In hermaphrodites the female and male sex cells, as well as the reproductive organs in which they are produced, have the same chromosomes and genes. At first sight this may seem strange. Why do some genetically similar cells develop into eggs and others into spermatozoa? Why, in dioecious plants, has the same flower ovules and pollen grains? Actually this is no more remarkable than that some body cells become, for example, liver cells and others brain cells, although they have, at least initially, the same genotype. It should be remembered that in a cell, as in an entire organism, the genotype determines the reactions to the environment. The fate of a cell may depend upon its position in the developing body, and on association with other cells. The male and female parts of a hermaphrodite are simply different organs of the same body.

Self-fertility and Self-sterility. Since hermaphroditism occurs chiefly among lower and not at all among higher animals, it is probable that hermaphroditism is the primitive condition, and that bisexuality arose later in the process of the evolution of sex. Plato was wrong, after all: it is the separation of sexes into female and male individuals, not the hermaphroditism, that may be regarded as the more "perfect" condition (see above). But the situation is actually too complex for any such facile judgment. Separation of sexes has no unconditional advantages over hermaphroditism.

In many hermaphroditic plants, such as wheat, self-fertilization occurs when the pollen falls on the stigma of the same flower. In some of these self-pollinating plants the flowers are so constructed that the pollination takes place before the flowers open and before the pollen can be transferred to other flowers by wind, by insects, or by other means. Such an arrangement has advantages as well as disadvantages. An obvious advantage of self-pollination is that a regular seed set is assured regardless of the vagaries of weather or of insects which transport the pollen in most cross-fertilizing plants. To offset this advantage, continuous self-pollination, like a very close inbreeding (see Chapter 9), leads to formation of homozygous pure lines. In the long run, these pure lines deplete the store of hereditary variability, and rob the species of the chief advantage of sexual reproduction, which is production of new gene combinations. Species in which self-fertilization is the only method of reproduction probably lack evolutionary plasticity.

Many hermaphrodites, therefore, have contrived in the process of evolution various more or less ingenious adaptations to avoid self-fertilization. Perhaps the simplest of such adaptations, found in many plants, is that the male reproductive organs (anthers) mature either before or after the female organs do. The pollen of a given individual is thus available only for fertilization of ovules of other individuals. A more radical method which accomplishes the same function is self-sterility. Thus in rye, which belongs to a genus (Secale) closely related to wheat (Triticum), most of the pollen grains fail to germinate on the stigma of the same plant which produces the pollen. Rye is an obligatory cross-fertilizer. Self-sterility occurs also in some hermaphroditic animals. For example, the sea squirt (Ciona) produces sperm which is incapable of fertilizing the eggs of the same individual, although there is usually no difficulty in making it fertilize the eggs of any other individual. Sea squirts in adult condition live attached to underwater rocks; they discharge their eggs and sperm in the sea water, and fertilization occurs outside the bodies of the parents. The sex cells that unite are derived from different individuals.

Origin of Bisexuality. Separation of sexes, bisexuality, is a radical method to insure that all reproduction takes place by cross-fertilization. Some individuals become females and produce only eggs, and others become males and give only spermatozoa. Fertilization involves necessarily a union of gametes coming from different individuals. Bisexuality has also the advantage over hermaphroditism that it permits a division of labor between the sexes. Among animals, males are often more mobile and active than females; or males furnish protection to the females and cooperate in raising the offspring; or, simply, the two sexes carry different organs which it might be difficult to combine in the body of one individual.

In many animals, though not in all, males actively search for females, and may be highly polygamous; females tend to be more passive but more choosy. Beyond doubt, the necessity for the two sexes to find each other and to perform the actions needed to bring about fertilization has raised numerous biological problems that could be solved only with the aid of highly developed nervous systems. Thus the evolution of mental abilities, culminating in man, might have been initiated by the separation of sexes.

Organisms are known with various intermediate stages between hermaphroditism and bisexuality. They make it easy to visualize the

transitions which may have occurred in evolution. Some plants produce female flowers, and male flowers, as well as hermaphroditic
flowers on the same individual. In corn (maize) the flowers at the
top of the stalk (tassel) are male and produce exclusively pollen,
whereas the flowers lateral to the stalk (ear) are female and produce
only ovules. The plant as a whole is a hermaphrodite. However,

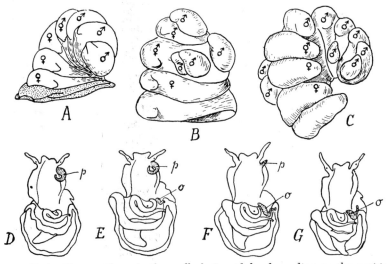

Figure 11.4. Change of sex in the mollusk Crepidula, depending on the position
of the individual in the colony. At the bottom are females (♀); in the middle,
hermaphrodites (♀̂); and at the top, males (♂). The lower part of the figure
shows the anatomy of the successive stages of the transformation of sex; *p*, penis;
o, oviduct. (After Orton and Coe, from Caullery.)

Jones and others found mutant genes which make corn bisexual. A
recessive mutant, called tassel-seed, causes development of female
flowers in the tassel, and makes the plant a female. Another recessive
mutant, silkless, suppresses the development of the silks in the female
flowers, making the plant function only as a pollen parent, that is, a
male. Some relatives of corn (Tripsacum, see Chapter 9) normally
have female as well as male flowers in the tassel.

A mollusk known as the boat shell or slipper limpet (Crepidula)
lives in small colonies consisting of several individuals firmly attached
to each other chain-fashion (Figure 11.4). The colony is started when
a larva of the boat shell settles and becomes attached to a stone or
some other support. A second larva settles and becomes attached to
the first, and then another, until a small pile is formed. The bottom

individual or individuals in the pile are females; the topmost individuals are males. The individuals in the middle are in the process of changing from the male to the female sex. According to Coe (1936, 1948), the maleness in the limpet is a juvenile characteristic, which an individual outgrows as it becomes older and as other individuals become attached to it. The transition from hermaphroditism to bisexuality occurs in the boat shell within the lifetime of an individual.

Chromosomal Sex Determination. In many groups of organisms, as among insects and vertebrates, hermaphroditism is rare, and the bisexual condition has become firmly established in the course of evolution. The reproductive organs and functions of females and males differ so greatly that any sexual intermediates (intersexes, see below) are sterile and useless to the species. It becomes, then, important to have the sex of every individual decided so firmly that it will develop either as a female or as a male. Any risk of the appearance of sexually abnormal individuals should be eliminated or minimized. The sex determination which satisfies the above requirement is by means of sex chromosomes. The populations consist of two kinds of individuals, females and males, which differ in their chromosomal complements and have different norms of reaction to the environment.

The pioneer microscopist Leeuwenhoek claimed in 1680 that he saw two kinds of spermatozoa in the seminal fluid of man, and also in that of the dog. He conjectured that one kind gave females and the other, males. The curious thing is that his conjecture was right even though his observation wrong. More than two centuries after Leeuwenhoek, it was discovered that in many animals half of the spermatozoa contain an X-chromosome and the other half a Y-chromosome, and that the former give rise to females and the latter to males (Chapter 3, pages 55–60). But even under modern microscopes the X-bearing and the Y-bearing spermatozoa cannot be distinguished by their appearance in the seminal fluids.

The chromosomal theory of sex-determination has elucidated the problem which excited man's curiosity for many centuries: what makes some individuals develop into females and others into males? The answer is that in most, though not in all, bisexual organisms, sex is decided at fertilization by the chromosomal constitution which the fertilized egg comes to possess. Just how the determination of the normal sexes takes place can be inferred best by studies of some instance of abnormal or experimentally modified sexuality.

Triploid Intersexes in Drosophila. The female flies of *Drosophila melanogaster* have two sets of four chromosomes, including a pair of

X-chromosomes (that is, a total of 8 chromosomes). The male flies have one of the X-chromosomes replaced by a Y-chromosome (Figure 11.5). Around 1920, Bridges discovered some females which were triploid, that is, had three sets of chromosomes, including three X's (a total of 12 chromosomes). Triploid females are normal in appearance and behavior, and they produce progeny when mated to normal diploid males. This progeny consists of ordinary diploid females,

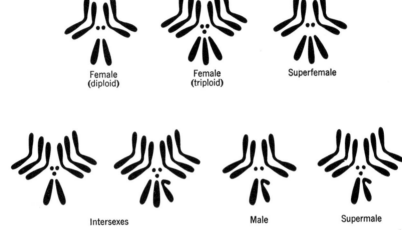

Female
(diploid)

Female
(triploid)

Superfemale

Intersexes

Male

Supermale

Figure 11.5. Chromosome complements of the different sexual types in *Drosophila melanogaster*. The X-chromosomes are rod-like, and the Y-chromosomes hook-shaped.

diploid males, triploid females, and three new sexual types known as intersexes, superfemales, and supermales.

The origin of these sexual types becomes clear if the meiosis in their triploid mother is considered. Let us distinguish between the X- and Y-chromosomes on one hand and the *autosomes* on the other—the latter being chromosomes which are alike in females and in males. A triploid female carries, then, three X-chromosomes and three sets of autosomes. It produces four kinds of eggs: (1) carrying one X-chromosome and one set of autosomes, (2) carrying one X and two sets of autosomes, (3) carrying two X-chromosomes and two sets of autosomes, and (4) carrying two X's and one set of autosomes (there are also some inviable eggs produced which need not be considered here). A normal male produces, of course, two kinds of spermatozoa, with an X- or a Y-chromosome, and with a single set of autosomes.

The fertilization yields, therefore, the eight kinds of offspring, which are shown in Table 11.1.

TABLE 11.1

SEXUAL TYPES IN THE PROGENY OF TRIPLOID DROSOPHILA

Sex	X-Chromosomes (X)	Sets of Autosomes (A)	Y-Chromosome (Y)	Ratio X : A
Superfemale	3	2	...	1.50
Triploid female	3	3	...	1.00
Diploid female	2	2	...	1.00
Diploid (XXY) female	2	2	1	1.00
Intersex	2	3	...	0.67
Intersex	2	3	1	0.67
Male	1	2	1	0.50
Supermale	1	3	1	0.33

Before the discovery of triploid females and their progeny, it was possible to entertain the hypothesis that the X-chromosome contains genes which impel the development towards femaleness, and that the Y-chromosome is the seat of genes which tend to maleness. Thus, XX = female, and XY = male. But this hypothesis is contradicted by the fact that individuals which have a Y-chromosome in addition to two X-chromosomes are normal females, provided that they have two sets of autosomes (Figure 3.14). Bridges concluded that, in Drosophila, the maleness is carried not in the Y-chromosome but in the autosomes, and the femaleness in the X-chromosomes. Sex is determined by a "balance" of the tendencies towards femaleness and maleness. This "balance" is decided by the ratio of the number of X-chromosomes and of sets of autosomes which an individual carries. This ratio for the various sexual types is shown in the rightmost column of Table 11.1.

The ratio is unity both in diploid and in triploid females, although the former have two and the latter three X-chromosomes. The ratio of 0.5 makes a male. An intermediate ratio of 0.67 gives an *intersex*, that is, an individual which is neither a male nor a female but intermediate between the two sexes (Figures 11.5 and 11.6). Intersexes are sterile (in contrast to hermaphrodites, which have both female and male organs, and are fertile). Finally the ratios of 1.5 and 0.33 give superfemales and supermales. These are weak and sterile individuals resembling females and males, respectively. The "super" parts of their names indicate that they have sex-determining ratios more

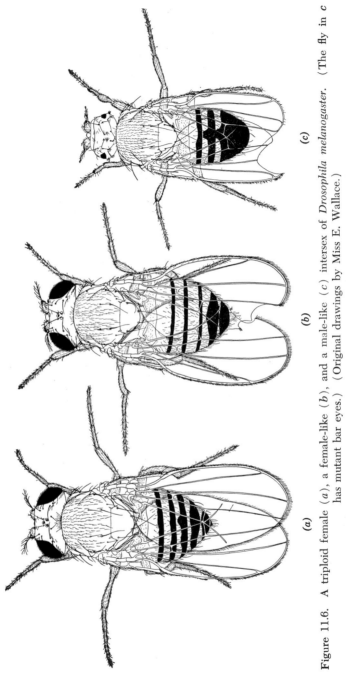

Figure 11.6. A triploid female (*a*), a female-like (*b*), and a male-like (*c*) intersex of *Drosophila melanogaster*. (The fly in *c* has mutant bar eyes.) (Original drawings by Miss E. Wallace.)

extreme than the normal sexes. The Y-chromosome carries, in Drosophila, no sex genes. Its presence or absence fails to modify the sexual characters as set by the other chromosomes.

Polyploids in Melandrium. The fact that in Drosophila the femaleness is carried in the X-chromosome and the maleness in the autosomes does not mean that this is so in all bisexual organisms. The same biological problem, sex determination, has been solved in different ways in different organisms. As an example of such diversity of ways we may consider the studies—carried out by Warmke and Blakeslee in the United States and by Westergaard in Denmark—of sex determination in the plant *Melandrium album.*

In this plant some individuals produce only female flowers and others only male flowers. Plants of both sexes have 22 autosomes (11 pairs), females have in addition a pair of X-chromosomes, and males one X- and one Y-chromosome. The investigators obtained also triploid (33 autosomes) and tetraploid (44 autosomes) plants, with one to four X-chromosomes and with none, one, or two Y-chromosomes. In contrast to Drosophila, Melandrium proved to be female regardless of the ratio between the numbers of X-chromosomes and sets of autosomes, provided only that the Y-chromosome is absent.

Individuals with two X-chromosomes and three sets of autosomes are pure females in Melandrium and intersexes in Drosophila. Again contrasting with Drosophila, plants which carry one or more Y-chromosomes are either males or hermaphrodites (which have flowers with both pollen and ovules). Diploid, triploid, and tetraploid plants are male when they carry one X and at least one Y. When two or three X-chromosomes are present, one Y-chromosome gives male plants with an occasional hermaphroditic flower, but two Y-chromosomes cause the plant to be a pure male. A tetraploid plant with four X's and one Y is a hermaphrodite.

It is clear from this evidence that in Melandrium the Y-chromosome carries a gene, or genes, for maleness. The X-chromosome is the carrier of femaleness; the autosomes seem to be sexually neutral. It should also be noted that in Drosophila sexual unbalance gives sterile intersexes. In Melandrium the sex intergrades are plants with more or less perfect hermaphroditic flowers, which are at least partially fertile.

Diploid Intersexes. The method of determination of sex which has proved most successful in evolution is by means of sex chromosomes. In Drosophila the sex of an individual is decided by the number of X-chromosomes in relation to the number of autosomes; in Melandrium it is the presence of a Y-chromosome and the number of X-chromosomes that make the plants females or males. But we know that chromosomes contain genes. If so, could a gene mutation alter sexual characteristics? It has, indeed, been observed. An individual which is chromosomally like a normal female or a male may nevertheless be intersexual.

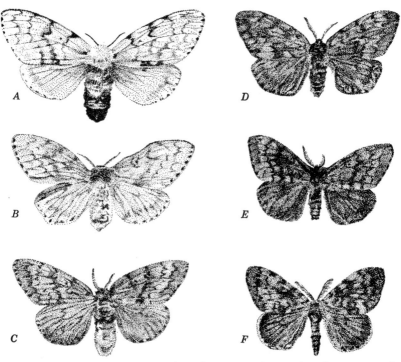

Figure 11.7. Female (*A*), male (*F*), and intersexes (*B* to *E*) in the gypsy moth, *Lymantria dispar*. (After Goldschmidt, redrawn.)

Spassky found a dominant mutant gene in *Drosophila pseudoobscura* which turns females into intersexes. The presence of the same gene in a chromosomal male (that is, in an individual which carries one X- and one Y-chromosome) has no effects on sex. The intersexes have their sexual organs reduplicated, one set being more or less female-like and the other male-like. These intersexes are evidently chromosomal females (that is, they have two X-chromosomes and two sets of autosomes).

The classical example of diploid intersexuality is the gypsy moth

(*Lymantria dispar*) described by Goldschmidt in numerous publications from 1911 to 1938. In this insect, the females and males differ strongly in coloration (Figure 11.7) and in behavior. The female is sluggish; the male is an agile flier. The species occurs in most of Europe and in northern Asia—from the Atlantic Ocean to Japan. It was also introduced, and became a pest, in the United States. Whenever female and male gypsy moths from the same locality in this enormous territory are crossed, the sex-determining mechanism functions perfectly—the offspring consists of normal females and males. But crosses between moths from Japan and those from Europe produce some normal females or males and also some intersexes.

The details of this case are complex, but the main features of the story are clear enough. All races of the gypsy moth are diploid, and in all of them the male has two X-chromosomes and the female one X- and one Y-chromosome. The X carries the gene (or genes) for maleness, whereas the femaleness is carried, according to Goldschmidt, not in the chromosomes at all but in the cytoplasm. The situation, then, is quite different from that observed in Drosophila or in Melandrium. Within the population of any one geographic region, the genetic determiners of femaleness and of maleness have become mutually adjusted by countless generations of natural selection. The result is that two doses of maleness brought in by two X-chromosomes overpower the femaleness of the cytoplasm, and produce a normal male. Yet one dose of maleness yields to the femaleness, and an XY individual is always a normal female.

The "strength" of the sex determiners in the race living in Japan is greater than that of the sex determiners in European races. An X-chromosome of the Japanese race meets, in the hybrids between the races, the cytoplasm and the Y-chromosome of European origin. The maleness of the zygote is, then, too strong to submit to the female tendency, and the result is an XY individual which is not a female but an intersex. On the other hand, a race hybrid may also have two X-chromosomes with "weak" European maleness, opposed by a "strong" Japanese femaleness in the cytoplasm. The result is an XX individual, which is not a male but an intersex.

Diploid intersexes teach us two important lessons. First, sex is not a rigidly fixed quality but a variable quantity. There may be more or less femaleness and maleness in an organism. Second, the strength of the sex determiners is a matter which is so adjusted by natural selection that in all environments to which a species is normally exposed the sex mechanism functions smoothly. Either females or males are produced, and sex intergrades which are useless to the species are avoided.

Sex and Environment. Many of the spurious solutions of the problem of sex determination which were in vogue before the discovery of sex chromosomes assumed that the sex of an individual is decided by the environment in which this individual develops. Such notions still crop up from time to time, especially in the popular press.

Can the environment influence sex? We know that most bisexual organisms produce either two kinds of spermatozoa (mammals, most insects), or two kinds of eggs (birds, butterflies, and moths), and that the chromosomal sex of an individual is decided at fertilization. It is, then, conceivable that methods will be found (though none have been found so far in higher animals) which will favor fertilization of eggs, for example, by male-determining spermatozoa and will discriminate against female-determining ones, or vice versa. On the other hand, what is fixed in the zygote at fertilization is its genotype. But the genotype sets only the norm of reaction of the organism to the environment, and does not necessarily decide any characters or structures. One may distinguish the sexual genotype from its actual manifestation, the sexual phenotype. Sexual traits of an individual may, then, depend on the environment as well as on the genotype. Modification of the sexual phenotype by the environment is, in principle, quite possible.

Triploid intersexes in Drosophila (see above) have two X-chromosomes and three sets of autosomes. Yet, despite their chromosomal uniformity, these intersexes are quite variable in sexual characters (Figure 11.6). Some of them resemble normal males in behavior and in the structure of reproductive organs; others are female-like. Still others have mixtures of malformed organs of both sexes. In short, all transitions between female and male states can be found among the intersexes.

What causes these great variations in the sexual phenotype? The environment has a great deal of influence in this matter. When triploid females are crossed to normal diploid males, the progeny consists of several sexual types, including intersexes (see Table 11.1). Cultures of triploid females were exposed to four different temperatures—15°, 20°, 24°, and 28°C. In cultures which developed at the lowest temperature most of the intersexes developed male-like characters. Conversely, at high temperatures the intersexes proved more female-like. Cold turns the development of Drosophila towards masculinity, and heat towards femininity. Changes in the sexual phenotype of the intersexes can also be produced by selection. If we select the triploid females which yield, in a given environment, most female-like, or most male-like, intersexes, strains are soon established which differ in their sexual tendencies.

Factor of Safety. The experiments concerning the influence of the environment on intersexes are made by exposing the progenies of triploid mothers to different temperatures or other influences. Now their progenies contain not only intersexes but also diploid females and males, triploid females, superfemales, and supermales. An astonishing fact, at first sight, is that the temperature variations which alter greatly the sexual phenotype of the intersexes have apparently no effects on the females and males. The sexual development of females and males is homeostatic (see page 13), that is, it is so buffered against environmental disturbances that a female chromosomal constitution always yields a normal female phenotype, and male chromosomes yield a normal male. The developmental pattern of the intersexes, on the contrary, is set so precariously that it is easily swayed towards either femaleness or maleness by both environmental and by genetic changes.

The reason for the more perfect homeostatic adjustments in females and males than in intersexes is not far to seek. The whole existence of the species depends upon the reproductive performance of the females and males of which it is composed. Natural selection, accordingly, has built in a "factor of safety" in the norms of reaction of females and males. This "factor of safety" operates in such a manner that in all environments to which the species is exposed the development always culminates in either femaleness or in maleness. The absence of the "factor of safety" in the intersexes is also understandable. Intersexes are rare or absent in nature, and their norm of reaction has not been perfected by natural selection. It is poised between femaleness and maleness, and can be turned towards or away from either.

Sex and Caste in Hymenopteran Insects. Once we understand that sex is a form of evolutionary adaptation, the many curious variations of the sex-determining mechanisms found in various creatures become intelligible. The same end may be attained by different means, and any method of sexual reproduction which safeguards the procreative capacities of the species may become perfected and established in evolution.

Bees, wasps, ants, saw flies, parasitic and gall wasps constitute the insect order Hymenoptera, which is generally regarded as the most progressive among insects. However, sex chromosomes of the usual kind are missing in this order. Instead, eggs which remain unfertilized develop parthenogenetically into males. Eggs of the same mother which are fertilized by spermatozoa develop into females. Thus females have twice as many chromosomes as males; the former are diploid and the latter haploid. Virgin females deposit eggs which yield only sons; females impregnated by males deposit some eggs which yield daughters and others which give sons. It appears that a female can control the access of spermatozoa to some of her eggs and can withhold them from others.

Where sex is determined by sex chromosomes (the XX-XY mechanism) the number of female and male zygotes that are formed is, with some rare and little understood exceptions, not far from equality. The diploid-haploid sex mechanism of the Hymenoptera permits the progeny to contain any proportions of sons and daughters. Females often greatly outnumber the males, especially among social insects, such as ants.

An ant colony contains several categories of individuals. An ant nest usually has numerous "workers," and in some species also "soldiers," which are diploid individuals, and hence genetically females. Their reproductive organs, however, remain underdeveloped. A relatively small number of sexually developed females and males suffice to take care of the perpetuation of the species. The males have haploid chromosome complements, whereas the sexually developed females ("queens") and the workers are chromosomally identical, having diploid chromosome complements. Whether a diploid zygote develops into a queen or into a worker depends, at least in the domestic honey bee and in some ant species, entirely upon the kind of food which the workers give to the growing larvae in the honeycomb or in the ant nest. The diploid chromosome complement thus sets a norm of reaction which permits the development of either a worker or a queen. What develops from a given egg is decided by the environment. However, the Brazilian geneticist Kerr has found that in stingless bees of the genus Melipona, the difference between queens and workers is brought about by their genotypes. Different reproductive mechanisms have arisen in evolution even in such closely related forms as different genera of bees.

Sex in Ophryotrocha and in Bonellia. We have seen above that in the boat shells the sex of an individual varies with its age and its position in the colony. Hartmann and his students (1936, 1938) found a somewhat similar situation in the marine worm *Ophryotrocha puerilis.* All young individuals of this worm are males, but as the worms grow they lose their male organs and acquire female ones. Older individuals are females. The females may be turned back into males by several means. One of these means is starvation; another is addition of potassium ions to the water in which the worms live; still another is amputation of the posterior part of the body. Ophryotrocha

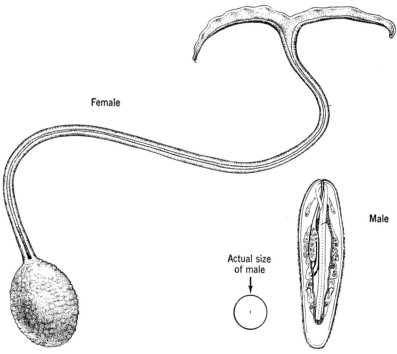

Figure 11.8. A female and a male *Bonellia viridis.* The female is shown slightly enlarged; the male is magnified since its real dimensions are so small that it can barely be seen with the naked eye. (After Baltzer, redrawn.)

thus seems to be a hermaphrodite which functions first as a male and later as a female. Bacci (1953) finds, however, that some individuals are genetically more predisposed towards maleness, and others towards femaleness. The genotype sets the response to the environment, some genotypes making the individual turn into a female or into a male more easily than others.

Perhaps the most spectacular example of a difference between females and males, and at the same time of sex determination by environmental influences, has been studied in the marine worm *Bonellia viridis* by Baltzer (from 1912 on). The female of this worm has a rounded body with a proboscis about an inch in length (Figure 11.8).

The male is barely visible to the naked eye; several such males live, parasite-like, in the genital ducts of each adult female. The male lacks digestive organs, and is accordingly quite incapable of independent

Figure 11.9. A gynandromorphic specimen of the butterfly, *Colias philodice*, the right side being female and the left male. (From Ch. L. Remington, courtesy of the Academic Press.)

existence. Females and males develop from eggs and larvae which look identical. The sex of the developing larva is determined by whether it lives free, swimming and feeding in sea water, or settles on the surface of the proboscis of a female specimen. The free-living larvae develop into females, those in contact with the female proboscis into males.

The proboscis must contain a chemical substance which exerts a masculinizing influence on the larvae. When larvae are placed in sea water containing an extract of the proboscis, they become inter-sexual or male-like. It may be that some larvae are more susceptible than others to the masculinizing action of the female proboscis. But even if this were proven, it would remain true that sex determination in Bonellia is effectively environmental.

Gynandromorphs. Where sex is determined by chromosomes, it is decided at the moment of fertilization. In Drosophila, as in man, a diploid zygote with two X-chromosomes is a female, and an XY zygote is a male. But early embryos look alike, and, in man, the females begin to be distinguishable from males only towards the third month of pregnancy. The female and male chromosomes determine developmental patterns, which in most environments result in "normal" girls or "normal" boys, and then in "normal" women or "normal" men. The ways in which the chromosomes determine these developmental patterns vary, however, in different organisms.

In man, in Drosophila, and in many other forms, every cell of a female body has a female chromosome complement, and every cell of a male has male chromosomes. However, in Drosophila as in most insects, the sexual characteristics of a body part depend entirely on the sex chromosomes in the cells which compose it, and are independent of the sex of other cells or parts of the same body. It is otherwise in man and in most other vertebrates. In these higher animals hormonal mechanisms have developed in the course of evolution; the sexual characters of a body part are influenced to a greater or lesser degree by the condition of other parts and of the body as a whole.

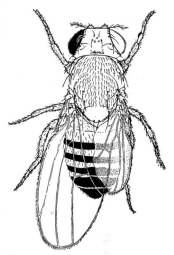

Figure 11.10. A gynandromorph *Drosophila melanogaster* obtained in a cross in which the sex-linked genes for eosin eye color and miniature wings were involved. The left side is female, and the right, showing the mutant genes, is male. (After Morgan and Bridges, redrawn.)

In many insects occasional individuals occur in nature as well as in laboratory cultures which have one side of the body of one sex, for example, female, and the other side of the opposite sex. Such sexual mosaics are called *gynandromorphs* (Figures 11.9 and 11.10). Gynandromorphs should not be confused with intersexes, which are sex intergrades, more or less intermediate between females and males (see above), or with hermaphrodites, which have more or less complete reproductive organs of both sexes. Sexual intermediates which occur in man are mostly intersexes (see below) and not hermaphrodites.

The origin of gynandromorphs in Drosophila has been clarified in the classical work of Bridges and Morgan (1919). Gynandromorphs begin their existence as female zygotes, having, of course, two X-chromosomes. Normally both X's are reduplicated at cell divisions, and are inherited by all cells of the developing embryo. But about once in some tens of thousands of eggs (and more often under the influence of X-ray treatments) one of the X-chromosomes may be accidentally lost, and a cell is formed which contains a single X-chromosome (and two normal sets of autosomes). A single X-chromosome results in a male chromosome complement. All the cells which arise by division from the cell that has a single X-chromosome are, then, male cells. A part of the body of a gynandromorph, therefore, is male, and the remainder is female. The relative sizes of the female and male parts depend, of course, on whether the X-chromosome is eliminated early or late during the development of the egg.

The important fact is that, in Drosophila, the dividing line between the female and male fractions of the body of the gynandromorph is usually sharp. Even when the male fraction is small and is completely surrounded by female tissues, or vice versa, the sexual characteristics are of one sex or the other. The sex of a tissue is independent of contacts with cells of the same or of the opposite sex.

Sex Hormones in Vertebrates. About a century ago the great physiologist Claude Bernard (1813–1878) pointed out that in some glands the secretions leave the gland by way of a duct, whereas other glands secrete their products in the blood stream. The latter are called glands of internal secretion or *endocrines*. Their secretions are *hormones*, chemical messengers which are carried to various parts of the body, where they influence the activities of cells and tissues.

Adrenalin, a hormone of the adrenal gland, was discovered by Abel in 1898, and secretin, prepared by certain intestinal glands, was found by Bayliss and Starling in 1902. Since then, numerous hormones have been discovered and studied in more or less detail; more than twenty compounds are produced by the cortex of the adrenal gland alone. Many hormones have been isolated, analyzed, and synthesized artificially. Thus adrenalin (or epinephrin) was isolated in 1901 and synthesized in 1904; thyroxin isolated in 1916 and synthesized in 1927; testosterone crystallized and synthesized in 1935, etc. Hormones may operate in incredibly low concentrations; epinephrin, for instance, is active in a dilution of 1 : 300,000,000.

Hormones exist not only in the higher but also in the lower animals and in plants. But it is in the vertebrates that they have become most important as coordinators of physiological functions, and particularly in the manifestations of sex. Furthermore, the effects of many endocrine glands in mammals and in man are so closely interlocked that the system of endocrines functions as an interdependent whole. Thus a deficiency or an excess of the hormones of the pituitary gland affects the functions of the thyroid gland, of the adrenal cortex, of production of insulin, of male and female reproductive glands, of parathyroids, of the rate of growth of the body, etc.

It has been known since antiquity that castration of boys results in lack of development of many secondary sexual characters, for example, of masculine voice, of facial hair, masculine body shape, and male sexual drive. Similar changes have long been known in castrated males of other animals, such as capons, geldings, and oxen (castrated roosters, stallions, and bulls respectively). These changes are caused primarily by the absence of testosterone, a hormone produced by the interstitial cells of the testicles (not by the cells which give rise to spermatozoa!). Testosterone belongs to the class of compounds known as sterols, and is related to cholesterol, which is present in many animal tissues.

In the adult human female an egg is shed, usually from either the right or the left ovary, once in about 4 weeks. During the reproductive age, from the first menstruation to menopause, a total of some 400 eggs is produced. Each egg cell grows in a so-called Graafian follicle, which is a liquid-filled vesicle under the surface of the ovary. The Graafian follicles are apparently the source also of the hormone estrogen. Estrogen stimulates the development of the lining and glands of the inner surface of the uterus. After the egg is shed, the Graafian follicle develops into a glandular structure of a different kind, the *corpus luteum*. This structure secretes a hormone progesterone, which causes further changes in the lining of the uterus, and assists in the implantation of the fertilized egg if pregnancy is achieved.

The estrogen hormone was isolated by Doisy in 1929 and synthesized by Butenandt in 1930. Progesterone was isolated and synthesized by Butenandt in 1934. The chemical structures of both hormones are related to cholesterol and to the masculine hormone, testosterone (Figure 11.11). However, their effects are, of course, quite different. The estrogens play an important role in the development of female secondary sexual characters, such as feminine body shape, voice, and feminine sexual drive.

Pezard (1918), Zavadovsky (1922), and many investigators since then have experimented with castration and with transplantation of gonads (testes or ovaries) in birds, particularly in poultry. Castrated roosters (capons) retain most of their "masculine" plumage, but the combs and wattles shrink and lose their turgidity, the animal ceases to crow, and loses its pugnacity and its sexual drive. Castrated hens acquire, after a molt, a capon-like plumage, and come to resemble in appearance the castrated males. The plumage of a capon and under-development of combs and wattles are thus sexually neutral characters; male plumage is suppressed by the hormones secreted by the ovaries, whereas testicular hormones stimulate the development of combs, wattles, and spurs. Implantation into castrated males and females

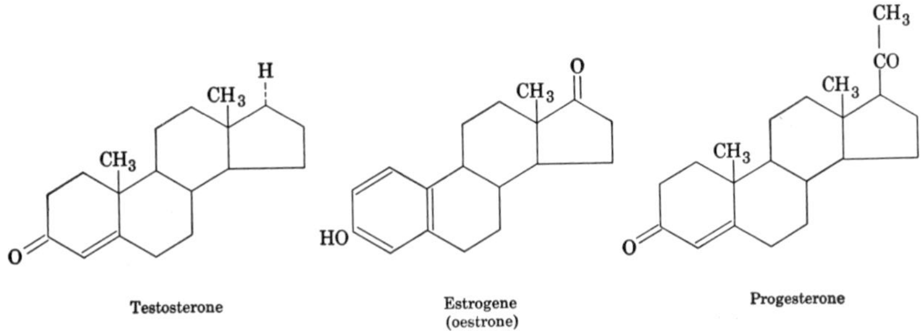

Testosterone

Estrogene (oestrone)

Progesterone

Figure 11.11. Chemical structure of three sex hormones.

of gonads from other individuals produces the characteristic feminizing or masculinizing effects, and these regardless of what the chromosomal sex of the individual may be. An implanted ovary causes the development of female plumage; implanted testes give cock's comb and wattles, together with behavior characteristic of the sex of the implanted gonad. However, the larger body size of roosters compared to the hens seems to be independent of the hormones.

Hormonal Intersexuality. Castration, transplantation of gonads, and injection of sex hormones obviously do not change the chromosomal sex of the individual. It is fallacious to speak of the effects on sex of genes and of hormones as though they were alternatives, which they are certainly not. The hormone system is a part of the developmental mechanism whereby the genotype becomes realized in a certain sexual phenotype. The functioning of the hormone-producing glands is itself determined by the genes; it is a part of the phenotype. Castration and hormone injections are environmental agencies.

Hormonal disturbances result, in man and in other animals, from many pathological conditions, caused in turn either by defective heredity or by environmental mishaps. Cases of sexual intermediacy were known even in antiquity, and some of them were immortalized in ancient art. Instances of individuals who "changed their sex" are reported from time to time in medical literature and in the daily press. More or less masculine women and woman-like men are not uncommon.

Some of the alleged "changes" of sex are simply cases where the sex was incorrectly determined at birth owing to malformation in the external sex organs. Others are instances of *hormonal intersexuality.* Hormonal intersexuality may be due either to developmental accidents or to genetic causes. At least one group of human pedigrees from Sweden, recently described by Pettersen and Bonnier, suggests a dominant mutant gene which has no effects in females (individuals with two X-chromosomes) but which transforms the males (XY individuals) into intersexes. The situation is comparable to diploid intersexuality in Drosophila (see page 266; in Drosophila it is, however, the genetic females which become intersexual).

Lillie, Tandler, and Keller (1916) have furnished a very clear analysis of one kind of developmental accident. It had been known for a long time that when a cow gave birth to a pair of twins of unlike sex, the female calf, called a freemartin, was often sexually abnormal and sterile. Freemartins have underdeveloped external genitals of female type, but the internal reproductive organs are intersexual, verging towards maleness. Lillie and his colleagues found that this condition occurs when the fetuses share a common placenta and common blood circulation which are often established between the twin embryos during pregnancy (Figure 11.12). Freemartin is the female member of a pair of fraternal twins (which arise from two separate eggs fertilized by different spermatozoa). The chromosomal constitution of the freemartin is certainly XX, but the sexual development is interfered with by the hormones received through blood from the male co-twin. A connection between the blood circulations of the two embryos may be established quite early during the pregnancy, and the male hormones may upset the development of the female twin in its most sensitive stages.

Sexual Selection. In 1871 Darwin published his theory of sexual selection, to account for the origin in evolution of conspicuous secondary sexual characters, such as the antlers of male deer, the bright plumages and elaborate displays and songs of many birds, the lion's mane, and facial hair growth in the human male. Since these characters, according to Darwin, are not sufficiently useful to the species to be formed by natural selection, he believed that their usefulness lay rather in the competition between males for the possession of females, or in making a male, or a female, particularly attractive to potential mates. The theory of sexual selection does not seem compelling to most biologists in its original form. In many animals the males do not engage in actual combat or rivalry for females, and, where they do, the victors do not father greater progenies as the theory demands. A. R.

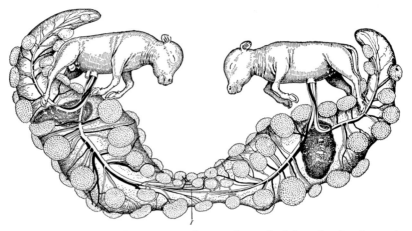

Figure 11.12. A pair of twins in cattle, a male on the left and a female on the right. Their blood circulations are united by the blood vessel marked *I*. The female twin becomes a hormonal intersex or *freemartin*. (From Newman, courtesy of the University of Chicago Press.)

Wallace, the co-author with Darwin of the theory of natural selection, rejected the theory of sexual selection. However, Wallace's counter proposal, that sexual characters arise because of a "superabundant vitality" of their possessors, is scarcely more satisfactory. The situation is really complex and should be considered from a different angle.

The very existence of a bisexual species depends upon the sexual drive which makes individuals of the opposite sexes come together and perform the acts needed to bring about fertilization and production of offspring. Elaborate physiological and psychological mechanisms which arose in the process of evolution by natural selection bolster the sexual drive and direct it into channels useful to the species. The fact that these mechanisms differ in different species, often in very closely related ones, is intelligible. As pointed out in Chapter 8, sexual isolation is one of the most important reproductive isolating mechanisms between animal species. Related species may look different, have different voices, and act differently in part because these differences are recognition marks that enable individuals to identify each other as members of the same species. These recognition marks may reach almost incredible degrees of complexity.

In many species of moths males locate females by scent. Experiments of Fabre (1823–1915), one of the keenest students of insect behavior, showed that males may be attracted from considerable distances, and may overcome various obstacles to reach a female confined in a cage. The scent, quite imperceptible to the human nose, is strictly specific, so that males of wrong species are seldom or never attracted. In other animals, including some insects, vision is more important than smell in finding a mate. This is probably true in many birds. In still others, sound stimuli are important. The "songs" of a bird, a cricket or a locust, the croaking of a toad, and the buzzing of at least some mosquitoes are among the methods whereby the sexes advertise their presence and find each other. How different may be the requirements of even very closely related species is shown by the flies *Drosophila pseudoobscura* and *Drosophila subobscura*. The latter species copulates only in the presence of light; the former copulates in the light or in the dark apparently indiscriminately.

Sexual Behavior. In many animals the behavior patterns connected with reproduction became complex "rituals" of courtship and mating. In a species of the fly family Empidae a courting male alights near a female and vibrates his wings. The vibration probably gives an auditory stimulus, and eventually the female responds by a similar vibration. The male now lifts up his front legs and waves them about, moving closer and closer to the female until they "caress" each other with their uplifted front legs; a tactile or a chemical stimulation seems to be involved in this "caressing." In a different species of the same family, the male catches another insect as a prey (these flies are predators); he then swaddles the prey in silk threads, seeks out a female, and presents the prey to her. She accepts the "gift," and mating takes place while she is busily unwrapping the food. The presentation of the "gift" is in some species, but not in others, accompanied by a special "dancing ceremony"; the dancing may be done by the male alone, or both sexes may take part.

Among birds, the greatest complexity of sexual behavior is reached probably in Australian bower birds. Here the male builds a kind of shelter consisting of boughs and twigs. Then he proceeds to "decorate" the shelter with colored materials, such as flower petals, feath-

ers, or fruits. Most remarkable of all, a race of bower birds displays
a definite color preference, selecting objects within a certain color
range for the decorations. If materials of a wrong color are placed in

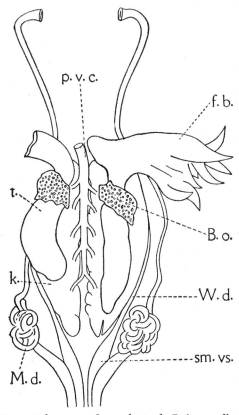

Figure 11.13.   Urogenital organs of a male toad, *Bufo woodhousei*, showing the
organ of Bidder (B.o.).   W.d., Wolffian duct; M.d., Müllerian duct, or vestigial
oviduct; sm.vs., seminal vesicles; t., testis; f.b., fat body; k., kidney; p.v.c., blood
vessel. (From Bhaduri.)

or near the bower by an experimenter, the bird removes them out of
sight. The male then locates a female, and entices her to the bower,
where the mating takes place.

The very elaborateness and complexity of sexual behavior patterns
make them vulnerable to environmental as well as to genetic breakdowns. One of such breakdowns is homosexuality, which occurs in a
minority of individuals in human as well as in animal populations. Its

precise causation is little known. Increasing complexities of human societies may at times lead to misdirection of the sexual urge. On the other hand, there is some evidence that certain forms of homosexuality may have a genetic basis. Kallmann and his collaborators (1953) found that, among 44 pairs of male identical twins one member of which had shown overt homosexual behavior as an adult, the co-twin in every case also evinced behavior of this kind. And yet, among 51 pairs of fraternal (two-egg) twins where one of the twins was known to be a homosexual, the co-twin showed evidence of similar condition in only 13 cases. It appears, then, that some human genotypes react by evolving homosexual behavior in at least some social and cultural environments.

Sex Reversal. A crucial proof that the genotype merely sets the stage for the development of a certain sex in a certain range of environments is afforded by sex reversals. Males of some species of toads have, next to the testis, a so-called organ of Bidder (Figure 11.13), which under the microscope reveals a structure resembling an ovary. The function of the organ of Bidder in normal males is unknown. But Harms, Ponse, Witschi, and others have shown that when a male toad is castrated (that is, when the testes are removed by a surgical operation), the organ of Bidder increases in size and becomes a diminutive ovary in which a certain number of fertilizable eggs are produced. The castrated male now functions as a female, and may produce progeny when mated to a normal male.

A castrated male must conserve, despite its sex reversal, its normal chromosomal composition. This can be proven by observing the sex distribution in the offspring of the cross, castrated male × normal male. Miss Ponse found this offspring to consist entirely of males, and interpreted the result to mean that in toads the male sex has two X-chromosomes (XX) and the female sex an X- and a Y-chromosome. All the sperms of a normal male, and all the eggs of a male transformed into a female will then carry an X-chromosome, and the experimental progeny will be purely masculine. The experiments of Harms, however, gave an entirely different result: about one-quarter of the eggs died, half of the eggs developed into males, and one-quarter into females. He interprets this to mean that a male toad had an X- and a Y-chromosome, and consequently that two kinds of eggs and two kinds of sperms were produced by his experimental animals. If so, half of the resulting zygotes will be XY (males), one-quarter XX (females), and one-quarter YY (these are inviable). The results of Ponse and Harms are not necessarily contradictory, since different

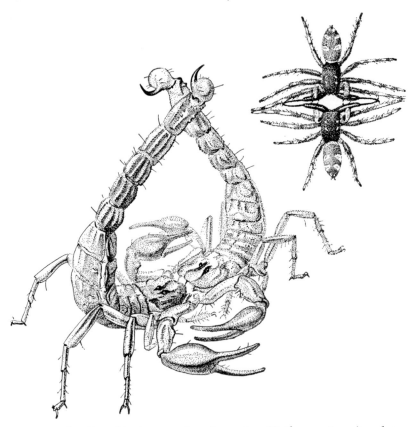

Figure 11.14. Courtship in a species of scorpion (*Buthus occitanus*) and two males sparring in a species of spider (*Salticus scenicus*). (After Vachon and Bristowe, redrawn.)

species and even races of toads may have different chromosomal mechanisms.

Suggestions for Further Reading

White, M. J. D. 1954. *Animal Cytology and Evolution.* 2nd Edition. Cambridge University Press, London.

Chapters XV to XVIII of this book contain an excellent account of the mechanisms of sex determination in different groups of animals. A briefer and more popular account may also be found in:

Crew, F. A. E. 1954. *Sex Determination.* 3rd Edition. John Wiley, New York.

Burrows, H. 1949. *Biological Action of Sex Hormones.* 2nd Edition. Cambridge University Press, London.

Koch, F. C., and Smith, P. E. (Editors). 1942. *Sex hormones. Biological Symposia,* Volume 9. Jaques Cattell Press, Lancaster.

Robson, J. M. 1947. *Recent Advances in Sex and Reproductive Physiology.* 3rd Edition. Blakiston, Philadelphia.

The literature on sex hormones is enormous, but it is reviewed very well in the three books just cited.

Burton, M. 1954. *Animal Courtship.* F. Praeger, New York.

A well-written review of courtship habits in various animals, but the interpretation given is out of tune with modern evolutionism.

Wenrich, D. H. (Editor). 1954. *Sex in Microorganisms.* American Association for the Advancement of Science, Washington.

This is a symposium on sexual processes in lower organisms.

Those familiar with the German and French languages will find also the following two books most useful:

Hartmann, M. 1947. *Allgemeine Biologie.* 3rd Edition. Gustav Fischer, Jena.

Caullery, M. 1951. *Organisme et sexualité.* 2nd Edition. G. Doin, Paris.

12

Historical Record of Organic Evolution

Almost one and one-half centuries ago (1809) Lamarck compared the process of evolution to the movement of the hour hand of a clock. A creature whose lifetime lasted one second would perceive no motion at all in the hour hand. Even thirty consecutive generations of such a creature might doubt whether the hand really moves. With respect to observing evolution in geological time, man is in the position of such a creature.

Since Lamarck, biologists did find ways to perceive some motion in the hour hand of the evolutionary clock. They used for this purpose the speeded-up processes of evolution by polyploidy, evolution under domestication (Chapter 9), and the experimental evolution, chiefly in microorganisms (Chapter 5). But with respect to the evolution which has actually taken place in the history of the earth, an observer of only the now-living animals and plants is still in a position of judging a long movie film by only the last picture frame. Let us, though, give the credit which is due to this observer: from the only picture at his disposal he has correctly inferred that there was a story back of this picture. Moreover, he has successfully used the experimental method to find out some of the mainsprings of action in the story. He can even make intelligent guesses as to what kinds of events could and could not have occurred. But to learn what events did actually occur and in what sequence, the last picture frame is not enough. Fortunately, some fossil remains of the living beings of the past epochs are preserved in the geological strata. They furnish us with some torn-up fragments of the preceding picture frames of the story. It is the business of paleontologists to restore these fragments as much as possible, and to arrange them in the proper sequence.

The Fossil Record Is Incomplete. Evolution is a continuous process, composed, though, of small discontinuous mutation steps. From the continuity of evolution it follows, of course, that forms intermediate between the now-living organisms must have existed in the past. Provided that man and the simplest virus are really descended from common ancestors, then, if all organisms which lived in the past were fossilized and recovered, we would see an unbroken chain of organisms intermediate between man and the virus. (This assumes, of course, that the entire living world is *monophyletic,* descended from a single common ancestor.)

In reality, only an infinitesimal fraction of individuals who lived in the past have become preserved as fossils. The fossil record is incomplete by the very nature of things. The remains of a creature are preserved in the sediments that form the stratified rocks of the earth's crust only as a result of rare accidents. Soft-bodied organisms are preserved only quite exceptionally, although some of them did leave their shadow pictures as prints in the rocks. For organisms which possess hard parts, such as solid calcareous shells or skeletons or teeth, the chances of preservation are relatively much greater, though still very small in the absolute sense. Moreover, fossilization of the remains of a creature is not enough. Many sedimentary rocks, which doubtless contained fossils, were eroded away at various stages of the earth's history, and the fossils were thus irretrievably lost. Very naturally, more ancient fossils were lost in this manner more often than relatively more recent ones. Other old rocks were buried under enormous weights of newer sediments, and consequently subjected to very high pressures and high heat. This heat has led to the rocks being metamorphosed and recrystallized, and again to the loss of the fossils which the rocks had contained. Ancient rocks are metamorphosed, of course, more frequently than recent ones. The paleontologists have thus far discovered and studied only an infinitesimal fraction of the fossils that are preserved.

In view of all this, it is not surprising that the known fossil record is nowhere near sufficient to reconstruct even approximately the phylogenetic relationships of all organisms. In fact, so obvious is the incompleteness of this record that Darwin expended rather more effort in his *Origin of Species* to show that paleontology does not contradict evolution than he did to show that it proves evolution. Since Darwin, the unrelenting efforts of paleontologists have filled many gaps in the fossil record, but many more remain to be filled. In some particularly favorable instances the fossils are so abundant that the changes from stratum to stratum appear very gradual, and the sequence of the changes is completely recorded. One of the famous examples of such gradual changes is in the shells of the snail shown in Figure 12.1. The snails are quite different in appearance in the youngest and the oldest strata in which they are found, but the intermediate strata contain an unbroken series of intermediates. The chief interest of paleontological data lies, however, not in their demonstration that evolution did occur but in their showing just how it occurred.

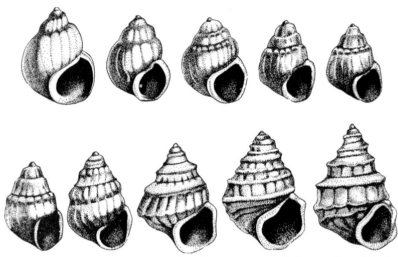

Figure 12.1. A remarkably gradual and continuous evolutionary change in the shape of the shell of the snail Paludina from successive geological strata of Pliocene age. (After Neumayr, modified.)

Geological Time. Earth's history did not always flow smoothly. There were times of more intense mountain building, and times of predominance of the mountain-leveling erosion; times of more uniform and humid climate, and times of more arid and diversified climate; times when many creatures died out and new ones appeared, and times of relative stability. Partly because of these variations and partly because strata of certain ages are poorly represented in geologically most widely studied countries, it is customary to divide the geological record in the eras, periods, and epochs shown in Table 12.1. (The epochs are given only for the Cenozoic era.)

The absolute chronology of these periods in terms of years is a more difficult matter, and until recently the estimates were quite unreliable. The discovery that the element uranium (of the now sinister reputa-

TABLE 12.1

THE GEOLOGICAL PERIODS AND THE GEOLOGICAL TIME SCALE

(After Colbert.)

Eras	Periods	Epochs	Duration in Millions of Years	Millions of Years Since Beginning
	Quaternary	{ Recent	0.025	0.025
		{ Pleistocene	1	1
Cenozoic		⌈ Pliocene	10	11
		│ Miocene	15	26
	Tertiary	⟨ Oligocene	10	36
		│ Eocene	19	55
		⌊ Paleocene	15	70
	Cretaceous		60	130
Mesozoic	Jurassic		35	165
	Triassic		35	200
	Permian		30	230
	Pennsylvanian		20	250
	Mississippian		30	280
Paleozoic	Devonian		50	330
	Silurian		30	360
	Ordovician		70	430
	Cambrian		90	520
Pre-Cambrian			1500(?)	2000(?)

tion because of the atomic bombs) inexorably and steadily decomposes into helium and an isotope of lead has furnished a more reliable method. The relative amounts of uranium and of that lead isotope in a given mineral are a function of the age of the mineral. For recent fossils the occurrence in them of certain carbon isotopes, as well as the contents of fluorine, give better estimates of age. Of course, the figures given in Table 12.1 may have to be revised in the future; they may conceivably be half as large or twice as large as the real ones, but they cannot be one-tenth as large or ten times as large. The best estimate for the duration of the time when the fossils are reasonably abundant, since the beginning of the Cambrian period, is, then, about half a billion years.

Most Ancient Life. Until the Devonian time, that is, from Cambrian through Silurian periods (Table 12.1), all the fossils known are remains of water-dwelling organisms, and chiefly of sea life. This is in agreement with the inference that life has originated in the sea, reached by evolutionists even before Darwin. The basis of this inference was that most of the now-living primitive organisms are water dwellers and particularly sea dwellers. Recent physiological studies have brought an unexpected corroboration of this view. The salt concentration in the blood and other body fluids of land animals is approximately like that in sea water and in marine animals. It is as though land animals still lived in the sea as far as their internal environment is concerned. It seems, then, quite natural that remains of land life appear in the fossil record some 150 to 200 million years later than do remains of marine life.

Another fact which seems appropriate from the evolutionary point of view is that the most highly organized phylum of animals, the vertebrates, are not represented at all in the Cambrian rocks. The vertebrates appear in the Ordovician period (see Table 12.1), and the first remains of the vertebrates are those of jawless fishes. This is the most primitive class of the vertebrates now living. (The best-known modern representative is the lamprey.)

But beyond the above two features, Cambrian remains do not strike us either as particularly primitive or lacking in diversity. These remains include representatives of most of the major groups of animals which live in modern seas. This means that at least some of the Cambrian creatures were quite elaborate and advanced in body structure. Such a situation may seem to be just about the reverse of what was expected at least by the nineteenth century phylogenetic school of evolutionists (see Chapter 10). They liked to picture the hypothetical common ancestors of the now-living organisms as lacking the special characteristics which these latter have, in other words as "types" or "ground plans" of the modern creatures. But evidently the seas and the continents of the past were not inhabited by mere schemes; these inhabitants were adapted to cope with their environments, just as modern life is adapted to modern environments.

Quite evidently, the Cambrian fossils represent organisms which were nowhere near the first to inhabit the earth. The origin of life from inanimate matter must have taken place very much earlier, and quite a lot of evolution must have intervened before the Cambrian sea dweller could have arisen. There is no doubt but that the earth was more than four billion, and possibly more than five billion, years old when Cambrian rocks were formed, but this enormous time span has left almost no fossil record (see Chapter 1, page 2). The pre-Cambrian rocks are mostly metamorphosed, and as such devoid of fossils. The exceptional non-metamorphosed rocks have yielded disappointingly little. It is possible that the remains of the most ancient life are lost forever; at any rate they have not been discovered.

Extinction and Replacement. Not even a brief group-by-group description of the fossil record of all forms of life can be given in this book. We must limit ourselves to consideration of only some examples which illustrate certain general principles.

One of the most striking facts of paleontology is that the inhabitants of a given period are descended not from all the inhabitants of prior periods, but from only a part of them. In other words, many creatures leave no descendants at all; their race becomes extinct. As a matter of fact, the most probable fate of any group of animals or plants in the course of time is extinction. If we examine the fossils of any remote geological age, say Mesozoic or Paleozoic, we find that most of them represent organisms which have no direct descendants living at present. They have succumbed at some point in time. On the other hand, some few of the denizens of the past have multiplied greatly, and their descendants, usually modified by evolutionary changes, fill the earth today. For one of the things which the fossil record shows beyond reasonable doubt is that the diversity of life has become greater and greater in the course of time. The dying-out groups of organisms are replaced not only by the surviving ones, but also by quite new organisms, which exploit the environment in novel ways, and are added from time to time. The known history of the land-dwelling vertebrate animals illustrates well the phenomena of extinction and replacement.

The Age of Amphibians and the Age of Reptiles. The most primitive backboned animals that live on land belong to the class Amphibia, of which frogs, toads, and salamanders are the best-known living representatives. The most ancient known amphibians have left some fossils in the late Devonian deposits of Greenland. The ancestors of these early amphibians apparently belonged to a group of fishes (crossopterygians), some of which inhabited fresh-water pools and streams of this remote age. It is a plausible guess that the development of the lungs for air breathing, and the development of walking legs in the place of the fins, occurred in response to a periodic drying-up of these pools and streams. Such periodic streams can still be observed in countries where rainy and dry seasons alternate. It is evidently a great advantage for the stream inhabitants in such climates to be able to respire both in water and in the air, and to be able to walk overland in search of bodies of water that have not dried up. Once provided with lungs and with walking legs, the ancient amphibians became able to exploit also a new source of food, which was not available to their water-dwelling ancestors, namely, the insects which were becoming numerous at about the same time. We see that the lungs and legs were "evolutionary inventions" which were made probably in response to peculiar aquatic environments—periodically drying-up pools and streams. But these same "inventions," so to speak, opened inadvertently much wider possibilities of adaptation to quite novel land environments hitherto unexploited by vertebrate animals.

However that may be, the amphibians have become very numerous and diversified in the Pennsylvanian period, some 30 to 40 million years after their first known appearance in the Devonian. Many strikingly large and powerful forms appeared, some of them resembling modern crocodiles in size and possibly in habits. Such rapid rises in abundance and diversity of novel groups of organisms adapted to novel ways of life are sometimes described as "evolutionary explosions"—a description more dramatic than accurate in view of the immense time spans actually involved.

The dominance of amphibians among the land life continued into the Permian period, but it was soon surrendered to another set of newcomers—the reptiles. Most of the ancient types of amphibians died out without issue. Some few of them, however, clung to life, and eventually produced new groups—frogs and toads, which are reasonably successful today but were rare or did not yet exist during the Age of Amphibians.

The reptiles may be described as the most successful descendants of a small group of ancient amphibians. It is reasonably clear which evolutionary invention caused their success. Amphibians are unable to live entirely on land, since they pass through larval stages (tadpoles, pollywogs) which live in water. It is interesting that a total emancipation from the necessity of beginning their lives in water has been attempted in some toads, in which the tadpoles develop in special skin pouches on the back of the parent. But, of course, it is the appearance of eggs provided with abundant food for the development of the embryo, and with a shell to prevent drying, that solved the problem of life on dry land. The reptiles, and among their descendants the birds and some few mammals, lay such eggs.

The first reptiles have been found in the Pennsylvanian deposits, and during the Permian period the reptiles became numerous. They increased in diversity and in importance during the Mesozoic Age of Reptiles, reaching a climax in the Cretaceous period. A great crisis came in late Cretaceous and early Tertiary times, when most groups of reptiles died out and were replaced by mammals and birds.

Adaptive Radiation. The skeletons of the earliest known reptiles (cotylosaurs) were so amphibian-like that, in the absence of information on what kind of eggs these animals laid, assigning them to either class is rather arbitrary. Such clear transitions between different classes and other large groups of animals and plants are so rare in the fossil record that their existence should be noted (some paleontologists even doubted that such transitional forms ever lived, see Chapter 14).

From the humble beginning in the cotylosaurs, the reptiles blossomed out during the subsequent geological periods in a variety of creatures ranging in size from a mouse to giants with bodies up to 87 feet long, some living on land and others in water or in the air. When a group of organisms becomes diversified in time into subgroups with different body structures and ways of life, it is said to undergo *adaptive radiation*. The following very brief account shows how great was the adaptive radiation of the reptilian stock.

By far the most famous of the fossil reptiles were the dinosaurs, some of which (though by no means all) reached enormous sizes. They belonged to two distinct orders, one of which developed a structure of the pelvis bones resembling that found in birds, although these dinosaurs were not the ancestors of birds. The similarity of the pelvis structure is, then, an instance of convergent evolution. Some of the dinosaurs were flesh eaters, preying probably on other reptiles. Tyranosaurus stood some 19 feet tall, which makes this Cretaceous dinosaur the largest known carnivore. The largest dinosaurs (Diplodocus and Brachiosaurus, the latter estimated to have weighed some 50 tons) were, however, vegetarians. It is hard to see how animals of such bulk could have moved on land, and some paleontologists conjecture that they waded partly submerged in shallow swamps or lakes. Stegosaurus and Ankylosaurus had bodies armored with bony plates, and were slow-moving herbivores, perhaps not unlike the living hippopotami. Triceratops had two horns above the eyes, and one on the nose, like a rhinoceros.

Other reptiles invaded the air, and produced the order of pterosaurs. These are again not the ancestors of the birds. Their flying apparatus consisted of wings formed apparently by a skin fold like the wings of modern bats, but supported only by a greatly enlarged fourth finger. The pterosaur wing is, then, completely homologous neither to a bird wing nor to a bat wing, although it performed the same function, that is, flying. At least two reptilian orders, ichthyosaurs and plesiosaurs, reverted to life in water, and transformed their walking legs into paddles or fin-like structures, although they, of course, continued to respire by lungs. Some ichthyosaurs probably looked superficially like the modern dolphins and porpoises, and led similar lives.

Just what caused the dying out of these varied and apparently well-adapted animals at the end of the Cretaceous period is obscure. The mammals at that time were undergoing an adaptive radiation of their own, and soon, together with the birds, replaced the reptiles. However, it is doubtful that the previously dominant reptiles could have been destroyed by the mammals. More probably the reverse was true: the removal of the reptiles opened the evolutionary opportunities to the mammals and birds, and they responded by adaptive radiations, which filled the "vacancies" in the economy of nature heretofore preempted by the reptiles.

It is also instructive to note that the ancestors of the now-living reptiles played rather inconspicuous roles during the Age of Reptiles. Lizards and snakes are the most successful of the modern reptiles, yet lizards have been known only since the Jurassic period, and snakes since the Cretaceous; and these orders can in no sense be regarded as replacing the extinct "ruling" reptiles—in the biological domains of the latter. Two other orders of reptiles, the crocodiles and the turtles, exemplify a different situation. Crocodiles have been known since the Triassic, and the turtles perhaps even since the Permian periods. Both orders were more abundant and diversified in the past than they are now, but by and large they underwent no major evolutionary changes. Although the dinosaurs and other orders had their time of rapid evolution, triumphant success, and then downfall and complete extinction, the turtles and crocodiles kept on placidly exploiting their peculiar ways of life without striking success but also without irrevocable disaster. They show an evolutionary conservatism, often met with in organisms specialized for some peculiar ways of life in which they have no serious competitors.

On an island off New Zealand, now carefully protected by the New Zealand government, there lives a superficially lizard-like reptile Sphenodon (or tuatara), which is a representative of a primitive reptilian order. This order may be a slightly modified descendant of the reptiles which gave rise to dinosaurs, true lizards, and perhaps other orders. Anyway, the living Sphenodon is not easily distinguishable from a fossil discovered in Jurassic rocks of an estimated age of more than 135 million years. This is a case of evolutionary conservatism, amounting to a complete stagnation, and bringing the animal to the very brink of extinction. The fact that Sphenodon has been preserved only in New Zealand will be commented upon below (page 296).

The Age of Mammals. This name is applied to the time span from the early Tertiary to the present, some 70 million years. During this time the earth came to be dominated by the two highest classes of backboned animals, mammals and birds, and also by the flowering plants and by insects (some people prefer to call it the Age of Insects).

Mammals and birds have reached a level of organization greatly superior to that of the reptiles and other animals (Figure 12.2). The most important advance, especially in the mammals, has to do with improved care of the young. Lower animals produce generally numerous offspring, most of which fall prey to environmental accidents and to predators. An individual matters little; the gamble is that a small part of the offspring will escape destruction. One of the trends observed in the progressive evolution of the living world has been to make the individual's survival not a matter of lucky chance but of his constitutional and genotypic fitness to survive (see Chapter 14). The progeny becomes, therefore, less numerous, but every infant is provided with maximum protection against the hostile world. Mammals are viviparous, the embryo developing inside the mother's body (except the Australian duckbill and spiny anteater, which lay reptile-like eggs). The great mammalian invention is the placenta, a nexus of blood vessels of the embryo and of the wall of the mother's uterus, through which the embryo is supplied with food and with oxygen (the marsupials, of which the opossums and kangaroos are representatives, have, however, no placenta or an imperfect one). Furthermore, all mammals, including the duckbill and the spiny anteater, nurse their young on milk secreted by mammary glands, which may be modified sweat glands.

Another evolutionary invention, made by birds as well as by mammals, is the warm-bloodedness, or, more precisely, a physiological homeostatic (see page 13) mechanism which maintains the body temperature constant. This mechanism permits the mammals and

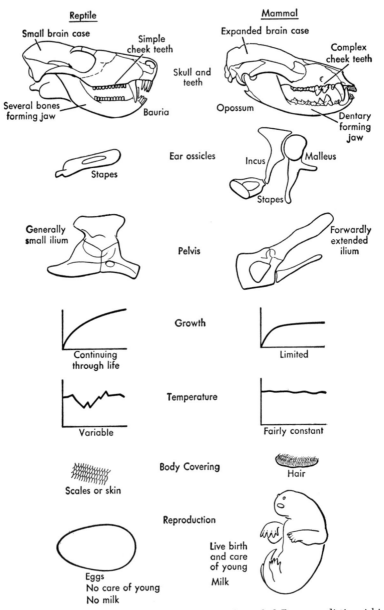

Figure 12.2.   Some of the structural and physiological differences distinguishing reptiles (left) and mammals (right).   (From Colbert.)

birds to remain active regardless of the temperature fluctuations in the environment. It is easy to see how great an advantage in the struggle for existence is such an independence of the organisms from the vagaries of weather. The development of hair (in mammals) and of feathers (in birds) in place of the reptilian scales was probably a concomitant of the regulation of the body temperature.

Mammals have developed also a leg posture superior to that of the reptiles. The legs of amphibians and reptiles, having evolved from the fins of their aquatic ancestors, are usually widely sprawled out sidewise from the body, so that at rest the belly lies on the ground. In mammals the legs have been placed under the body, which now rests on the legs. This change, minor though it may seem, has necessitated widespread alterations of the skeleton and the musculature. Finally, mammals have greatly elaborated their teeth. Instead of the simple peg-like teeth of the reptile, there is a great variety of mammalian teeth adapted for nipping, grasping, piercing, cutting, pounding, or grinding food, the same jaw having different teeth in front and on the sides. To be sure, mammals have sacrificed the indefinite amount of tooth replacement; barring artificial ones, mammals have just two sets of teeth, the "milk" and the "permanent" dentition (Figure 12.2).

A remarkable thing about the evolutionary history of mammals is that they appeared long before they became dominant and the Age of Mammals began. In fact mammal-like reptiles, the so-called therapsids, had appeared already at the beginning of the Age of Reptiles, in the Triassic and even in the late Permian periods. The mammalian-like characters of the therapsids are found in the structure of their skeletons, since, obviously, there is no way of telling whether they had already embarked on the development of the temperature regulation and the improved care of the young. In the Jurassic period four different orders of mammals already existed, none of which survives today. They were small, rare, and inconspicuous animals. Unfortunately, very few of them were preserved as fossils, and those that were are represented not by complete skeletons but by fragments, mostly by teeth. There is, again, no way of telling how rapid was the progress in the evolution of mammalian physiological adaptations, since only bone fragments are found. But by the late Cretaceous, as the Age of Reptiles was drawing to its close, some mammals appeared whose bones are indistinguishable from those living now, particularly opossums and small insectivores not very different from modern shrews. And only in the early Tertiary, during Paleocene and Eocene, did the adaptive radiation of mammals burst forth, and every mammalian order now living, and some that are extinct, became represented by more or less numerous forms. (This radiation appears, however, less sudden if we recall that the Paleocene and Eocene together lasted for some 35 million years!) As indicated above, the coincidence of the adaptive radiation in mammals with the disappearance of the previously dominant reptiles can hardly be due to chance, but the causal relations between the two events are far from clear.

Evolutionary Rates. It should already be clear from the foregoing d.scussion that the evolutionary changes do not proceed at anything like uniform rates in all organisms. Organic evolution is in this respect radically different from such inexorably even-paced processes as the decomposition of radioactive elements. The evolution of some groups appears to have come to a halt (Figure 12.3). The opossum, which in late Cretaceous was one of the evolutionally most progressive forms, has changed little during the 75 or more million years since. The Sphenodon (see page 292) has not changed appreciably for some 135 million years, since the Jurassic. A "living fossil" which became famous in 1939 is a coelacanth fish (Latimeria) which belongs to a group believed to have been extinct since the Cretaceous period until a fisherman caught it alive in the Indian Ocean, off South Africa. Incidentally, the coelacanths are regarded as the descendants of the order of fishes which probably gave rise (during the Paleozoic time) to the land vertebrates, and consequently to ourselves. The horseshoe "crab" (Limulus), which is a familiar sight on the Atlantic Coast beaches in late spring and early summer, is not very different from some fossils which were alive some 200 million years ago. But the animal that can be used as a symbol of a really staunch conservatism is the little marine brachiopod Lingula, which has not changed, at least on the outside, for about 400 million years, since the Ordovician times (Figure 12.3).

At the opposite extreme are the dangerous radicals, which change so rapidly that the fossil record becomes quite inadequate to register the changes. The class of mammals as a whole belongs here, since, with few exceptions indicated above, none of the modern forms existed in the late Cretaceous. Few of the modern species of mammals existed even in the late Tertiary (although all the modern orders and many families and genera did). The human species is one of the worst radicals, since it evolved so rapidly that our ancestors only one million years ago were quite appreciably different from ourselves.

Evolutionary progressiveness or conservatism are not permanent

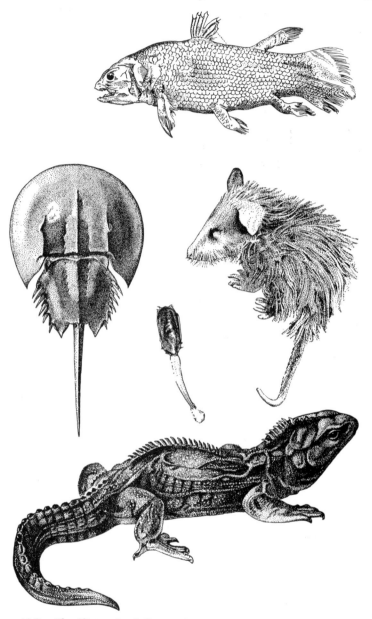

Figure 12.3. The "living fossils," animals which underwent little change during long geological periods. From top downward: A coelacanth fish (Latimeria); horseshoe crab (Limulus); a young opossum (Didelphis); a brachiopod (Lingula); and the tuatara (Sphenodon). The figures are not drawn to the same scale.

properties of a group of organisms. Even Lingula must have at some time evolved from more primitive ancestors. A rapidly evolving group may enter upon a period of evolutionary stagnation, and the opposite change may also occur. Some biologists supposed that every group of organisms has its "evolutionary youth" when it evolves rapidly, its maturity when it is common and produces many species and varieties in different parts of the world and in different habitats, and its "evolutionary old age," when it stops evolving or evolves in wrong directions, leading to extinction. This matter will be discussed in the concluding chapter of this book. For the time being it is sufficient to say that evolutionary "youth" and "senility" are words which are misleading, since they suggest a wrong analogy between the development of an individual and the evolution of a species, a genus, or a class. The evolutionary fate is to a great extent determined by the relationships between the organism and its environment, and has no inexorable course, as the life of an individual does. This fact can be seen best by considering a concrete evolutionary history, and we choose for this purpose the example of the evolution of the horse family (Equidae), which has been studied in detail by some of the most eminent paleontologists.

Evolution of Horses. According to Simpson, the foremost authority on mammalian origins: "It may be, indeed, that the lion and the lamb are cousins." He has said this because the ungulate mammals, to which horses and lambs belong, and the carnivores, to which lions belong, are greatly modified descendants of the closely related condylarths and creodonts. Condylarths and creodonts were rather common animals during the earliest Tertiary epoch, Paleocene. They became extinct as such during the next epoch, Eocene, presumably being replaced by their own modified or better fit to survive descendants. The best-known condylarth, called Phenacodus, resembled a horse about as little as it did a lion or a lamb. It was an animal rather smaller than the smallest pony, with feet having five toes, each toe provided with a small hoof (Figure 12.4). Its teeth were small and pointed, the canines being somewhat larger and remotely dog-like. Such teeth suggest that Phenacodus was probably omnivorous, eating the various foods, both vegetable and animal, that it could get.

During the Eocene, Hyracotherium lived. It is more widely known under the name of Eohippus, the "dawn horse." There is a break in the fossil record between the condylarths and Eohippus, that is, no intermediates between them have yet been found. It is chiefly for this reason that Eohippus is placed in the order of ungulates and in the family of horses (Equidae), whereas Phenacodus is placed in the extinct order Condylarthra. Otherwise, Eohippus resembles Phenacodus more than it does a modern horse. Eohippus was, in fact, even

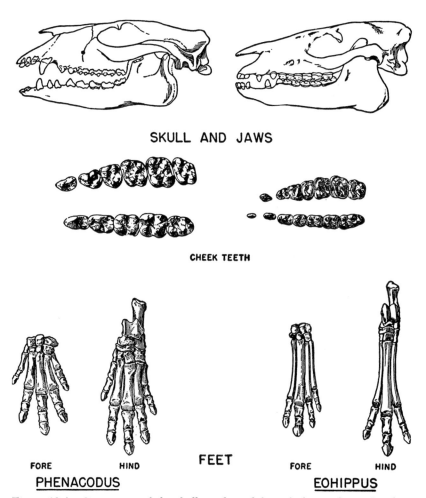

SKULL AND JAWS

CHEEK TEETH

FORE HIND **FEET** FORE HIND

PHENACODUS   EOHIPPUS

Figure 12.4. Comparison of the skull, teeth, and feet of Phenacodus and Eohippus. (From G. G. Simpson, by permission of the Oxford University Press.)

smaller than Phenacodus, various species of the former ranging from 10 to perhaps 20 inches tall at the shoulders—the height of a medium-sized dog. But its front feet had only four toes, and the hind feet only three toes, each toe ending in a separate hoof (Figures 12.5 and

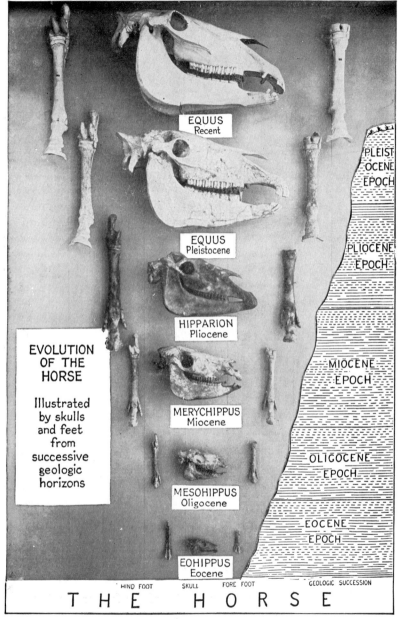

EVOLUTION
OF THE
HORSE

Illustrated
by skulls
and feet
from
successive
geologic
horizons

EQUUS
Recent

PLEIST
OCENE
EPOCH

EQUUS
Pleistocene

PLIOCENE
EPOCH

HIPPARION
Pliocene

MIOCENE
EPOCH

MERYCHIPPUS
Miocene

OLIGOCENE
EPOCH

MESOHIPPUS
Oligocene

EOCENE
EPOCH

EOHIPPUS
Eocene

HIND FOOT   SKULL   FORE FOOT   GEOLOGIC SUCCESSION

T H E   H O R S E

Figure 12.5.　Evolution of the horse, as illustrated by an exhibit at the American
Museum of Natural History, New York.　(From Weimer.)

Figure 12.6. Restorations of the fossil horses Neohipparion (*A*), Mesohippus (*B*), and Eohippus (*C*). (From Weimer, courtesy of the American Museum of Natural History, New York City. Painted by Charles R. Knight.)

12.6). The head of Eohippus was, again, not very different from the head of Phenacodus, but the molar teeth had already begun to develop the crests which serve to grind the food, whereas the front teeth (incisors) became modified for nipping and picking up leaves, and a gap (diastema) appeared between the incisors and the canines. This gap is present in the later and in the modern horses. Eohippus did not graze on grass, but probably browsed on leaves, buds, and perhaps on fruits and seeds. Having the benefit of hindsight, we recognize that Eohippus was evolving not in the direction of lions, but in the direction of lambs, or rather of horses.

Many textbooks and popular accounts of biology represent the evolution of the horse family as starting with Eohippus, and progressing in a direct line towards the modern horse, Equus. This evolutionary progress involved, allegedly, the animals getting steadily larger and larger, while their feet were losing toe after toe, until just a single hoof was left. According to Simpson, this oversimplification really amounts to a falsification. In reality things happened in a far more complex, yet more meaningful way, summarized in Figure 12.7, which still shows only the principal events of a long history.

During the Eocene epoch Eohippus evolved slowly, and produced several species and related genera (Orohippus, Epihippus) which lived both in North America and in Eurasia. Later on, all the Old World species died out, while one or more American species gave rise to a new genus, called Mesohippus. During the Oligocene epoch, Mesohippus became a very common animal in North America to judge by the large number of its remains that have been discovered. It was taller than Eohippus (24 inches tall on the average), and it had long and slender legs, each with three toes. The brain casts of Mesohippus show another important advance—an increased size of the cerebral hemispheres. The success of this animal may have been due as much to its growing more intelligent as to growing more fleet-footed.

During the next epoch, the Miocene, the Mesohippus stock blossomed out in a variety of new genera, among which Anchitherium, Hypohippus, and Merychippus are most important (see Figures 12.6 and 12.7). The first two were great travelers, and spread out from their native North America to the Old World, where they became quite common. These successful colonizers were getting somewhat taller as time went on, but they still had three toes on each foot, and their teeth indicate that they were, like their ancestors, browsing on foliage. Merychippus stayed at home in North America, but it made an evolutionary invention which affected all subsequent evolution of

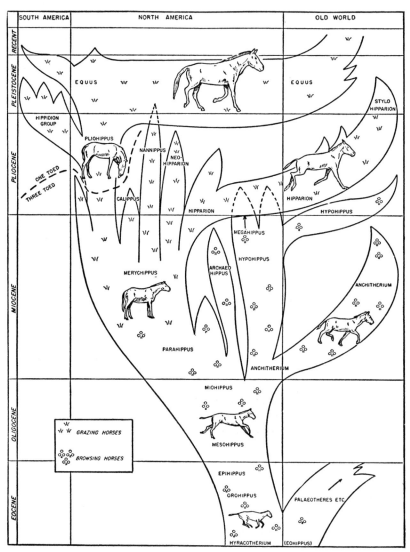

Figure 12.7.   A schematic representation of the evolution of the horse tribe, showing the geographic distribution of the different forms, and their mode of securing food by browsing or by grazing.   (From G. G. Simpson, by permission of the Oxford University Press.)

the horse family. This invention is the high-crowned teeth with a complex pattern of crests and ridges; the horses now living have teeth of this kind, though, of course, they are much larger than those in Merychippus. Such teeth made possible a change in diet: Merychippus and its numerous descendants, including the modern horses, fed by grazing on grass instead of by browsing on leaves.

It was not a fortuitous chance that the switch from browsing to grazing took place in horse evolution during Miocene. In Eocene and during much of Oligocene, most of the earth enjoyed warm and humid climates. Tropical evergreen and temperate broad-leaved forests were the widespread types of vegetation, and they offered ample food to browsing horses. But as time went on, the climates tended to become cooler, and in many parts of the world also drier. Grassy steppes, prairies, and savannas were becoming more and more widespread. And yet, during Miocene, few animals, or at least few mammals, were adapted to utilize grass as their main diet. Grass is very harsh food, and the low-crowned teeth of the browsing horses would have been worn down to the gums by tough grass. Merychippus evolved teeth which enabled it to feed on grass, and its descendants "inherited the earth," or at least the grass-covered part of it. But the new way of life necessitated also qualities other than high-crowned teeth. On grassy plains, animals can be seen from greater distances than in forests. Accordingly, natural selection favored larger, stronger, and faster grazing horses, which could defend themselves or could escape from their enemies.

The net result of the change in the diet was a quickening of the pace of evolution in the Merychippus line. The horses of the next epoch, Pliocene, were derived chiefly from Merychippus, whereas the browsing horses lingered on, and eventually became extinct (Figures 12.5 to 12.7). One of the most successful descendants of Merychippus was the genus Hipparion, which repeated the exploits of the Miocene browsing horses, and spread from North America to the Old World, colonizing not only Asia and Europe but Africa as well. This was an animal of about the size of a modern cow pony, but it still had three toes on each foot. Meanwhile, in North America there arose still another horse, Pliohippus, in which the side toes were finally lost, leaving just a single toe on each foot. Pliohippus appears to be the progenitor of the genus Equus, to which belong the modern horses, zebras, and asses (see Chapter 9).

The last chapter of the history of the horse family is a puzzling one. During the Ice Age (Pleistocene) the genus Equus spread from North

America to Eurasia, giving rise to species of horses and asses, to Africa where zebras were formed, and finally to South America. Just what the indigenous North American horses were like in color and in habits is anybody's guess, but it is fairly certain that the early human inhabitants of the Americas (Indians) found horses abundant in many parts of the continents. It is quite certain, however, that by the time white men came to the Americas, the native horses had died out, and horses were re-introduced from Europe. What or who killed the native American horses? Was it an infectious disease, or animal predators, or hunting by the Indians? The cause is unknown, and serious objections can be raised against all these hypotheses.

Another puzzle of the horse evolution is that all major evolutionary advances have taken place on the North American continent. As Figure 12.7 shows, horses repeatedly invaded the Old World from North America, had a brief efflorescence there, but each time died out without leaving descendants. Remains of Eohippus, Anchitherium, and Hipparion were found in Europe before fossil horses were discovered in America. The pioneer Russian paleontologist Kovalevsky, who made a classical study of the European fossils in 1873, concluded that Eohippus–Anchitherium–Hipparion–Equus formed a line of descent. This was one of the first triumphs of evolutionism in paleontology. Kovalevsky, of course, was right in his conclusion that the fossils he was studying represented successive stages of horse evolution, but he had no way of knowing that the forms which he had at his disposal were blind offshoots of an evolutionary development which took place on the other side of the globe. Only since the American paleontologists Marsh, Cope, Osborn, Matthew, and Simpson have discovered and studied the American fossil horses has the evolution of the horse family become one of the best-known and most instructive examples of the historical development of a group of living beings.

Evolution and Opportunity. Although this interpretation is not universally accepted (see Chapter 14), it seems probable that the important advances in the evolution of the horse family occurred when the animals adopted new ways of life. Thus the high-crowned teeth with complex grinding surfaces arose presumably when the horses were becoming grazers instead of browsers. In turn, the development of the grazing habit was a response to the existence of an abundant and hitherto little exploited food supply—grass. Such a causal connection between ecological opportunity (a new and plentiful food supply) and evolutionary change (development of organs able to utilize this food) is exactly what is expected if evolution is brought about by natural selection of fit gene combinations. Modern paleontologists and biologists are certainly not yet in a position to give causal explanations along similar lines to all the evolutionary changes of which the fossil record bears witness. We can, however, take comfort in the fact that as our knowledge both of living and of fossil organisms increases, the ecological factors responsible for evolutionary changes emerge more and more clearly in more and more evolutionary histories.

One of the most fascinating and suggestive phenomena which can be understood in the light of the above theory is evolutionary parallelism. It has been pointed out in Chapter 10 that organisms which are not closely related often develop analogous organs, serving similar functions, when these organisms have similar ways of life. Thus fishes, ichthyosaurs, and whales and porpoises evolved remarkably similar streamlined body shapes. Comparison of the inhabitants of certain countries reveals evolutionary parallelism on even grander scale. We shall consider two examples in this category: comparison of the mammals of Australia with those of the rest of the world, and comparison of the histories of the mammals inhabiting North and South America.

It has already been stated (page 293) that the mammals which give birth to living young can be divided into placentals and marsupials. In the former, the fetus obtains its nourishment from the mother's body through the placenta, and is born at an advanced stage of development. In the marsupials the young are born quite small, and are taken care of in a special pouch on the mother's belly, which serves as an incubator and a perambulator combined. In the world at large, placental mammals greatly outnumber the marsupials. Thus in North America the only marsupials are the opossums; in Europe there are none at all. Australia, however, is an exception. The most conspicuous and characteristic Australian mammals are marsupials. Furthermore, and this is the point worth a particular emphasis, among the Australian marsupials many kinds of animals exist which resemble, both in appearance and in ways of life, placental types living elsewhere.

Figure 12.8 shows some examples. There exist wolf-like marsupials (Tasmanian "wolf"), mole-like, squirrel-like (phalangers), rodent-like (wombats corresponding to our woodchucks) and even anteater-like marsupials. There is nothing quite like horses, deer, antelopes, or other ungulates in Australia, but their place is taken by the herbivorous kangaroos, which are represented by many species of different sizes.

There are no marsupial bats, and this exception truly proves the rule, for placental bats are a group of placental mammals abundantly represented in Australia.

The reason the marsupials have developed in Australia many ecological and structural types represented by parallel placental forms

Figure 12.8. Adaptive radiation of marsupial mammals in Australia, which has given rise to a great variety of forms resembling certain kinds of placental mammals which live outside Australia. (From Colbert.)

elsewhere is reasonably clear. It is the absence in Australia of these placentals. Australia is an "island-continent," separated from other continents by wide oceans, or (from Asia) by deep and relatively broad sea straits. Australia has been an island-continent for a long time, although there is no unanimity among geologists as to just how long. During the Cretaceous and the early Tertiary periods, both the primitive marsupials and the placentals were widely distributed. The marsupials happened to reach Australia at an early time (just when, however, is unknown), whereas the placentals did not reach there until much later. Such accidents, when some creatures do and others do not happen to colonize an island, are quite common (see page 313). Australia offers about as rich a variety of ecological opportunities as larger continents. It has temperate and tropical forests, steppes, deserts, mountains, and plains. To the existence of these opportunities life has responded by evolving parallel adaptive organizations. A marsupial "mole" is astonishingly like a "real" placental mole, both in general appearance and in habits. And yet any competent anatomist sees easily that the similarities are due to analogy and not to homology (see page 231). But the opportunity to develop a marsupial "bat" was cut off by the invasion of placental bats from Asia; the bats can negotiate marine straits perhaps more easily than non-flying mammals can.

The Mammalian Inhabitants of North and South America. The drawback to the story of the Australian mammalian fauna is that its geological history is little known. In this respect a comparison of the mammals of North and South America is more instructive. For South America was an island-continent on and off during its history, and again it was repeatedly connected to North America by land bridges, such as the Isthmus of Panama is at present. It happens that during most of the Tertiary Age of Mammals, South America was an island. On the contrary, North America, at least during the Tertiary, was always connected with, or separated by only a narrow strait like the present Bering Strait, from the great Eurasian land mass. The connection was through Alaska and northeastern Siberia, and organisms able to negotiate the climatic conditions of that region passed freely between the New and the Old Worlds. We have seen that ancient horses made use of this route several times.

By Eocene times both placental and marsupial mammals were spread widely over the surface of the earth. Their fossilized remains have been discovered in both North and South America. Of course they belonged not only to extinct species, but also with few exceptions (such as the opossum) to families and even to orders which have since become replaced by greatly modified descendants. From Eocene onward, however, South America became an island, since there was a sea strait in place of the Isthmus of Panama. The mammals of South America evolved, then, independently from those of North America, with little or no interchange of inhabitants between the two continents. The results of these independent developments were remarkable.

During the later part of the Tertiary period (Miocene and Pliocene epochs) both North and South America had diversified mammalian inhabitants, more than twenty different families having been preserved as fossils on each continent (see Table 12.2). The striking fact, how-

TABLE 12.2

NUMBERS OF DIFFERENT FAMILIES OF MAMMALS WHICH ARE KNOWN TO HAVE LIVED ON THE NORTH AMERICAN AND THE SOUTH AMERICAN CONTINENTS AT DIFFERENT TIMES, INCLUDING THE FAMILIES WHICH WERE COMMON TO BOTH CONTINENTS

(According to Simpson.)

Time	Families in North America	Families in South America	Families in Both Continents
Recent	23	30	15
Pleistocene	32	36	21
Late Pliocene	27	26	5
Early Pliocene	28	26	2
Late Miocene	26	24	1
Mid-Miocene	27	23	0

ever, is that almost all the North American mammals were quite different from the South American ones. Only a few families, and no genera, lived on both continents. In other words, the independent evolutionary developments have produced different animals in the two Americas.

And yet, the North American and the South American Tertiary mammals often represented strikingly parallel biological types. Thus in North America (and in the Old World) there appeared dog-like and cat-like carnivores, the order Carnivora belonging, of course, to the placental mammals. In South America there also appeared some animals resembling wolves and others resembling saber-toothed tigers. But these South American carnivores are marsupials, not placentals! In the Old World (including North America) herbivorous ungulates developed, including horses, camels, rhinoceroses, etc. In South America two now completely extinct orders evolved, known as litopterns and notoungulates, which have produced some forms amazingly similar to ungulates (Figure 12.9). Thus the family Proterotheriidae, belonging to the Litopterna, became horse-like, including the reduction of the number of toes in one line to three and in the other to a single toe on each foot. These one-toed litopterns had already appeared in Miocene, whereas one-toed horses are known only from Pliocene on. Curiously enough, the three-toed and one-toed litopterns did not develop grazing teeth; but another group (Notohippidae) did acquire grazing teeth but not the legs specialized for running that horses have.

Still other litopterns became camel-like, whereas the toxodonts (belonging to an extinct South American order Notoungulata) were rhinoceros-like.

Of course the South American litoptern pseudo-horse is in no sense identical with a real horse, just as the Australian marsupial "wolf" is

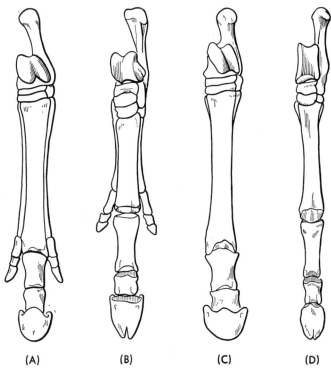

(A)   (B)   (C)   (D)

Figure 12.9.   Convergent evolution of the foot bones in the horses (*A* and *C*) and in the South American litopterns (*B* and *D*). *A* and *B*, three-toed forms; *C* and *D*, one-toed forms. (From Colbert.)

still a marsupial and not a placental wolf. According to Simpson, "it would be a stupid anatomist who could not distinguish the two ('wolves') from any single bone or organ in the body." And yet, the two "wolves" do appear strikingly similar externally, and it is certainly not a coincidence that they lead more or less similar lives. The modern placental wolf, the Australian marsupial "wolf," and the extinct South American marsupial "wolves" (borhyaenid) are made out of different genetic materials, but they are cast, as it were, in the same mold. Because of the similar mold these different animals were able to preempt the ecological niche, the profession, of a wolf-like animal. Most of the peculiar and fascinating South American mammals of the Tertiary have become extinct. In late Pliocene or in Pleistocene times the Isthmus of Panama rose from the sea and made a land corridor linking the two continents. Through this corridor the North American mammalian families, including horses, tapirs, deer, camels, cats, wolves, rodents, and many others, invaded South America. Similarly, North America acquired armadillos, porcupines, sloths, and other forms from South America. During Pleistocene and Recent times more than half of the mammalian families occurring on either continent occur also on the other continent (Table 12.2).

The invasion from the North had disastrous effects on many native animals of South America: several whole orders and many families died out. The litoptern pseudo-horse and the marsupial pseudo-wolf were simply no match for the real horse and the real wolf. Strangely enough, the immigrants from the South did not wreak any havoc in North America, and the extinction of only a few North American natives is ascribable to the competition of the invaders from the South. Just why this should be so is a matter of speculation. One guess, put forward originally by Matthew, is that, among land organisms, the successful products of evolution are most likely to arise close to the center of large continental masses, where the numbers of competing forms are largest and the competition is toughest. Isolated islands, and remote corners of continents, on the contrary, may harbor some organisms relatively less resistant to the rigors of competition. During the Tertiary, South America was an island while North America was exchanging inhabitants with the great Asian-European-African land mass. Many of the native South American mammals were, then, supplanted by the tougher invaders.

Oceanic and Continental Islands and Their Inhabitants. In 1835 Charles Darwin, then a young naturalist, visited the Galapagos Islands, located on the Equator some 600 miles off the West Coast of South America (Figure 12.12). He was greatly impressed by finding that most of the animals and plants in Galapagos were *endemic*, that is, occurred nowhere else in the world. At the same time many of them resembled the inhabitants of the neighboring South America. Darwin correctly surmised that the Galapagos endemics were more or less profoundly modified descendants of immigrants from the South American continent. Here, then, the occurrence of an evolutionary process was reasonably obvious. Some two decades later, A. R. Wallace, the co-discoverer with Darwin of the principle of natural selection, reached similar conclusions by studying the inhabitants of islands on the opposite side of the globe—in Indonesia.

Two kinds of islands may be conveniently distinguished—the oceanic

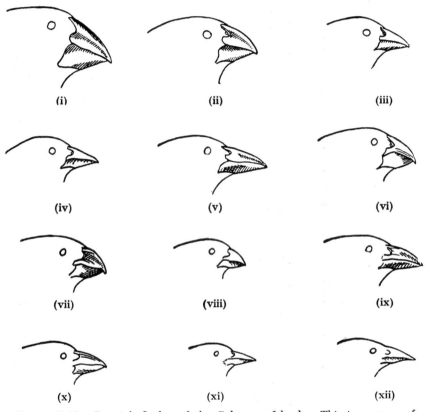

Figure 12.10. Darwin's finches of the Galapagos Islands. This is a group of birds which became adapted to diverse modes of life and developed a great variety of adaptations, particularly in the structure of the beak. (From Lack, courtesy of Cambridge University Press.)

and the continental ones. Oceanic islands have never been connected by land with any continent, or were so connected only long ago. Galapagos and the Hawaiian islands are good examples of the oceanic kind; they are islands of volcanic origin, and they rose from the bottom of the ocean far from any land. Continental islands are separated from the mainland generally by shallow straits, and were parts of the mainland in geologically recent times. Long Island near New York,

Newfoundland off the coast of Canada, or the British Isles off Europe are examples.

Continental islands have rather few or no endemic plants or animals. Their flora and fauna differ little from the adjacent mainland. The flora or fauna of an oceanic island, on the contrary, are more or less strongly different from those of other islands or continents. Not only do oceanic islands have many endemics, but their floras and faunas are usually "unbalanced," that is, they lack whole groups of plants and animals which occur pretty much everywhere in the world where suitable climatic and other conditions are available. Thus we know that the oceanic island-continent of Australia has few placental mammals. The oceanic Galapagos Islands have their mammalian inhabitants restricted to some bats and some rats, but they have instead a remarkable fauna of reptiles, including the famous giant tortoises and herbivorous lizards. Many kinds of birds familiar on the South American continent are also missing on Galapagos, but one group of birds, the finches, are represented by numerous and diversified forms. These "Darwin's finches," recently subjected to penetrating study by Lack, have evolved on Galapagos species with beaks adapted for feeding on large or on small seeds, with strong woodpecker-like beaks feeding on insect larvae, with parrot-like beaks feeding on buds and fruits, with slender beaks feeding on small insects, etc.

These facts are comprehensible only in the light of the history of life on oceanic islands. An island arising in the midst of an ocean can be populated only through accidental introductions of plants and animals by oceanic currents, by winds, storms, etc. Just which kinds of plants and animals will arrive and when will depend, of course, on their ability to remain alive during the transport. But it will depend also on chance or luck; Simpson has called the accidental methods of colonization of new territories *sweepstakes dispersal*. How low are the chances of winning in these sweepstakes has been estimated by Zimmerman for the Hawaiian Islands. These islands have about 3700 endemic species of insects and about 1000 endemic snails; Zimmerman reckons that they may have arisen from about 250 insect and 25 snail species introduced in Hawaii from elsewhere. On geological grounds Hawaii is estimated to be of the order of 5 million years old. This means a successful introduction of a new insect species once in 20,000 years, and of a snail species once in 200,000 years on the average!

The peculiar floras and faunas of oceanic islands are, therefore, due to the accidental nature of their colonization. A finch, arriving in Galapagos when these islands had few or no other bird inhabitants, started an adaptive radiation of finches which eventually resulted in elaboration of adaptive types. They exploit kinds of food which on continents are eaten by groups of birds other than finches (wood-

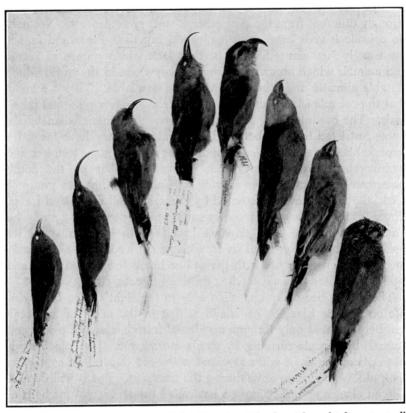

Figure 12.11. Drepaniid birds of the Hawaiian Islands. These birds, not at all closely related to Darwin's finches (see Figure 12.10), gave rise to diverse adaptations, particularly different forms of the beak used to subsist on different kinds of food. (Courtesy of Dr. Dean Amadon.)

peckers, parrots, warblers, etc.). In Hawaii it is a different family of birds which underwent a similar adaptive radiation—the honey creepers—Drepaniidae. The history of a flora or a fauna of an oceanic island teaches us the same lesson as does the history of the living world as a whole. The existence of unexploited possibilities of life, of unfilled "ecological niches," acts as a challenge to which the living matter may respond by evolution of forms adapted to occupy these ecological niches.

Zoogeographic and Phytogeographic Regions. The second half of the eighteenth century saw the completion of the first phase of the geographic exploration of the world. By that time all the continents and the major islands had been discovered. At the same time, the descriptive studies of the geographic distribution of living creatures began to reveal that every land area and every section of the sea have their own sets of animals and of plants. Much depends, of course, on the climate, but this is far from the whole story. Parts of California, of Mediterranean countries, of Australia, South Africa, and western South America have rather similar climates, and yet the native inhabitants of these countries are quite different. Tropical rainforests occupy extensive territory in the basin of the Amazon in South America, the Congo Basin in Africa, and in southeastern Asia and Australasia, but the plants and animals of these rainforests are different. These facts were generalized during the second half of the nineteenth century, when the world was subdivided into several zoogeographic (faunal) and phytogeographic (floral) regions. Although the details of this subdivision are not even now fully agreed upon, the map in Figure 12.12 summarizes the essentials of the story.

The United States, Canada, and the highlands of Mexico are inhabited by the *Nearctic* fauna. This fauna is not very different from the *Palearctic* fauna—in Europe, Asia down to the southern slope of the Himalaya Mountains, and Africa north of Sahara Desert. The Nearctic and Palearctic fauna may, consequently, be parts of a larger *Holarctic* fauna. South America, Central America, and the Mexican lowlands are inhabited by the *Neotropic* fauna. Africa south of Sahara has the *Ethiopian* fauna, southern Asia and Indonesia the *Oriental* or *Indo-Malayan* fauna; and Australia is a world unto itself—here is the *Australian* fauna.

Darwin, Wallace, and among their successors particularly Lydekker (1896) and the Sclaters saw clearly that the existence of this regional differentiation of the living world is comprehensible only as an outcome of an interaction between the geological history of the earth and the organic evolution. We have already discussed the history of the Australian region (page 307). The marsupial mammals underwent there an adaptive radiation, being protected from competition of the placental mammals by the island nature of Australia. The Australian tree flora is dominated by species of eucalypts and of acacias, which have evolved almost every conceivable ecological type of tree. Outside Australia the eucalypts are native only on some of the neighboring islands, and nowhere else in the world.

The divergent features of the fauna and flora of the Neotropic regions arose because of a situation similar to that obtaining in Australia. South America was an island during the Tertiary times, but it became linked to North America and interchanged inhabitants with the latter

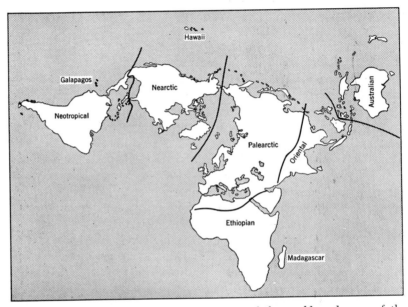

Figure 12.12. Zoogeographic or faunal regions of the world, and some of the oceanic islands having peculiar faunas mentioned in the text.

from Pleistocene times on (page 311). Conversely, the relative uniformity of the enormous Holarctic region, including parts of four continents, is understandable because these continents interchanged inhabitants more or less continuously. In particular, North America was for a long time close to Eurasia in the vicinity of the Bering Strait (page 204). The inhabitants of Africa (Ethiopian region) developed in relative isolation from those of Eurasia, because of the existence until geologically relatively recent times of a sea in place of the present Sahara Desert (Figure 12.12).

The above facts have now been familiar to biologists for so long that it is useful to point out that the history of the world fauna and flora is still far from completely known, and that many basic problems in the field still await solution. One of the most controversial issues arose in connection with the hypothesis of *continent drift* developed by the German geologist Wegener. According to this hypothesis, continents are blocks of relatively light rocks floating on the surface of the viscous and heavier strata of the earth's crust. Wegener visualized that the present continents during the Paleozoic and earlier times formed one or two enormous land masses. Africa was united with southern Asia, and through South America also with Antarctica and Australia, into a single mass. This mass broke up into the present continents, which then proceeded to drift apart, the Atlantic, Indian, and Antarctic oceans forming between them.

Some zoologists and botanists believed that the continental drift hypothesis explained some faunal and floristic resemblances, particularly between Africa and South America, South America and Australia, and Africa and Australia. Indeed, there are examples of animals and plants which occur on almost any pair of continents now separated by wide oceans, and not in the territories linking these continents. In Chapter 9 we saw a situation of this sort exemplified by species of cottons. However, the hypothesis of continental drift has encountered grave and apparently insuperable difficulties, and is now abandoned by most geologists. The biological facts which were adduced in its favor were never compelling, and most of the modern biogeographers believe that this hypothesis should be rejected also on biological grounds. The scattered instances of discontinuous distribution of animals and plants on remote continents have to be considered, each on its own merits. Sometimes we are dealing with organisms which were widely distributed in the past, but now survive only in some widely separated territories. Thus species of incense cedar (Libocedrus) are now known in California, Chile, and New Zealand. Sometimes there are instances of "sweepstakes distribution."

Suggestions for Further Reading

Simpson, G. G. 1944. *Tempo and Mode in Evolution.* 1st Edition. 1953. *The Major Features of Evolution.* 2nd Edition. Columbia University Press, New York.

Simpson, G. G. 1949. *The Meaning of Evolution.* Yale University Press, New Haven.

Many paleontologists questioned whether the evidence of the fossil record could be reconciled with the biological theory of evolution. Simpson's books have shown that a synthesis of paleontology and the rest of evolutionary biology is, indeed, possible. In fact, these works have to a considerable extent created the modern version of this theory. They should be read by every evolutionist.

Dunbar, C. O. 1949. *Historical Geology.* John Wiley, New York.

Colbert, E. H. 1951. *The Dinosaur Book.* 2nd Edition. McGraw-Hill, New York.

Colbert, E. H. 1955. *Evolution of the Vertebrates.* John Wiley, New York.

Gregory, W. K. 1951. *Evolution Emerging.* Macmillan, New York.

Romer, A. S. 1941. *Man and the Vertebrates.* University of Chicago Press, Chicago.

Romer, A. S. 1945. *Vertebrate Paleontology.* 2nd Edition. University of Chicago Press, Chicago.

Simpson, G. G. 1950. *History of the fauna of Latin America. American Scientist,* Volume 38, pages 361–389. Also in Baitsell's *Science in Progress,* Volume 7.

Simpson, G. G. 1951. *Horses.* Oxford University Press, New York.

The basic facts of historical geology and paleontology can be found in the eight books (Dunbar to Simpson) cited above.

Mayr, E. 1944. *Wallace's line in the light of recent zoogeographic studies. Quarterly Review of Biology,* Volume 19, pages 1–14.

Mayr, E. 1946. *History of the North-American bird fauna. Wilson Bulletin,* Volume 58, pages 3–41.

Matthew, W. D. 1939. *Climate and Evolution.* 2nd Edition. New York Academy of Science, New York.

Simpson, G. G. 1953. *Evolution and Geography.* Oregon State System of Higher Education, Eugene.

Stebbins, G. L. 1950. *Variation and Evolution in Plants.* Columbia University Press, New York.

Chapter XIV contains a concise discussion of phytogeography. The works of Mayr, Matthew, and Simpson discuss fundamentals of zoogeography.

The following three works are concerned specifically with the faunas of oceanic islands:

Amadon, D. 1950. *The Hawaiian honeycreepers. Bulletin of the American Museum of Natural History,* Volume 95.

Lack, D. 1947. *Darwin's Finches.* Cambridge University Press, London.

Zimmerman, E. C. 1948. *Insects of Hawaii.* University of Hawaii Press, Honolulu.

13

Human Evolution

Darwin's discovery that man is a descendant of non-human ancestors seemed repugnant to some of his contemporaries. The story goes
that, on hearing about Darwin's theory, a lady cried: "Descended
from the apes! My dear, we will hope that it is not true. But if it is,
let us pray that it may not become generally known." To her, it was
terribly degrading to be related, however distantly, to an ape. But
the news became rather generally known, and most people grew
reconciled to the strange relative.

At present the dust has settled sufficiently to see things more clearly.
Man is a biological species, subject to the action of biological forces,
and a product of a long evolutionary development. It does not matter
whether the evolutionary origin of man is called an "hypothesis" or
a "fact." Events which occurred before there were observers capable
of recording and of transmitting their observations must of necessity
be inferred from evidence now available for study. But the evidence
shows conclusively that man arose from forebears who were not men,
although we have only the most fragmentary information concerning
the stages through which the process has passed. Nobody has seen
that the earth is a sphere or that it revolves around the sun, rather
than vice versa; nobody has caught a glimpse of atoms or of things
within atoms. Are atoms, then, factual or hypothetical? The least
that can be said is that in our activities we take the earth to be a
sphere and treat atoms as though they were facts. For similar reasons,
it is not a matter of personal taste whether or not we "believe in"
evolution. The evidence for evolution is compelling. Moreover,
human evolution is going on at present, and, what is more, biology is

in the process of acquiring knowledge which may permit man to control and to direct this evolution.

Biologists have been so preoccupied with proving that man is a product of organic evolution that they have scarcely noticed that man is an extraordinary and unique product of this evolution. He is unique in a purely biological sense. Some forces which are important in the evolution of man occur at most as vestiges in the evolution of other creatures. The leading forces of human evolution are intelligence, ability to use linguistic symbols, and the culture which man has developed. These exclusively, or nearly exclusively, human phenomena affect the biological evolution of man so profoundly that it cannot be understood without taking them into account. Conversely, human society and culture are products of the biological evolution of our species. Human evolution is wholly intelligible only as an outcome of the interaction of biological and social forces. Biologists and sociologists are equally guilty of underestimation of this fact.

Characteristics of the Class of Primates. Although Linnaeus was not an evolutionist, he correctly placed man, *Homo sapiens,* in the order of primates, of the class of mammals, of the vertebrate phylum.

Except for man, who now lives in all climates which the earth has to offer, primates are tropical or subtropical animals. Several groups of primates are known, as shown in Table 13.1 and Figures 13.1 and 13.2.

TABLE 13.1

Systematic Position of Man and His Living Relatives Belonging to the Order of Primates of the Class of Mammals

(After Simpson.)

Suborder	Infraorder or Superfamily	Vernacular Name and Geographic Distribution
Anthropoidea	Hominoidea	Family Hominidae, Men (World-wide) Family Pongidae, Apes (Tropical Asia and Africa)
	Cercopithecoidea	Old World Monkeys (Tropical Asia and Africa)
	Ceboidea	New World Monkeys (Tropical America)
Prosimii	Tarsiiformes	Tarsiers (Indonesia, Philippines)
	Lorisiformes	Loris and Galagos (Tropical Asia and Africa)
	Daubentonioidea	Aye-Aye (Madagascar)
	Lemuroidea	Lemurs (Madagascar)
	Tupaioidea	Tree-Shrews (Tropical Asia)

Very few distinctive traits are common to all primates. Most, though not all, occur in tropical forests and are tree dwellers. The thumb, and usually also the great toe, are opposable to the other digits—an advantage for creatures that must climb and jump among tree branches. Man, however, has lost the "opposability" of the great toe which his ancestors possessed. Most, though again not all, primates use their hands and feet for grasping and handling objects rather than for walking. Man's ancestors lost the use of their feet for grasping as they attained their erect posture. The emancipation of the hands from walking duties made possible their use for delicate manual operations of which man alone is capable. The teeth of primates are not specialized for just one kind of food, as the teeth are specialized in, for example, grazing animals, in rodents, or in carnivores. Primate teeth deal successfully with diversified diets, both vegetable and animal. In mammals the eyes are placed usually on the two sides of the head, permitting a very broad field of vision (consider the position of the eyes, for example, in a rabbit or in a horse). In most primates both eyes are directed forward, as in man. This position facilitates binocular vision and correct estimation of distances, which is vitally important in animals which dwell among branches of tall trees.

Living Relatives of Man. Man resembles the anthropoid apes (family Pongidae, Table 13.2) in body structure more than any other group of animals. This family comprises two species of gibbons, living in southeastern Asia, orangutan on the islands of Sumatra and Borneo, and chimpanzee and gorilla in equatorial Africa. Not only do the anthropoid apes share with man a relatively large size and many details of the structure of the brain and the skull, but they approach each other in posture, in position of internal organs, absence of a tail, and in many physiological traits, especially those dealing with reproduction (menstruation, the position of the fetus in the womb, etc.). The differences between the families Hominidae and Pongidae are those which are expected between animals which walk erect on the ground and animals which dwell among tree branches.

About 140 species of New World monkeys and some 200 species of Old World monkeys have been named. The number of species is in reality only a fraction of the above numbers, because of the habit of some taxonomists of giving species names to races of the same species. Nevertheless, a considerable diversity of forms is involved. Monkeys vary in size from marmosets, which are about as small as squirrels, to baboons, which are of the size of large dogs. Some have long and

Figure 13.1. Representatives of prosimians and monkeys. *A*, squirrel monkey; *B*, macaque monkey; *C*, tarsier; *D*, lemur; *E*, galago; *F*, tree shrew. (Not drawn to exact scale. Redrawn after Ashley Montagu and other sources.)

Figure 13.2.   Representatives of anthropoids.   A, chimpanzee; B, orangutan; C, gorilla; D, gibbon.   (Not drawn to exact scale.)

powerful prehensile tails which act as a "third hand," but others (dwelling on the ground rather than in trees) are tailless.

The primate suborder Prosimii (Table 13.1) stands between the anthropoids on one side and the non-primate mammals on the other. Lémurs and lorises (Figure 13.1) vary in size from that of a cat down to that of a newborn kitten. In contrast to monkeys and apes, they have movable and usually large ears, and elongated snouts rather than flattened "faces." Their tails are usually long and bushy but not prehensile. Lemurs do not menstruate. True lemurs are a relict group which is now confined to the island of Madagascar in the Indian Ocean off Africa (see Figure 12.12). Their fossil remains, however, occur over much of the Old World and North America. A curious creature called aye-aye (Daubentonia) has remarkably large front teeth which resemble those of mice and other rodents, and has claws on all digits except the big toes, which have flat nails. The third finger of each hand is much longer than the others; the animal uses this long finger to extract insects, on which it feeds, from cracks in the bark and similar places.

The spectral tarsier (*Tarsius spectrum*, Figure 13.1) is the only living representative of a group of primates which was much more common and widespread in the past, to judge from fossil remains described from Eocene strata of North America and Europe. The structures of the face, lips, and brain of the spectral tarsier make this little animal (about the size of a two-week-old kitten) a connecting link between the Prosimii on one side and the anthropoids on the other. And yet the tarsier shows several features which make him quite unique. His eyes are relatively larger than in any other primate (it is an exclusively nocturnal animal), and his hind legs are modified to enable him to make powerful jumps among tree branches. The tarsioids of the past may have given rise to the lemuroid stock on one hand and to the anthropoid stock on the other. The spectral tarsier is an aberrant and greatly modified relic of the primitive tarsioids known only as fossils. Wood Jones has even conjectured that the human stock arose directly from the tarsioids, rather than through monkey-like and ape-like ancestors. This conjecture is far-fetched, and it is mentioned only to emphasize the interest of the tarsioids as a group which may have been ancestral to other groups of primates.

Even more remarkable than the tarsioids are the tree shrews (Table 13.1 and Figure 13.1). These animals have a superficial resemblance to squirrels, both in size and in general aspect. But their body structures are such that some zoologists have placed them in the order of insectivores (to which belong moles, ordinary shrews, and hedgehogs), but other zoologists have placed them among the primates. Now the insectivores are generally considered to be the most primitive order of living placental mammals (see Chapter 12), whereas the primates, to which we belong, are at or near the top. The tree shrews indicate, then, the probable origin of the ancestral primates from ancient insectivores. Tree shrews have claws instead of nails on their fingers and toes, which give to their feet a non-primate-like appearance, but their digits have a greater range of movements than those of mammals other than primates. Their brain is too small for a primate but too large for an insectivore, and it shows a considerable development of the part of the cortex concerned with the function of vision.

Fossil Non-human Primates. The fossil record of primates is unfortunately meager. As stated above, most primates dwell in tropical forests, an environment highly unfavorable for the preservation of the remains of living creatures as fossils. Furthermore, whatever remains are found are usually fragments of bones and teeth. It is a difficult matter to get from such fragments an idea of what the whole animal might have been like. Because of this difficulty the disagreements between different authorities on fossil human and prehuman beings are often extreme and rather exasperating to non-specialists. Nevertheless, so great is the interest in human evolution that the utmost efforts are expended to find fossil evidence, and whatever is discovered is studied in the minutest detail. It is not too optimistic to hope that much more satisfactory fossil evidence than is now available will be forthcoming before very long.

During the Paleocene and Eocene (see Table 12.1), there existed several families of animals, about rat-like or mouse-like in size, which had an unmistakable resemblance to modern tree shrews. During the Eocene, Europe and North America enjoyed tropical climates, and among their inhabitants were some tarsioids and lemurs. By the Oligocene and Miocene, the prosimians disappeared in Europe and North America, which became climatically unsuitable. Traces of them, however, have been found in the Miocene of eastern Africa, and in the Pliocene abundant remains were preserved on the island of Madagascar, where living lemurs are found now.

The most ancient known ape is represented by a fragment of a mandible found in the lower Oligocene strata of Egypt to which the name Parapithecus has been given. In some respects this mandible resembles the tarsier, which agrees with the notion that the Anthropoidea arose from a tarsioid stock (Table 13.1). By the Miocene a variety of ape-like animals existed in Africa and in Asia. A number of fragmentary remains have been dug up in Kenya (east-central Africa); a small form, called Limnopithecus, may have resembled the gibbon (which now lives only in southeastern Asia). A larger one, Proconsul, discovered in 1948 by Leakey, may have been an ancestor or a relative of the living chimpanzee, but it had certain human features which are absent in the chimpanzee. A little later, by the middle and upper Miocene, there lived in Africa, India, and southwest Europe (Spain) the fossil apes Dryopithecus and Sivapithecus. They show many similarities with the now living great apes (chimpanzee, gorilla, orangutan), and yet some characters of their teeth adumbrate those known in fossil men. Fragments of a thigh bone and of an arm bone suggest that Dryopithecus did not have the long and powerful limbs which the modern great apes have developed to enable them to live in the tropical forest trees. The human ancestors probably were not as strongly specialized tree dwellers as the modern apes are. Discovery of complete remains of Dryopithecus must be awaited before we can judge whether this animal can be regarded as one of the ancestors of man.

Man-Apes of South Africa. It is clear that a large-scale adaptive radiation of anthropoid primates took place during the Tertiary period, particularly in Africa. Some of the most interesting products of that radiation lived in the southern part of that continent. Exceptionally abundant, if fragmentary, relics of the animals concerned, coming from at least 65 individuals, have been discovered in recent years by Dart, Broom, Robinson, and their collaborators. Counting isolated teeth, the remains may belong to over 100 individuals. The rate of discovery has been so high that unprecedentedly abundant material on fossil man may soon be accumulated. Those fossils have been described under several generic names (Australopithecus, Plesianthropus, Paranthropus, etc.), although it is most probable that the animals of which these fossils are fragmentary remains belonged to only one or two closely related species of the same genus, Australopithecus.

No agreement has been reached concerning the position of Australopithecus among the primates. Some authorities regard it as a peculiar ape which had nothing to do with human descent. Others, and probably a majority, put it in a special subfamily, Australopithecinae, which has no living representatives, but in which the characteristics of the human family (Hominidae) and of the ape family (Pongidae) are blended in such a way that it is arbitrary to say whether the Australopithecinae are to be considered apes or hominoids.

Evolutionists of the past, and especially popular writers, frequently spoke of a "missing link" between apes and man, the discovery of which was eagerly awaited. One school of thought among those who study fossil human remains believes that Australopithecinae come close to having the skeletal structure which such a link might be expected to have had. The skull of Australopithecus resembled in ap-

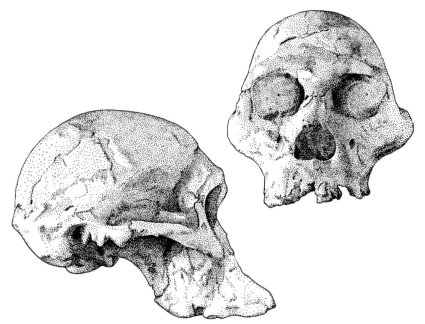

Figure 13.3. A fossil skull of an australopithecine (*Plesianthropus transvaalensis*) from South Africa. (After Ashley Montagu.)

pearance (Figure 13.3) an ape such as a chimpanzee or a gorilla; the volume of its brain is estimated as about 600 cubic centimeters, which is only about half as large as that of man. The forehead, however, was more rounded and consequently more human-like than that of the living apes. The form of the palate and the teeth are more human than ape-like. In addition, the structure of the part of the skull which is attached to the spinal column shows that Australopithecus had a standing body posture approaching that of man rather than of an ape. This is borne out by the structure of its pelvic bone.

Since some of the Australopithecus skulls are found in caves, together with remains of crushed bones of other animals and of cracked shells, Dart and others conclude that Australopithecus was "an animal-hunting, flesh-eating, shell-cracking, and bone-breaking ape." Certainly no living ape subsists on such a diet. The possibility that Australopithecinae were ancestors of mankind is seriously considered by some authorities. For the time being this is only a possibility. Most unfortunately, the geological conditions in which the Australopithecinae fossils were found make precise determination of their age doubtful. They may extend in time from as early as the Upper Pliocene to as late as the Middle Pleistocene; in other words, they may be appreciably older or appreciably younger than one million years. If they lived well into the Pleistocene, it would follow that they were contemporaries, rather than ancestors, of early man. Robinson believes that Australopithecus in fact coexisted with man.

Java and Peking Men. Early hominoids which possessed enough intelligence to fashion and use stone tools and yet had some unmistakably ape-like features lived during the Pleistocene (Ice) Age in Asia. In 1891 the Dutch anthropologist Dubois found the first remains, a skull cap and a thigh bone, of Java Man, whom he called *Pithecanthropus erectus* (ape-man walking erect). In 1936 and later, von Königswald and others found in the central part of the island of Java the remains of two more Java men. Between 1929 and 1940, Black and Weidenreich found in caves near Peking, China, the remains of perhaps as many as forty individuals of Peking Man, which became known as *Sinanthropus pekinensis.* These Latin names, however, are misleading, since we are dealing undoubtedly not with distinct genera and species but merely with races of a single species of man. A better terminology is (according to Mayr):

Homo erectus erectus = Java Man = *Pithecanthropus.*
Homo erectus pekinensis = Peking Man = *Sinanthropus pekinensis.*

Java Man lived during the Pleistocene age (first Interglacial to second Interglacial times), perhaps some half million or more years ago (Figure 13.4). He was rather undersized by modern standards (average height estimated at about 5 feet); and the brain size varied, in the known skulls, from 750 to 900 cubic centimeters, compared to 900 to 1200 cubic centimeters in Peking Man, and an average of about 1350 cubic centimeters in modern man. The skull bones are consistently thicker than in modern skulls, the foreheads slope gradually backwards from very prominent eyebrow ridges which are continuous above the root of the nose. The lower jaws are large and powerful, with large teeth and without a chin. This must have made the face of *Homo erectus* markedly prognathous, that is, the mandible, front teeth and lips must have projected forward beyond the level of the nose and the rest of the face. The limb bones, however, are very similar to those of modern man, making it certain that *Homo erectus* walked

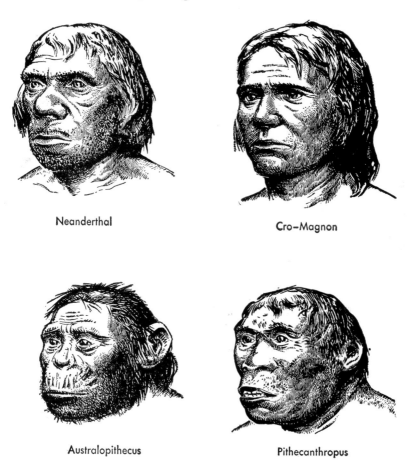

Neanderthal

Cro-Magnon

Australopithecus

Pithecanthropus

Figure 13.4. Hypothetical restorations of fossil human and pre-human forms. (From Colbert.)

erect as we do. Primitive stone tools have been found near the remains of Peking Man; he lived in caves and rock shelters, used fire and was a hunter who pursued and killed deer. There is even a suspicion that he had already discovered the gentle art of cannibalism, since the remains of his skulls are broken in a fashion suggesting extraction of the brain.

Neanderthal Men. Europe and North America offered some very harsh environments during the Pleistocene Age. Four times enormous ice sheets covered large parts of these continents, making climatic conditions perhaps not unlike those now found in Greenland. The four Ice Ages were separated by warmer interglacial times (Table 13.2). We are living during what may prove to be the Fourth Inter-

TABLE 13.2

Relative Chronology of Human Physical and Cultural Evolution during the Ice Age

(After Vallois and Movius, Oakley, Le Gros Clark, and other sources.)

Time	Fossil Human Races and Species	Cultures (in Europe)
Modern	Races of *sapiens*	Historic
		Neolithic (New Stone Age)
		Mesolithic (Middle Stone Age)
Fourth Glacial (Würm)	Cro-Magnon and relatives	Magdalenian
		Solutrean
		Aurignacian-Perigordian
	Neanderthal	Mousterian
	Mount Carmel	
Third Interglacial	Neanderthal	
	Fontechevade	Levalloisian
	Ehringsdorf	
Third Glacial (Riss)	Steinheim	Acheulian, Clactonian
	Peking Man(?)	
Second Interglacial	Swanscombe	
	Peking Man	
	Java Man	
Second Glacial (Mindel)	Peking Man(?)	Clactonian, Abbevillian
	Java Man	
First Interglacial	Java Man, Australo-pithecus(?)	Abbevillian
First Glacial (Günz)	Australopithecus(?)	Villafranchian

glacial Age. Concerning the duration of the Pleistocene Age and of its glacial and interglacial stages, specialists are not in agreement. One school (Milankovitch and Zeuner) thought that the Pleistocene might have been about 600,000 years long, and that the Fourth (Würm) glaciation lasted from about 125,000 to about 20,000 years ago. Now it seems more probable (according to Movius, Flint, and others) that the Pleistocene was perhaps one million years long. There are as yet no definitive estimates of the dates of the various Glacial and

Interglacial ages, and therefore we are giving in Table 13.2 what is known as "relative" chronology of various findings of fossil man, rather than "absolute" chronology (in years).

In any case, during the Third Interglacial and the Fourth Glacial ages, Europe, western Asia, and north Africa were inhabited by a very distinctive Neanderthal race of man (*Homo sapiens neanderthalensis*), of which the remains of close to 100 individuals in varying degrees of preservation have been found in places ranging from the Atlantic coast of Europe to Asia (France, Gibraltar, Italy, Germany, Yugoslavia, southern Russia, Turkestan, Palestine).

The Neanderthalians (Figure 13.4) were of short stature, about 5 feet, but of exceedingly rugged build. They had a stooping posture, powerful neck muscles, and massive heads with surprisingly large brains—1450 cubic centimeters on the average, that is, as large as or larger than in modern man. The bones of the skull were thick; the brow ridges were large, although not as prominent as in Java Man. The forehead was retreating, and the braincase flattened. The lower jaw was heavy, without a chin, but with rather large teeth, and with attachments for strong muscles which operated the jaws.

The Neanderthal race attained a relatively high cultural level. Although the stone tools which they used were primitive, belonging to the Old Stone Age types, the Neanderthalians had a social organization which enabled them to hunt large and powerful game such as mammoths and the woolly rhinoceros which at that time inhabited Europe. There are evidences of religious activities, since their bones are found under conditions suggesting ceremonial burial. In a Neanderthalian cave in Switzerland an altar has been found on which a bear skull was placed.

Emergence of Modern Man. Some 75,000 years ago, while Europe was in the grip of the last Ice Age, the Mousterian culture of Neanderthal man was replaced by the Aurignacian culture, and the Neanderthalian inhabitants by another race, which, to judge from its bones, was like the modern man—*Homo sapiens sapiens*. The Aurignacian stone tools are more expertly made than the Mousterian ones; the makers, named Cro-Magnons from the cave in which the first remains were discovered, were fine physical specimens, up to 6 feet tall and with brains up to 1650 cubic centimeters in volume (Figure 13.4). There is, of course, no way to tell what they were like in such external traits as skin color and hair shape. Some of the remains in southern Europe yield measurements which can be matched in the skeletons of certain living Negro populations in Africa, but it does not follow that these early Europeans were Negroes in appearance or, even less, in culture. Anyway, from the Aurignacian-Perigordian times on, Europe and probably the rest of the world as well, was inhabited by *Homo sapiens sapiens.*

Where did modern man come from? Where did he first arise? The problem is very complex, speculation concerning it rife, and no convincing solution is yet in sight. Some students have conjectured that modern man developed in Africa, others that he came to Europe from Asia, and destroyed the Neanderthalian natives. According to some authorities, Europe had some human inhabitants who resembled modern men during the second interglacial period (350,000 or more years ago), before the appearance of the Neanderthalians. Very few remains of this hypothetical race have been found, and those which have come to light are fragments not easily interpretable. The skull fragments found at Fontechevade in France, at Swanscombe in England and at Steinheim and at Ehringsdorf in Germany may have been rather *sapiens*-like, despite their great age. It looks as though there lived in Europe during the middle of the Ice Age a race rather like ourselves and yet not ancestral to us. Some experts, in a kind of desperation, regarded all fossil hominoids, except the Cro-Magnons and more recent races, as collateral branches of the human family tree, which became extinct without contributing to the direct ancestry of modern man. This makes the origin of modern man more puzzling than ever.

Light is shed on this problem by the work of McCown and Keith (1939), who studied a fine series of human remains found in the caves of Mount Carmel in Palestine. These people lived at about the same time that Europe was inhabited by the Neanderthalians. But the dwellers of Mount Carmel range in physical type all the way from indubitable Neanderthalians to more *sapiens*-like individuals. The most reasonable explanation of this is that Palestine formed, at that age (probably the third Interglacial), the geographic boundary between the Neanderthal race (*Homo sapiens neanderthalensis*), which lived to the northwest, in Europe, and a more nearly modern race (*Homo sapiens sapiens*) which lived perhaps farther southward, in Africa. The inhabitants of Palestine were, then, either hybrids between the two races, or else they were an intermediate population of a kind usually found at race boundaries (see Chapter 7).

In either case, one thing that is certain is that the Neanderthalians belonged to the same species as ours. The replacement of the Neanderthalians by the Cro-Magnons in Europe may have occurred partly by destruction and partly by hybridization with the incoming race,

which possessed a superior technology. Coon and other anthropologists are probably right that some modern European populations show
persistence of genes derived from the Neanderthalians. In like fashion, within the last few centuries the white race has displaced the
red-skinned men in the Americas and the blackfellows in Australia.
It is possible that the Neanderthalians themselves had, at a much
earlier time, displaced the Swanscombe and similar populations which
had inhabited Europe before them.

The cultural development of the Cro-Magnons and other related
races who soon appeared in Europe was superior to that of the Neanderthalians, which might explain the rapid replacement of the latter
by the former. The Cro-Magnons and their relatives fashioned more
efficient stone tools; they probably knew the use of the bow and of
harpoons. Most remarkable of all, they have left superb drawings
of animals on the walls of the caves which they inhabited (Figure 1.1).
The artistic feeling which these drawings display is admired even
by modern man.

Specific Unity of Mankind. It is important to keep in mind that
new species do not arise in any single place but in large territories
(except polyploid species, see Chapter 9). A species is a Mendelian
population which lives in a more or less extensive area and which gradually alters its genetic composition. Students of fossil man have a
habit of giving resounding Latin specific and generic names to almost
every bone fragment which they discover, which conveys the mistaken impression that there existed in the past many different man-like
species and genera. Weidenreich, however, has pointed out that when
the remains of human or prehuman forms which lived more or less
simultaneously are compared, the differences between them are only
of the order of those found between the now living human races (see
above). There is no fossil evidence of the existence at any one time
of more than a single human or human-like species, except, possibly,
in the case of the Australopithecinae (see above). Mankind preserved
its specific unity throughout its evolutionary development during the
Pleistocene times, although it always was, as it still is, subdivided into
races. Human evolution never led to differentiation of a single species
into a group of derived species, some of which might have become
lost and others survived. Mankind was and is a species which evolves
as a body.

Any living species, race, or population tends to expand in numbers
as soon as it encounters favorable environment. In doing so, a population often overflows into neighboring territories occupied by other

populations, and the immigrants usually intermarry with the natives. If the genotype of the immigrants is adaptively superior to that of the natives, the population resulting from the mixture comes to resemble the former immigrants. Our species, *Homo sapiens*, evolved from its ancestors, *Homo erectus*, and perhaps other species as yet undiscovered, in an extensive territory, comprising perhaps most of the Old World. Evolutionary improvements, that is, new and adaptively superior genotypes, arose from time to time in various parts of this territory. The populations in which these improvements arose expanded and transmitted their advantages to more widespread populations. Where two genetic improvements met, new populations of still superior adaptedness were formed, and expanded in turn.

To ask where *Homo sapiens* first appeared is therefore meaningless. Races and local populations are evolutionary trial parties which explore the various possibilities of adaptation. The gene pool of the now living mankind contains genetic elements which were present in many and perhaps in all major populations of the past.

Development of the Brain as the Moving Force of Human Evolution. However incomplete our knowledge of human ancestry, there is scarcely any doubt that the development of brain power, of intelligence, was the decisive force in the evolutionary process which culminated in the appearance of the species to which we belong. Natural selection has brought about the evolutionary trend towards increasing brain power because brain power confers enormous adaptive advantages on its possessors. It is obviously brain power, not body power, which makes man by far the most successful biological species which living matter has produced. The unprecedented and unparalleled success of man as a species has led to an increase in the numbers of living individuals from perhaps some hundreds of thousands during the Ice Age to about two and a half billion at present. Man has spread and occupied all continents and major islands except, perhaps, the interior of Antarctica. He has destroyed or reduced to insignificance other organisms which were his competitors, or which preyed on him as predators or parasites. He has domesticated many animal and plant species, made them serve his needs, and changed them genetically to improve their serviceability to him. Finally, man is in the process of the acquisition of knowledge which may permit him to control his own future evolution.

The human skeleton, and particularly the skull, underwent many changes during the evolutionary transition from ape-like ancestors (such as the Australopithecinae) to modern man. At first sight some of these changes, such as those in the shape of the skull, the presence of brow ridges, or in the presence or absence of a chin, may appear fortuitous and without meaning. Actually, careful comparative analysis of these traits in different races and species shows that most of them are part and parcel of the basic trend—the development of the brain. To quote Weidenreich: "One of the most impressive experiences a student of human evolution can have is to realize the extent to which all the smaller structural alterations of the human skull are correlated with and depend upon each other, and the extent to which they are governed by the trend of the skull transformation as a whole."

Examples shown in Figures 13.5 and 13.6 illustrate what is meant by such correlations. The brain of an Irish wolfhound, a large dog breed, is only about twice as heavy as that in the King Charles spaniel; the weight of the body, however, is about ten times greater in the large than in the small dog. In other words, a small dog has a relatively much larger brain than a large one. The relatively large brain can be accommodated in the small skull only by reducing the parts other than the brain cavity. According to Weidenreich, transitions between the gorilla skull, that of Java Man, and that of modern man entail changes strikingly parallel to those found in large and small dogs. Of course, man is not strikingly smaller than the gorilla in body size, but his brain is both absolutely and relatively larger. A greater size of the brain does not necessarily prove a higher intelligence. Among living men the brain size varies greatly, and there is no strict relation between its size and intellectual capacity. Among the great writers, the brains of Jonathan Swift and of Ivan Turgenev measured about 2000 cubic centimeters each, while that of Anatole France was only 1100 cubic centimeters in volume. This does not contradict the fact that groups of animals with larger brains show a higher intelligence on the average.

The trend towards increasing brain size has played an important role in the evolution not of man alone but of the whole primate order. The sequence of forms beginning with the tree shrews and going to other prosimians, monkeys, apes, and man, is characterized above all by a growth of the brain and of intelligence. There have been other evolutionary trends among the primates interacting with the brain development. Washburn (1951) regards the achievement of erect posture and of efficient bipedal locomotion a critically important stage of human evolution. To be able to walk and to run on the ground, instead of climbing on tree branches, our ancestors had to modify their

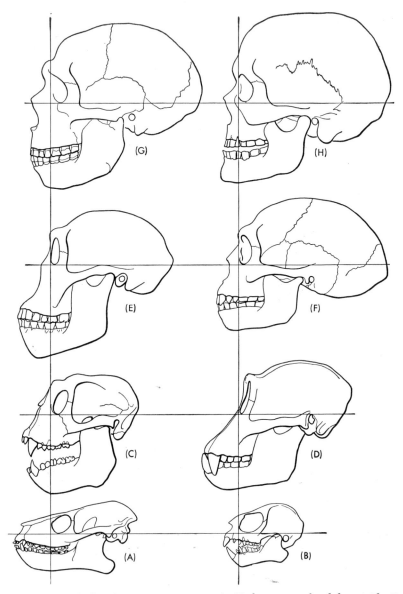

Figure 13.5. Skulls of various primates. *A*, Notharctus, a fossil lemuroid; *B*, Tetonius, a fossil tarsioid; *C*, Mesopithecus, a fossil Old World monkey; *D*, chimpanzee; *E*, Australopithecus; *F*, Java man; *G*, Neanderthal man; *H*, Cro-Magnon man. (From Colbert.)

pelvis bones and the musculature attached thereto, as well as their thigh, leg, and foot bones and muscles.

The use of the arms for handling objects rather than for walking was stimulated by the developing brain, and has in turn stimulated further progress in intelligence. Living in the crowns of tropical

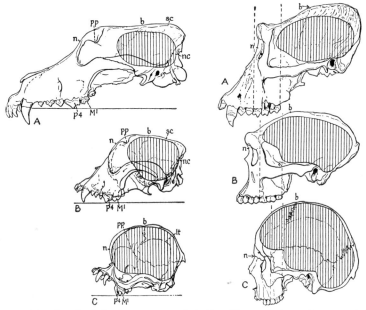

Figure 13.6. On the left: Comparison of skulls of large (*A*), medium-sized (*B*), and small (*C*) breeds of dogs. On the right: Skulls of male gorilla (*A*), Java man (*B*), and modern man (*C*). The brain cavities are shown shaded. The three dogs' skulls are drawn to the same scale, and so are the three anthropoid skulls. (From Weidenreich, courtesy of the University of Chicago Press.)

forest trees has made the primates rely more on good vision, rather than on the sense of smell which is paramount in most other mammalian orders, and to rely on speed, agility, and cunning, rather than on concealment, for protection against their enemies. This condition not only led to changes in the skull, making the eyes look forward instead of laterally, but also necessitated the development of the parts of the brain concerned with vision. Although the ancestors of man at some time abandoned the trees and the tropical forests and became animals walking on the ground and living in more arid and treeless terrain, they have kept their good vision and turned it to other uses, such as fashioning of tools.

The Humanity of Man. It is hard to tell at what point in the evolution of the hominoid stock the prehuman animal became a human being. To some extent this is a matter of definition of what constitutes a "human being." According to Le Gros Clark (1953) the segregation of the family Hominidae (including Australopithecinae) from the ape family (Pongidae) occurred in the Miocene, ten or more million years ago. The most ancient and primitive tools (eoliths) appear at the transition from the Pliocene to the Pleistocene periods in Europe. However, the eoliths are so much like ordinary stones that their nature is a matter of controversy. Unmistakable stone artifacts date from early to middle Pleistocene, perhaps close to a million years ago, and more than 100,000 years ago expertly made tools were available.

Man is not simply a very clever ape, but a possessor of mental abilities which occur in other animals only in most rudimentary forms, if at all. Many animals utter sounds as warning signals or as manifestation of emotions. A dog may bark, howl, growl, and whine in many different ways, the meaning of which may be comprehensible to his master and to other dogs and human beings. But only man uses words to express concepts or to designate categories of objects or acts. A word, after all, is a noise which the human larynx and mouth are able to produce. But to become a word this noise must be invested with a conventional meaning. Thus the sounds of the word "table" are in no way descriptive of the object they denote; they become so by virtue of a certain group of people having learned to associate them with definite objects. Furthermore, the use of sounds for objects involves abstract thinking: "table" means not only an individual piece of furniture but many and diversified pieces having certain properties in common.

Cultural Heredity. Man has developed cultural heredity or *culture*. There are several definitions of culture. One of them is: "The total life way of a people, the social legacy the individual acquires from his group. Or culture can be regarded as that part of the environment that is the creation of man" (Kluckhohn). The essential thing about culture is that it has to be acquired by each individual by learning from others; it is not transmitted from parents to offspring through the sex cells as is biological heredity. For example, nobody is born able to speak, read, and write any language. Children have to be taught speaking, reading, and writing.

And yet human infants are born able to perform the complex series of muscular movements needed to obtain milk from their mothers' breasts. This is a biologically inherited behavior pattern, an instinct. Many animals have wonderfully complex and efficient behavior patterns of courtship, copulation, and care of offspring. These behavior patterns need not be learned. They are set by the genes. Of course cultural and biological heredity are not isolated from each other; they constantly interact. For example, although we have to learn reading and writing, the ability to learn is genotypic. The human sexual drive, though instinctive at base, is overlaid with so great a mass of culturally acquired conditionings and elaborations that it is chiefly non-genetic in its manifestations.

Culture is acquired, and like all acquired traits it is not transmitted through genes in the sex cells. This may at first glance seem to diminish the adaptive effectiveness of culture. In reality the opposite is true: culture is a powerful means for controlling human environments exactly because it is not biologically inherited. We inherit our genes only from parents and other direct ancestors. We transmit them only to children and to direct descendants. There is no way to transmit our genes to even the most dearly beloved friends. The biological heredity of populations can be changed only by the relatively slow process of breeding and selection. By contrast, culture can be transmitted to any number of contemporaneous individuals or to future generations, regardless of biological descent or relationships. The founders of great religions, scientists, inventors, poets, philosophers, and men of action have influenced the cultural heredity of mankind for many generations and perhaps forever. Cultural evolution is vastly more rapid and efficient than biological evolution (see further discussion of this in Chapter 14).

Because of the great efficiency of the transmission of culture, man has been able to master an immense variety of environments. Organisms other than man become adapted to their environments by changing their bodies and their genes by the relatively inefficient process of natural selection. Man alone adapts himself, in a large part, by actively or even deliberately changing the environment, and by inventing and creating new environments.

He uses his immense powers to modify the environment not always wisely, but on a scale so grand that he has become an important not only biological but also geological agent. He has plowed up the soil and changed it by destruction of forests and other vegetation. The adaptive advantage of the ability to acquire even the most rudimentary forms of culture must have been so great in the early stages of human evolution that natural selection rapidly propagated the genotypes which permitted the acquisition of culture throughout the human species. The gene-controlled capacity to learn, absorb, and use new techniques and tools was, then, developed, intensified, and diffused by means of biological evolution, making our species more and more human.

Rudiments of Cultural Transmission among Animals. Human intellectual abilities seem to be not only quantitatively but also qualitatively different from those of animals other than men. It is important, therefore, to demonstrate that rudiments of these specifically human abilities can be found in certain animals. Natural selection found in the ancestors of our species the raw materials from which the present genetic endowment of mankind was compounded.

It can easily be observed that, at least among mammals and birds, the offspring acquire certain behavior patterns by imitation and learning from their parents. Wolves and cats instruct their young in hunting techniques. But all this does not necessarily result in the formation of learned tradition comparable to human culture. In animals, the individuals of one generation transmit to those of the next what they themselves learned from their parents—not more and not less. Every generation learns the same thing which its parents have learned. In only very few instances the evidence is conclusive that the learned behavior can be modified or added to, and that the modifications and additions are transmitted to subsequent generations.

Promptov, Sick, and others found that some details of the song of some birds vary in different local races, and that young birds learn them by imitating their parents and other birds in the neighborhood. (The ability to produce certain notes is, of course, a genetic trait of each bird species, just as the ability to learn to read is a genetic trait of the human species.) Three populations of the chaffinch, near Stuttgart, Germany, each live in a definite neighborhood, and differ in the calls which males utter in their breeding territories. One of these populations is confined to a certain large park, which is known to be about 300 years old. It is probable that the special "dialect" of the chaffinches in this part has evolved within this period of time.

A spectacular instance of development of a "custom" has been observed in the kea parrot (*Nestor notabilis*) in New Zealand. At some time late in the last century the kea started to attack and kill sheep and rapidly became a serious pest and an economic problem. Until the arrival of the white man, New Zealand had no sheep and no animals of similar size and character; the sheep killing is a new habit which has spread among the kea parrots by imitation and learning.

According to Lack, the finch *Camarhynchus pallidus* on the Galapagos Islands uses a cactus spine which it carries in its beak to poke into crevices of tree bark to get at insects on which it feeds. This animal is, then, using a primitive "tool"; it would be interesting to ascertain whether this tool-using habit is acquired by young birds by a process of learning and whether it can be modified.

Brilliant experiments of von Frisch have shown that honey bees have a "language" which, as recently pointed out by the anthropologist Kroeber, involves the use of some genuine symbols, which otherwise are known for sure only in man. A bee which has located a source of food returns to the hive and performs a special "dance," which imparts to the hive mates information concerning the direction from the hive where the food is to be had. The movements of which the "dance" is composed indicate the direction in a purely symbolic fashion.

Insect Societies. Allee (1951) and Ashley Montagu (1950) maintain that all animals are social to some extent. Indeed, even the relationships between the sexes and between parents and offspring involve some cooperation ("protocooperation" according to Allee) and social behavior. Some animals, however, live in complex and highly organized societies. Most monkeys and apes are social animals; they live in bands or herds, warn each other of approaching danger, announce the finding of food, etc. It is probable that the development of cooperation in the social life of prehuman primates was quite important in the origin of human mental abilities.

Apart from man, the most highly organized societies occur not among mammals or birds but among insects—wasps, bees, and especially ants and termites. The study of the social life of these insects has yielded some of the most fascinating stories which biology has to offer. Ants and termites live in colonies which may consist of many thousands of individuals. A colony builds a nest, often of elaborate and species-specific architecture. Food is collected and stored in special chambers. Larvae and different classes of adults may be provided with different diet. Some species of ants engage in "agriculture" —they collect pieces of leaves, store them in their nests, seed them with spores of special fungi, harvest the fungus growth when it reaches a certain degree of maturity, and use it for food. Ants and termites often have in their nests other kinds of insects or other animals which stand to their hosts in a relation analogous to that of domesticated animals to man. Some of these "guests" of the ant and termite nests are unable to live independent lives, since they are fed and cared for

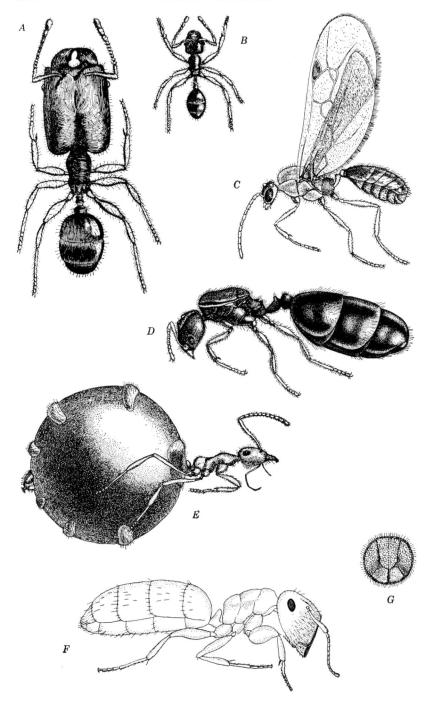

by their hosts. The benefits which the hosts derive from their charges sometimes appear far-fetched; for example, some ant guests produce odoriferous secretions which the hosts lick with avidity.

Most remarkable of all is the division of labor between the different kinds, or "castes," of individuals in ant and termite colonies (Figure 13.7). A colony of ants has one or more "queens" and "kings," which are females and males whose business is reproduction and who are fed and cared for by the workers. Workers are sexually underdeveloped females who collect food and build the nest; soldiers, also underdeveloped females, who take care of the defense from outside invasions; and such curious castes as door-keepers with heads fashioned into plugs to close the nest entrances, and living barrels, with enormously swollen abdomens in which certain provisions are stored. All members of a colony show complete "unselfishness" and "devotion" to the common good.

Innate and Learned Behavior. In describing insect societies, it is hard to avoid expressions like "unselfishness" and "devotion," borrowed from the human social and ethical vocabulary. We must, however, beware of the fallacy of anthropomorphism, which ascribes to animals human motivations and emotions. Yet some biologists have again and again tendered the quaint advice, that human societies ought to be reformed to emulate the "virtues" of insect societies. How nice it would be if our society were organized for the benefit of all, if every person was an expert in some useful function and performed it to the best of his ability, and if all men were heroes ready to sacrifice themselves for mankind!

Such counsels are naïve, because the behavior of social insects is innate or instinctive, and is fixed by heredity; human social behavior is learned from others or devised through reasoning and choice. It is important to realize the implications of this distinction.

Innate behavior is a wonderful instrument which efficiently serves the needs of the species in the environments in which this species normally lives. The behavior of an insect building a nest or arranging things for its progeny appears highly competent and wise. Most important, their behavior needs not to be learned. Among the marvels of ant and termite societies one thing is conspicuously absent. Nowhere is there a school for the young workers or soldiers! An ant just

Figure 13.7. Specialized individuals (castes) in ants. *A*, soldier; *B*, worker; *C*, a winged male; *D*, a female who has lost her wings, of *Pheidole instabilis;* *E*, a "replete" or honey barrel of *Myrmecocystus hortideorum;* *F*, a soldier door-keeper of *Colobopsis etiolata;* and *G*, its head in front view. (After Wheeler, redrawn.)

344 Human Evolution

hatched from a pupa, or just having reached a certain stage of its development, is just as expert at performing its work as it will be after having done this work repeatedly. By contrast, human infants are utterly helpless and must undergo prolonged training and education before they can take care of themselves and become useful members of society. In no other animal is this period during which the young require protection and care so long as in man. But during this period the young absorb the accumulated cultural experience of the human species; they need not learn things only by trial and error or make all the mistakes and discoveries which others have made before them. However time-consuming may be the individual apprenticeship, a very much longer process of cultural development is telescoped in the upbringing and education (see Chapter 14).

There is an all-important limitation to the apparent wisdom of innate behavior: it may no longer function to the advantage of either the individual or the species in new environments, which the species has seldom or never encountered in the past. The classical experiments of Fabre (1823–1915) illustrate well the rigidity of instinctive behavior. One example will suffice here. The mason-bee (Chalicodoma) constructs pot-shaped cells from pellets of clay, fills them with honey and pollen, deposits an egg on these provisions which the larva hatching from the egg will eat, and finally seals the opening of the pot with a clay cover. While the bee is in the process of constructing the cell, she notices and repairs any damage which the construction suffers. As soon as the building is finished and the insect begins to collect the provisions, repairs are no longer made. Fabre made in a cell a hole through which the honey then escaped. The bee went on trying to fill the bottomless barrel. Similarly, while the provisions are being collected, the insect removes and throws away any extraneous particles that may happen to get into the cell. But when the egg is laid and the opening is to be sealed, it is sealed regardless of the presence of conspicuous debris on the surface of the food.

This does not mean that instinctive behavior is absolutely fixed. Innate behavior patterns, like other traits determined by the genotype, can be modified within certain limits by the environment. As always, the genotype determines the norm of response to the environment. Environmental variations which the species often meets evoke modifications of the innate behavior patterns which are, as a rule, beneficial to the organism. For example, the drive which makes birds of a given species migrate in spring and in autumn to different countries is innate, and is released by a physiological mechanism of a hormonal nature. But the birds do adjust their wanderings to some extent to weather conditions. Similarly, ants can use a certain range of materials for the construction of their nests and adjust the shape of the nest to local conditions. Innate behavior, however, is less plastic and less versatile than learned behavior.

Human Diversity. Man inhabits all parts of the world and all climes. He is consequently exposed to a great variety of environments. Moreover, he uses his ingenuity, his technological competence, to invent ever new environments. Consequently, environments in which men live change rapidly with time. To be sure, the diversity and changeability of human environments are due chiefly to cultural rather than to physical causes. The physical environments in which men live are, in fact, becoming progressively more standardized. The clothing which men wear, the houses in which they live, artificial heating, lighting, and assured food supply make the physical environments perhaps more uniform now than they were during the formative period of the biological evolution of our species.

Quite the reverse is true of social and cultural environments. Here the diversity is enormous and ever increasing. Even in primitive societies there is a division of labor among their members. Some individuals gather or produce food; others make implements and vessels; still others act as priests, witch doctors, or leaders. In advanced societies the functions to be performed are not only highly diversified, but new ones constantly appear and the old ones vanish. Finally, every individual performs different functions as a child, an adolescent, an adult, and an old man or woman.

We know that a living species adapts itself to diverse and variable environments by two methods (Chapters 6 and 7). First, a variety of genotypes is produced, each specialized to fit a certain part of the available range of environments. Second, genotypes are evolved which permit their possessors to adjust themselves successfully to a certain spectrum of environments by homeostatic modification of the phenotype. The first method involves genetic specialization; the second emphasizes the adaptive plasticity of the phenotype.

The first method of adaptation makes the inhabitants of different regions of the earth diverge genetically and form allopatric geographic races. It also makes people living in the same region genetically diversified, and causes genetic variation between individuals and polymorphism in human populations. The second method makes people able to adjust themselves to circumstances. Human plasticity and educability make it possible to have most normal human beings trained to perform competently whatever functions the society may need to have ministered to, although some persons may be genetically conditioned to succeed in the performance of some functions more than of others (see Chapter 14).

Classification of Human Races. The fact that human populations of different countries are visibly and genetically different is, then, a reflection of the diversity of environments in these countries. Human races have developed through the adaptation of human populations to their surroundings.

It has, however, been shown in Chapter 7 that the number of races which one chooses to recognize in a species by giving them names is largely a matter of convenience. It is not surprising, therefore, that different authorities have held widely divergent opinions concerning the number of human races.

Perhaps the simplest division of the human species is in three major races: Negroid, Mongoloid, and White or Caucasoid. Negroids have dark brown to black skins, frizzly or kinky hair, broad flat noses, and usually thick lips. In Mongoloids the face is flattened, hair straight and coarse, nose flat at the root and with moderately spread nostrils. Whites have usually, though not always, pale skin, narrow and often long noses, and straight, wavy, or curly hair. By distinguishing the natives of Australia from the Negroids, the pre-Columbian inhabitants of the Americas from the Mongoloids, and the inhabitants of the South Sea Islands, from Hawaii to New Zealand, which are hard to place in the three-race scheme, we arrive at the following six races: (1) Negroid, (2) Mongoloid, (3) White or Caucasoid, (4) Australoid, (5) American Indian, and (6) Polynesian.

The six-race scheme obviously fails to do justice to differences easily observable among human populations. For example, the white race of this scheme includes people as different as the predominantly blond northern Europeans, the brunet Arabs, and the tawny Hindus. Very naturally, anthropologists attempted to split the races further and further in the vain hope of making them more uniform and more clear-cut. The result has been a useless multiplication of racial names. The dividing lines between the small races are often completely blurred by the intermarriage and gene exchange which have been going on for centuries and millennia and are becoming more and more frequent as time goes on. Moreover, no classifications satisfactory to all anthropologists has been arrived at; different authorities have proposed different numbers of races.

A reasonable proposal, made in 1950 by three outstanding American anthropologists, Coon, Garn, and Birdsell, recognizes thirty races, listed in Table 13.3 and Figure 13.8. Without attempting to describe the races in any detail, some interesting features of this classification deserve to be mentioned.

In the first place, Coon, Garn, and Birdsell claim no finality for their thirty-race classification. They recognize that race is not a static but a dynamic entity. Old races may disappear, either because human populations may die out or because races may merge together owing to frequent intermarriage. New races are formed by selection, hybridization, and genetic drift. Some of the races listed in Table 13.3 did not exist a thousand years ago; others were relatively more numerous than now; many have become distributed more widely, while some have contracted the areas of their habitation. Thus the Murrayian race in Australia (1) and the Ainu race (2) in eastern Asia are on the verge of extinction or of being engulfed by intermarriage with other races. Both these races showed high frequencies of heavy brow ridges, large teeth, and thick skull bones, which are traits often met with in early human races and species known as fossils (see above). Lapps (6), Negritos (9), Bushmen (10), Carpentarians (13), and Dravidians (14) may also be engulfed by the more numerous races near whom they live.

On the other hand, the beginnings of the formation of the races (19), (20), (28), and (30), Table 13.3, date back only some centuries. The North American Colored race (19) is a result of admixture of genes of European origin, and of some American Indian genes, in the gene pool formed by a mixture of several races native to Africa. An analogous population is South African Colored (20) which arose by hybridization of races (10) and (11) with immigrants from western Europe. The Ladinos (28) are a series of populations which exist as castes or classes in some Latin American countries; they arose by hybridization of the immigrant Mediterraneans (17) with the native Indians (27, some 26), and, in places, some Negroes. Finally, the Neo-Hawaiians (30) are a very recent population arising from hybridization of the Polynesian race (29) with migrants from various parts of Asia, America, and Europe.

These new races are biologically no less "real" than the old ones which have contributed to their formation. No race of a sexual and cross-fertilizing species ever consists of genetically identical individuals. It cannot be too often emphasized that "pure races" exist only in asexual organisms and are figments of the imagination as far as man is concerned. Gene exchange between races of a sexual spe-

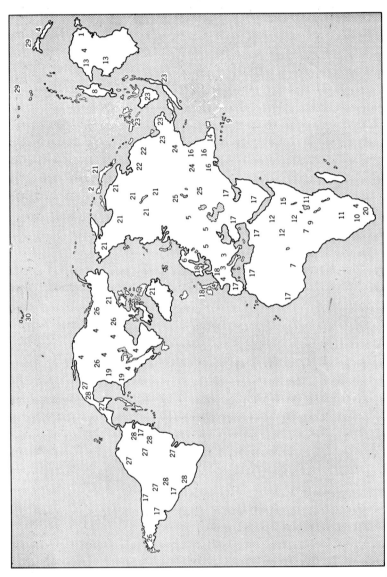

Figure 13.8.   Geographic location of the races of man listed in Table 13.3.   The numbers on the map refer
to those in the table.   (After Coon, Garn, and Birdsell, redrawn.)

TABLE 13.3

RACIAL CLASSIFICATION OF MANKIND, ACCORDING TO
COON, GARN, AND BIRDSELL

Name of the Race	Country of Origin or Residence
1. Murrayian	Aboriginal population of southeastern Australia
2. Ainu	Aboriginal population of Japan
3. Alpine	Central Europe to western Asia
4. Northwest European	Native in northern and western Europe, now world-wide
5. Northeast European	Russia and Poland
6. Lapp	Northern Scandinavia
7. Forest Negro	Western Africa and Congo
8. Melanesian	New Guinea to Fiji and New Caledonia
9. Negrito	Enclaves in Africa, Philippines, New Guinea, Andaman Islands
10. Bushmen	Aboriginal population of South Africa
11. Bantu	East and South Africa
12. Sudanese	Upper Nile, Sudan
13. Carpentarian	Aborigines of northern and central Australia
14. Dravidian	Aboriginal population of southern India
15. Hamite	East Africa and Sudan
16. Hindu	India
17. Mediterranean	Southern Europe, North Africa, Near East
18. Nordic	Northern and western Europe
19. North American Colored	The "colored" population of United States
20. South African Colored	The "colored" population of South Africa
21. Classic Mongoloid	Eastern Siberia, Mongolia, Korea, Japan, Eskimo
22. North Chinese	Northern and central China
23. Southeast Asiatic	Southern China, Siam, Indonesia, Philippines
24. Tibeto-Indonesian Mongoloid	Tibet, northern Burma, parts of Indonesia
25. Turkic	Turkestan, Central Asia
26. American Indian, Marginal	Most of American Indians
27. American Indian, Central	Southwestern United States to Bolivia
28. Ladino	Mexico to Bolivia
29. Polynesian	Islands of central Pacific Ocean
30. Neo-Hawaiian	Hawaiian Islands

cies is always likely to take place. It occurred between the Neanderthalians and the more modern-looking races of *Homo sapiens* during
the Ice Age (see page 332). In organisms other than man, biologists
can study only the situation as it appears today and can at best make
conjectures concerning the past. The history of human populations

Figure 13.9. Representatives of some of the races of the human species. A, Murrayian (No. 1); B, Polynesian (No. 29); C, Melanesian (No. 8); D, Neo-Hawaiian (No. 30). Numbers refer to the racial classification of Coon, Garn, and Birdsell, summarized in Table 13.3. (After Coon, Garn, Birdsell, and other sources, redrawn.)

Figure 13.10.   Representatives of some of the races of the human species.   A,
Classic Mongoloid (No. 21); B, Turkic (No. 25); C, Southeast Asiatic (No. 23);
D, American Indian (No. 26).

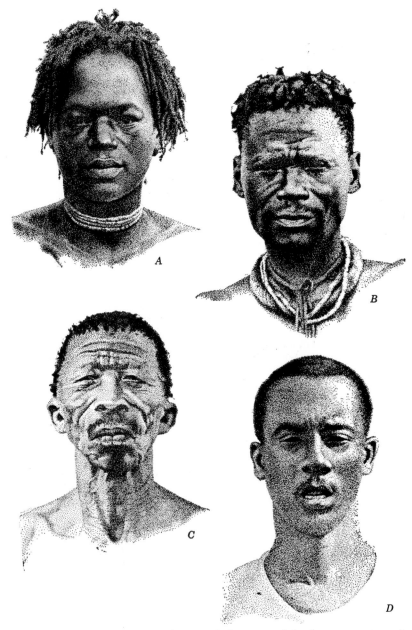

Figure 13.11. Representatives of some of the races of the human species. *A*, Forest Negro (No. 7); *B*, Bantu (No. 11); *C*, Bushman (No. 10); *D*, Hamite (No. 15).

Figure 13.12. Representatives of some of the races of the human species. *A*, Alpine (No. 3); *B*, Northwest European (No. 4); *C*, Mediterranean (No. 17); *D*, Hindu (No. 16).

is known much better, and this allows some insight to be gained into the processes of race formation and amalgamation.

Adaptive Nature of Human Races. Man's most powerful means of adaptation to his environments is learned and acquired knowledge, the ability to choose consciously and to create new environments, in short his culture. In the concluding chapter of this book it will be argued that the genetic endowments which permit the acquisition and maintenance of culture are the property of the human species as a whole, not of any one race. Relative to the efficacy of cultural adaptation, the importance of the genetic differences between the races is very small indeed. It is also diminishing with time, as civilization discovers ever new methods of controlling environments. In fact, surprisingly little is known about the adaptive significance of the particular traits which distinguish human races. Coon, Garn, and Birdsell (1950) and Coon (1954), however, have made some tentative suggestions which may be reviewed here.

People with black or chocolate-brown skin are native to the forests and grasslands of Central Africa, Melanesia (New Guinea and islands to the southeast), southern India, and some islands on the fringe of southern Asia. All these regions are located in the torrid zone along the Equator, where the sunlight is intense and the danger of sunburn is great. The skin pigment absorbs the ultraviolet radiation which is responsible for the sunburn. No dark-skinned population has yet developed in the American tropics, partly because human occupancy of these lands is relatively recent, and partly, according to Coon, because most populations there live either in the shade of dense forests or in the mountains. People native in temperate and cold climates can develop the protective tan following skin exposure to light, or can bleach if covered with clothing or if the weather is cloudy. Bleached skin is supposedly advantageous because it permits the scarce ultraviolet rays to produce enough of the vitamin D, the "sunshine vitamin" which is necessary for health. Skin which can either darken or bleach is, therefore, advantageous where the amount of sunshine is variable with the season (cf., however, Chapter 7).

In bodies of similar shape, the surface grows as the square, and the volume (or weight) as the cube, of the linear dimensions. In other words, the smaller the body, the greater its surface in relation to the volume. Body surface is relatively greater in tall and slender people than in short and rotund people of similar bulk; long arms and legs and large flat hands and feet also increase the body surface. The body surface acts as a radiator of an automobile does, causing dissipation of heat and cooling of the body. It follows that an increase of the body surface relative to the body mass is desirable in hot climates, and a decrease in cold climates. There is some evidence that the observed racial variation is on the whole in accord with these requirements. In Europe the bulkiest people inhabit the North, whereas the Mediterranean people tend to be more slight and gracile. Among the Mongoloids, northern Chinese are larger people than their southern countrymen, Annamites, and Siamese. In the Americas, the Maya of southern Mexico and Guatemala, and the Amazonian Indians are small, whereas the Indians of Alaska, Canada, the northern United States, aₙd of southern Argentina are more bulky. In Africa, the Nilotic Negroes are among the tallest people in the world, but they are also exceptionally slim. Coon is also of the opinion that the characteristic features of the Mongoloid face may represent an adaptation to the cold, dry, and windy climates of the great interior of Asia.

Not all racial traits need be so utilitarian as suggested above. Some facial features, hair shapes, and perhaps body forms may have become established by natural selection in response to the vagaries of popular tastes and ideals of bodily beauty. The possessors of traits considered comely and pleasing may have been favored as mates and placed in superior positions to raise large families. Much study and research are necessary before the origin of human racial characters can be fully understood.

Suggestions for Further Reading

Darwin, Ch. 1871. *The Descent of Man.*

This book remains a great classic of evolutionary literature.

For more up-to-date information on human origins consult the following five books:

Coon, C. S. 1954. *The Story of Man.* Knopf, New York.
Howells, W. W. 1945. *Mankind so Far.* Doubleday, New York.
Howells, W. W. 1954. *Back of History. The Story of Our Own Origins.* Doubleday, New York.
Ashley Montagu, M. F. 1951. *An Introduction to Physical Anthropology.* 2nd Edition. Ch. Thomas, Springfield, Ill.
Weidenreich, F. 1946. *Apes, Giants, and Man.* University of Chicago Press, Chicago.

Concerning human origins, as well as concerning the problems of human race and racial classification, consult also the books of Count, Boyd, Coon, Garn and Birdsell, and the *Symposium on the Origin and Evolution of Man,* cited among the suggested readings in Chapter 7.

The story of social insects and the relations between the innate (instinctive) and the learned behavior are discussed in the following books:

Allee, W. C., Emerson, A. E., Park, O., Park, Th., and Schmidt, K. P.   1949. *Principles of Animal Ecology.*   Saunders, Philadelphia.

See particularly Chapters 23, 24, and 35.

Haskins, C. P.   1945.   *Of Ants and Men.*   Allen & Unwin, London.
Haskins, C. P.   1951.   *Of Societies and Men.*   Norton, New York.
Lorenz, K.   1952.   *King Solomon's Ring. New Light on Animal Ways.*   Crowell, New York.

14

Chance, Guidance, and Freedom in Evolution

The idea of evolution, of transformation of one kind of organism into another, certainly antedates Darwin. Before scientific biology appeared, even the weirdest stories of transformation were often credited (see page 166). In classical antiquity, the creation myths of Anaximander, Empedocles, and Lucretius fancied that living beings arose from very different progenitors and from inanimate matter (page 111). H. F. Osborn (1857–1935) and others claimed that Aristotle was also an evolutionist, since he maintained that nature advances from the inanimate to the animate, and from less perfect to more perfect creatures (page 224). It is not, however, certain whether Aristotle meant this advancement as a concrete historical event, or only as a part of his more general philosophical view that a vital force, a soul, gives a recognizable actuality and "form" to potentiality and "primary matter." Aristotelian views were taken over by medieval philosophers and theologians, particularly by St. Thomas Aquinas, who did not interpret them in any recognizably evolutionist sense. On the other hand, Descartes (1596–1650) and Buffon (1707–1788) apparently did arrive at evolutionist views of nature. But in their day such views were regarded as subversive, and Descartes and Buffon accepted the dictates of authority and were in no mood to risk their privileged positions. They saw fit to disguise their views as mere amusing paradoxes or idle play of the intellect. Maupertuis (1698–1759), Erasmus Darwin (grandfather of Charles, 1731–1802), Goethe, and several others mentioned in Chapter 10, approached the problem of evolution in various ways. The possibility that the world of life might be a product of evolution was, indeed, "in the air" when Charles Darwin started his work.

The greatness of Lamarck and of Darwin was that they not only adduced new and compelling evidence of evolution (which they certainly did), but that they also made the occurrence of evolution intelligible. Lamarck and Darwin agreed that the evolution of life on earth had been brought about by causes which continue to be in operation even now. These causes can, then, be observed and experimented with. It happens that a century and a half of observations and experiments have failed to confirm Lamarck's surmise of what these causes are. Darwin's ideas have stood the test of time much better. Both Lamarck and Darwin were innovators who proved that life has had history, and that this history is not unfathomable. Although we shall never be able to have the evolution of the living world re-enacted as a whole before our eyes, at least some elementary evolutionary events have been reproduced (Chapters 5 and 9). Man may yet learn to direct the future course of the evolution of species, including his own.

The general biological theory of evolution outlined in this book developed, by an unbroken continuity of thought, from the Darwinian prototype (Chapter 6). However, biology has not stood still since Darwin; therefore, the modern theory differs greatly from Darwin's. Not all biologists, however, are satisfied that this theory is valid. Quite properly, they have tried to suggest alternative possibilities. and these alternatives should be given consideration. Even though none of them may prove acceptable, a clearer perspective of evolutionary biology will be gained in the process.

Autogenesis and Finalism. The longing to know the future is deeply ingrained in human nature. Science helps to understand the present, to comprehend the past, and to predict the future. Astronomers can foresee the second when a sun eclipse will be visible from any given point of the earth's surface, and can describe eclipses which happened centuries ago. The astronomer Laplace (1749–1827) asserted that, given for one instant a knowledge of the positions and the velocities of all the masses composing the universe at any particular moment, "an intelligence vast enough to submit these data to analysis would embrace in the same formula the motions of the greatest bodies in the Universe and those of the lightest atoms; for such an intelligence nothing would be uncertain, and the future, as well as the past, would be present to its eyes." Of course, no human intelligence is anywhere near so vast, but Laplace's proud hope became a basic tenet of mechanistic science.

The present state of the universe, then, is the consequence of its previous states and the cause of its future states. Once this is granted, it inevitably follows that the evolution of life, of man, and indeed of the whole cosmos, was predetermined and fixed from the start. This conclusion harmonizes very nicely with the biological preformation theory (Chapter 10). Primordial life contained within itself all the evolution to come, as a flower bud contains all parts of the future flower. Evolutionary changes arise, some biologists suppose, from inside the organism, *autogenetically,* and lead only to the unfolding of what was there from the beginning. It was not natural selection at all which has shaped the diversity of living creatures. If evolution is brought about by autogenesis, then natural selection can accept only what is fit to survive in a given environment and reject what is unfit. An analogy will make clearer what is meant by autogenesis. The element uranium decomposes into helium and lead; the rate of decomposition is constant and largely independent of the environment; it is possible to predict that after a certain number of years a certain fraction of the uranium will have turned to lead. May organic evolution be caused by a similar process? L. S. Berg (1926) thought that it might. According to him, evolution is "nomogenesis," that is, "development according to law" residing in the living matter itself. What evolution produces is what it is destined to produce, just as a flower bud is destined to produce a flower. Rosa's "hologenesis" (1931) is a similar notion.

We need not be mechanistic materialists to believe in autogenesis. A modern brand of vitalism, known as *finalism,* credits this notion. Cuénot (1941) and Vandel (1949) in France, their popularizer Du Noüy (1947) in the United States, Naef (1919) and Dacqué (1931, 1940) in Germany, and other finalists have no use for crude material forces such as mutation and selection. The problem of evolution is resolved more simply. Evolution strives to reach a predetermined goal or end. This goal is assumed to be the production of man. To Dacqué, the amoebae, fishes, amphibia, etc., are "disguised states of mankind," whatever this may mean. To Vandel, "Matter was at its origin rich in power and in unrealized possibilities, able to engender the organic as well as the inorganic, the living and the inert. In giving birth to life, matter passed to the latter the essence of its creative energy, and this effort reduced matter to a degraded relic, devitalized, and having lost most of its ancestral qualities." Having produced man, the evolution of life has done its job, and has terminated. Organisms other than man are "by-products, slags, left over after its (man's) production." H. F. Osborn (1934) held opinions close to those of the modern finalists. To him, the important principle which brings forth evolution was "aristogenesis," an urge towards greater "perfection," assumed to be inherent in life.

Orthogenesis. To most biologists the speculations of the finalists and other believers in autogenesis seem frankly puzzling. Nevertheless, the validity of a scientific theory, however startling it may seem, is tested by its ability to account for facts which are incompatible with other theories. The alleged basis of autogenetic theories is the apparent directedness of evolutionary changes, revealed especially by the fossil evidence. Consider the succession of the shell forms in the snail shown in Figure 12.1. In each successive geological stratum the shells become more and more angular, as though the evolution of these snails were directed by some force straight towards attainment of the greatest possible angularity. For such apparently directed trends of evolutionary changes Eimer (1897) introduced the word "*orthogenesis.*"

One of the most famous examples of orthogenesis is the development of gigantic antlers in the males of the Irish elk, Megaloceros (Figure 14.1). Starting with late Tertiary times (Pliocene) the ancestors of Megaloceros were getting progressively larger in size, and, as they were getting larger, the antlers in the males were getting more and more enormous, until during the Ice Age the antlers reached seemingly absurd dimensions; and finally these animals died out. Some paleontologists surmised that such huge antlers must have been injurious to their carriers, and concluded that Megaloceros died out *because* its antlers got too big for it to carry. In other words, the evolutionary trend towards large antlers developed such a momentum that it could not stop, even when it got to be harmful and led to extinction. Simpson's fitting comment about this surmise is: "I can only feel awe for any one who *knows* that structures were disadvantageous in animals that were very abundant for tens of thousands of years and more."

The evolutionary history of the horse tribe, considered briefly in Chapter 12, has often been alleged to represent another clear instance of orthogenesis, and has been cited as such in many books on biology and evolution. Indeed, starting with the little Eohippus, the horses were getting larger and larger, the modern thoroughbred horse (Chapter 9) being a veritable giant compared to Eohippus. Furthermore, beginning with the Condylarths and the Eohippus, the ancestors of the horse were losing toe after toe, until the modern horses have just a single toe left on each foot to stand on. The **teeth** became progressively bigger and bigger, their structure getting more and more suitable for grazing.

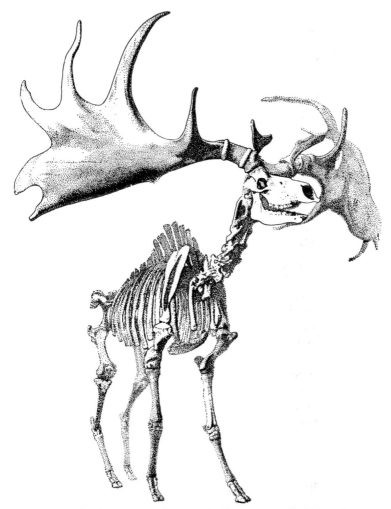

Figure 14.1. A fossil stag (Megaloceros, also known as Irish elk) with enormous antlers, which some authors imagined to be harmful to the animal. (After Cuenot, redrawn.)

The evolution of the human family (Chapter 13) shows a progressive development of the brain, with corresponding changes in the bones which house this noble organ, and in the body which is presided over by its function. This is an orthogenesis of sorts. But does it follow that the Australopithecinae, or the tarsiers, or any other human ancestors or relatives were men in disguise, who needed millions of years to slough off their animal masks? There is nothing to necessitate such a view. Not all primates, nor all anthropoids, evolved in the direction of man, and there is no reason to think that they will do so in the future.

Orthoselection. The above examples of orthogenetic trends are not exceptional. Fossil histories of many groups of organisms may be interpreted as showing trends of one kind or another. Many paleontologists and some biologists believed that a theory of evolution of the type outlined in the foregoing chapters of this book could not explain the apparent prevalence of orthogenetic trends. If so, we would have to turn to one of the theories with names ending in—genesis mentioned above. The German paleontologist Schindewolf (main works in 1936 and 1950) has been particularly emphatic in expounding the view that an explanation on autogenetic or finalistic lines is necessary. Simpson (1944, 1953) and Rensch (1947) have performed a great service to science by demonstrating that there is actually nothing in the known fossil record to contradict the modern biological theory of evolution.

In speculating about the evolutionary trends disclosed by the fossils, we must be on guard in order that, seeing the obvious, we do not miss the significant. Simpson, having analyzed the fossil evidence of horse evolution in greater detail than any one else, has concluded that the orthogenetic interpretation can here be sustained only by disregarding important facts. As shown in Chapter 12, there were not one but many evolutionary lines of horses, and not all of them by any means were getting bigger all the time, or getting rid of toes, or developing teeth fit for grazing. True enough, these things happened in some lines of descent, including the one which gave rise to the horses which are now alive. The horses which were largest and strongest, which could run fastest, and which were able to utilize the most abundant food supplies by grazing on grass, survived, while those animals which did not develop these characteristics died out. On the whole, the fossil evidence lends no support to the idea that there was, or is, a built-in propensity to develop in any particular evolutionary direction. It is quite consistent with the view that the evolutionary changes took place owing to natural selection of genotypes which were most suited to exploit certain environmental opportunities, particularly living on open grassy plains which were becoming widespread on earth during the Tertiary geological period.

Of course the evolutionary changes did go in the same directions and often for prolonged periods of time in many groups of organisms. Moreover, the same or parallel evolutionary trends are often observed in different organisms. Perhaps the most widespread and best-known trend concerns gradual but steady increase in body size. This growth has occurred in quite different animals, making them grow larger and larger as time went on. The most ancient mammals (living during the Mesozoic times, see Chapter 12) were only as big as modern mice or, at most, rats. Larger quadrupeds appeared during the Tertiary. The known history of the elephants begins in late Eocene times with animals about as big as a hog. As early as the Oligocene, forms appeared that were as large as a bull. During Miocene and Pliocene came elephants as large or larger than the modern ones, and the giants like the woolly mammoths lived during the Ice Age and died out, perhaps with the active assistance of man who must have regarded them as excellent sources of meat. The increase of the body size in horses has already been discussed, as well as the body size progression among the primates, which may have been our own ancestors (Chapter 13). The primitive reptiles of the Pennsylvanian and Permian ages were only as big as some big lizards, yet they appear to be the ancestors of the most gigantic land animals ever produced, which lived during the Jurassic and Cretaceous periods (see Chapter 12). Evolutionary size increases have been observed also in some invertebrate animals, particularly in mollusks.

There is, however, no iron-clad law that would make evolution produce ever larger animals. For one thing, many animals have remained as small as their ancestors, and some even became smaller. For another, the prevalence of the tendency towards bigness is quite understandable, since larger individuals are usually also stronger, better able to resist some enemies and escape from others. In addition, a more massive body is advantageous in cold climates (see page 355). No wonder, then, that natural selection by and large favors bigger animals over smaller ones. The selection becomes, according to Simpson, *orthoselection*, which operates generally in the same direction. Orthoselection brings about the appearance of orthogenesis. The basic difference is here that orthoselection lasts only as long as the environmental opportunity which favors it; orthogenesis has usually meant a change independent of, or even contrary to, such opportunity. Orthoselection is simply selection long continued.

Allometric Growth. A human infant has a relatively much bigger head and smaller legs and arms than an adult person. This amounts to saying that as our bodies grow, the different organs and parts do not grow in the same proportion. The head grows less than the extremities, so that an adult is not just like a baby magnified, nor is a baby a diminutive adult. Such difference in relative growth rates of body parts is known as *allometry* or allometric growth. Allometry occurs in many kinds of animals and also in plants. Allometry can be observed also when adult bodies of different species or races are compared. Larger species and races often show predictably different body proportions, as illustrated in Figure 13.6 for the skulls of the larger and smaller breeds of dogs.

Allometry is a reasonable explanation of some otherwise very puzzling evolutionary changes. Consider again the Irish stag Megaloceros (Figure 14.1). This extinct form had not only much larger antlers than its ancestors and relatives, but it was a larger animal. The evolution of the ancestors of Megaloceros brought about an increase in body size as well as in antler size. Now among deer and their relatives, as the body grows larger, the antlers increase in size even faster. If natural selection for any reason favored larger and more powerful bodies, the antlers would be expected to overtake the body in the rates of increase. This prize example of orthogenesis (see above) is most likely an instance of orthoselection. Seeing the monstrous antlers of Megaloceros we wonder why selection should ever have created such an unwieldy structure. But it is as certain as such things can be that natural selection does not bring into being antlers separate from heads, or heads separate from the shoulders, etc. It is an individual's body as a whole that lives, grows, reproduces, and dies. And natural selection is opportunistic: So long as bigger stags transmitted their genes to the following generations more efficiently than smaller stags, the selection favored increasing size. Assuming that the huge antlers were a burden to the animals (and this is an assumption which may easily be wrong), a genotype which would have produced a bigger body with relatively smaller antlers would have had an advantage. There is, however, no warrant to believe that any combination of relative sizes of body parts will always be ready when circumstances favor it. This belief would imply a miraculous prescience of the future on the part of the genotype (see page 107), and genes are, after all, things of this imperfect world.

Evolutionary Youth and Senescence. The way of all flesh is from birth, childhood, exuberance of youth, vigor of maturity, senility to inevitable death. The fossil record shows group after group of organisms which appear, become diversified and abundant, and then decline to extinction. An analogy is tempting: Are youth, senescence, and death the destiny of species, genera, and orders, as they are of individuals? Some believers in autogenesis-orthogenesis thought so. But analogies are a precarious method of scientific cognition. Growth and senescence of individuals are brought about by physiological causes and presumably do not involve changes in the genes; evolution is genetic change. The two things cannot be equated hastily.

Let us see what is meant by evolutionary youth and senility of a group of organisms. The reptiles were "born" in Pennsylvanian times as an offshoot from the amphibians, and the "infant reptile," called Seymouria, was so amphibian-like that, according to Romer, "the academic question has been raised as to whether Seymouria was an amphibian which was almost a reptile or, on the other hand, a reptile which had just ceased to be an amphibian." Very soon (geologically speaking), namely during the Permian, there were present representatives of several (six) orders into which the class of reptiles is divided. Several more orders appeared during the Triassic, including the small ancestors of the future giant "ruling" reptiles. This, then, is the "youth" of the reptiles. The Age of Reptiles, when they were most numerous and diversified, and when the gigantic forms were living, occurred during the late Triassic, Jurassic, and Cretaceous. This is "maturity." But, remarkably enough, no new orders of reptiles appeared when as a class they were dominant. The "senility" came with a crash in the late Cretaceous and in early Tertiary, when all but four previously inconspicuous orders (turtles, crocodiles, lizards and snakes, and the order of the New Zealand tuatara, or Sphenodon) died out. These four orders are still hanging on, but the class of reptiles as a whole is "senile."

Mammals have a similar story. They appeared as an offshoot of the reptiles when the latter were "young." The "infancy" of the mammals was a prolonged one, extending through the whole Age of Reptiles; their vigorous "youth" came in the early Tertiary (Paleocene and Eocene), coincidentally with or immediately after the dying-out of the ruling reptiles. Most living orders of mammals, and some of the extinct ones, appeared at that time, inaugurating the Age of Mammals (see Chapter 12). The greatest blooming of the class of mammals, when they were most diverse and included some spectacularly large or peculiar forms, came in late Tertiary (Miocene and Pliocene). A "senility" may have begun during the Ice Age and the Recent, when there appeared a curious mammal called man. This upstart has succeeded, however, in making the present time the Age of Man.

The careers of the classes of reptiles and of mammals have nothing in them that would compel us to assume that evolutionary "youth" comes inescapably after "infancy," or "senility" after "maturity." Despite the fossil record's being incomplete and in many ways baffling, we may entertain a working hypothesis that the evolutionary events for which this record stands were brought about by natural selection in response to environmental opportunity. Mammals lingered inconspicuously for many millions of years while the reptiles were dominant, but underwent an exuberant adaptive radiation as soon as the dominant reptiles died out. Was this just a coincidence? Is it not more likely that the decline of reptiles opened up biological opportunities which were quickly seized upon by mammals (and by birds)? Again, while most orders of reptiles died out, that of the lizards and snakes suffered no eclipse and is doing nicely even now. They have a place in the sun which is not much encroached upon by the mammals.

The birth of a new group of organisms usually means that an evolutionary "invention" has been made which permits life to exploit novel environments, or to exploit old environments in novel ways. Thus amphibians were the first vertebrates to live on land; reptiles became free from dependence on water as an abode of the early developmental stages (tadpoles); mammals and birds evolved regulation of the body temperature that makes them less dependent than the reptiles are on the vagaries of weather; besides, mammals "invented" superior ways of taking care of their young, while birds became able to exploit the food resources of the air (Chapter 12). Clearly, natural selection would be expected to perpetuate such useful "inventions." It would also be expected to encourage the adaptations to the various aspects of environment, hence the adaptive radiation of the evolutionary "youth" period (Figure 6.1).

Causes of Extinction. Extinction is a frequent finale to many evolutionary histories. The causes which brought about the extinction of many groups of organisms are quite obscure, which is not really surprising, since, even if the fossil record were much more complete than it is, we would often be unable to visualize all the manifold and complex interrelations of the inhabitants of the remote past. But the supposition that extinction occurs "obeying certain internal impulses concealed in the constitution of the organism" (Berg) is barren as a working hypothesis. A diligent study of the interrelations of now-living organisms, however, throws some light on causes of extinction.

Fossil remains of reptiles very much like Sphenodon occur in Triassic and Jurassic rocks in different parts of the world. Then they disappear from the record for at least 130 million years (Cretaceous to Recent, Table 12.1). A population of Sphenodon is nevertheless living on an isle off New Zealand, quite oblivious that it should have long ago felt "internal impulses" towards extinction. However, it is hardly an accident that the living Sphenodon is preserved in a locality so far out of the way. The animal life of New Zealand is limited in variety and lacks representatives of many kinds of creatures which are common elsewhere. The competition of these creatures would probably make short shrift of the Sphenodon. On a larger scale, the marsupials are now restricted chiefly to Australia, where the placental mammals were few until man came (Chapter 12). The marsupials, with the notable exception of the opossum, have died out outside Australia, presumably because they were no match for the placentals.

Every species is enabled by its body structure to occupy and exploit certain ecological, or adaptive, niches in the economy of nature (page 311). Extinction occurs either because the ecological niche disappears, or because it is wrested away by competitors. The ecological niche of a parasite is its host; if the host species dies out, so does the parasite, provided that it cannot victimize alternative hosts. The more narrowly specialized is an organism for life in only certain environments, the greater the risk of extinction. Evolutionary "senility" may be a consequence of specialized adaptation to only a restricted ecological niche. A narrow specialist may live quite happily so long as his exclusive abilities find an assured outlet. The Teddy-bear-like marsupial koala (Phascolarctos, Figure 12.8) deigns to eat nothing but the young foliage of only a few species of eucalypts. Nevertheless this slow and defenseless animal was quite common in parts of Australia until white men started to use it for target practice. Compare this with the dietary versatility, aggressiveness, and watchfulness of such an animal as the gray rat. Koala is now kept in existence only by conservationist laws, whereas the rat is far from rare despite determined campaigns of extermination.

It may seem surprising that evolution controlled by natural selection leads so often to overspecialization and consequent extinction. But this is only a consequence of the fact repeatedly emphasized above that natural selection is opportunistic and, like any natural process other than the human mind, lacks foresight. Selection perpetuates what is advantageous here and now, and fails to perpetuate what may be beneficial in the future unless it is also immediately useful. To take up again the case of the unwieldy antlers of the stag Megaloceros. Provided that larger stags produced more surviving progeny than smaller ones, there must have been an "orthoselection" for size increase. It is, then, conceivable that because of some environmental changes the cumbersome antlers may have become injurious; if the reversal of the size trend could not be accomplished quickly, the animal died out.

Origin of Complex Adaptations. A difficulty, fully realized by Darwin, which any rational theory of adaptation has to face is the formation of complex organs and physiological functions. Consider the human eye with its many wonderfully coordinated parts, each part necessary for the organ to be fully serviceable. Or consider the processes of pregnancy and childbirth. Here is a series of hormones, each with a separate function, and yet acting in an ordered sequence like different instruments in a symphony orchestra; even a slight disturbance may make the process of reproduction end in failure.

Can such delicately engineered systems possibly arise through natural selection acting on the genetic variability supplied by mutation? A mutation is, essentially, a "mistake" in the process of gene reproduction, and most such "mistakes" are detrimental to the organism (Chapter 4). Yet these "mistakes" must be woven by natural selection into such patterns as give rise to useful organs and functions. Let us keep in mind that selection has no foresight and cannot build organs useful only in the future. An organ must be continuously useful, or else selection will neither advance its construction nor even maintain it. To some biologists this requirement seemed too great. "We might just as well expect that if the wheels, screws and other component parts of the mechanism of a watch were to be put into a vessel, we could, by a simple process of shaking, get them to combine in such a manner as to become a watch that would function as such" (Berg). Theories of autogenesis have been urged on this basis.

The objection that theories of evolution by natural selection rely too much on "blind chance" has been made repeatedly since Darwin's day. Mutations are accidents of gene reproduction; gene recombination yields by chance various genotypes; selection improves the chance that some genotypes will leave more offspring than carriers of other genotypes. Can these chances add up to building a complex organ such as an eye? The "watch analogy," however, contains a subtle fallacy. It tacitly assumes that the human eye arose in all its present perfection all at once, by a lucky throw of genetic dice. Such a supposition would, indeed, stretch our credibility to the breaking point.

What actually happened was that eyes were gradually formed and perfected among man's close and remote ancestors. These ancestors had eyes for at least 400 million years (the appearance of the vertebrates in the fossil record). Reptiles have eyes, and so do amphibians and fishes, and even the lowly lancelet (Amphioxus) has pigment cells which make it able to perceive light. Many of man's ancestors had eyes which were simpler in structure and less perfect in function than our own, yet the eyes were always useful to their possessors. Natural selection had ample opportunity to press onward toward high degrees of perfection of the eyes.

The most misleading implication of the "watch analogy" and of similar arguments is that the eye was formed by summation of independent mutations, each responsible for a certain part of the organ—the lens, or the iris, or the rods or the cones of the retina, or the muscles which move the eye, etc. If this were the true nature of genes and mutations, the eye could not function until the last part of the eye mechanism had been installed in its proper place. An automobile motor does not work until every component part is put where it belongs. But genes and mutations do not work that way, and this makes the difference. Genes determine not body parts but developmental processes. The genes make a fertilized egg develop by stages in a body which has, among other parts, eyes of a certain kind. Evolution of the eye, then, is not like the building of a unit motor; it is rather more comparable to the gradual development of internal combustion engines from the first hesitant model to the present powerful and efficient makes.

Preadaptation. Another dialectical tangle in which some evolutionists have ensnared themselves concerns the origin of genetic changes which prove to be adaptive. As we have seen, mutations may be described metaphorically as "mistakes" in the processes of the self-synthesis of genes. These "mistakes" occur regardless of the need of the organism to maintain or to improve its adaptedness to the environment. Nevertheless, some of them occasionally prove to be adaptive. Such occasional mutations may be said to be "preadapted" to certain environments actually before the organism has had any chance to make use of them. From this is only a short dialectical step to saying, as some finalists and vitalists actually did say, that evolutionary changes are in general preadapted to certain environments, whether these environments do or do not actually exist in reality. Thus the ancestors of the ancient amphibians were becoming "preadapted" to exploit the food resources of land before they actually started to walk on it (cf. Chapter 12, page 290); some genetic changes altered the teeth of Tertiary horses in ways to make the latter "preadapted" to grazing instead of browsing (page 305). Man's erect posture made his hands "preadapted" towards performance of delicate manual operations (Chapter 13).

The difficulty is chiefly a verbal one. When some ancient anthropoids made the first tentative attempts to walk erect, not even the shrewdest evolutionist could have predicted that the fore paws of these anthropoids would some day handle surgical instruments used for delicate operations. When these anthropoids were increasing their brains in response to the need for more cunning in escaping enemies it was quite unpredictable that the brains of their remote descendants would eventually develop the ideas of Plato or of Darwin. In other words, we must have the benefit of hindsight to decide whether a given change was preadaptive for anything. "Preadaptation" is a meaningless notion if it is made different from "adaptation."

Progress in Evolution. We have seen in Chapter 10 that according to Aristotle all living beings range in a single series from the least perfect to the most perfect. Lamarck thought that this single ladder of perfection reflected evolution, and this unfortunate mistake was largely responsible for the rejection of Lamarck's whole theory. The belief in progress, however, was too dear to the nineteenth century mentality, and Darwin's theory was promptly interpreted to mean that "no good thing was ever lost and that no lost thing was any longer any good" (Barzun). Indeed, natural selection generally does maintain or improve the adaptedness of a living species to its environment.

The situation, however, is complex. In the first place, there is no single line of evolution but very many different lines. Furthermore, every kind of organism occupies its own adaptive niche, to which it is fitted by its body structure and by its mode of life. The mighty lion may be the king of beasts, but it cannot fly through the air like a bird, nor live in water like a fish, nor subsist on simple organic compounds like bacteria, nor utilize the sunlight as a source of energy like green plants. By and large, every species is superior to all others in its own adaptive niche, for if another species were superior it would drive the first out. But it is ridiculous to conclude on this basis that there has been no progress in evolution, and that man is not a more perfect organism than a worm or an amoeba. There are several possible criteria of progress and perfection, and we must make it clear which one is being used.

Evolution has brought about a tremendous increase in the range of environments in which life is possible, in the diversity of living creatures, and in the total mass of living matter. We do not know what the primordial life was like, but it is certain that it could exist only in some very restricted range of environments. The fossil record of the early Paleozoic consists of only water-dwelling creatures, while land was apparently lifeless. At present life extends almost everywhere on the earth's surface, including such apparently inhospitable places (from the human standpoint) as deserts, high mountains, and subpolar regions. Some forms of life seem so grotesque in appearance (Figure 14.2), or live in such strange places, that we naïvely wonder why such creatures ever appeared. This is another instance of the opportunism of evolution: whatever can perpetuate itself in any accessible environment does so. The appearance and spread of a new species constitute progress, whereas extinction is ⸱⸱⸱ᵒⁿ. Although evolution has been, in this sense, progressive oɪ the living matter (biosphere) is still, on a planetary scɑ thin film at the boundary of the earth's crust (lithospɦ gaseous envelope (atmosphere).

Another kind of progress is the increasing complexity tion of living beings. Simplest plant viruses consist app a single chemical substance—nucleoprotein. Bacteriophage more so, bacteria and unicellular organisms are immensely plex, since their bodies are structured systems involving chemicals. Then follow multicellular organisms; these aga complexity from such relatively "simple" things as Pandoriɴ 1.2), which are merely colonies of semi-independent cells, complex systems of cells, such as the "higher" animals and man. this respect, too, evolution has been on the whole progressive, althoug not always so. For example, parasitic organisms, such as Sacculina (Figure 10.6), are often much simpler in structure than their free-living relatives. There even exists a view that the viruses may be degenerate descendants of more complex bacteria-like organisms.

Furthermore, it is not just a love of complexity which makes evolution produce ever more intricately organized living bodies. Although there is no strict relationship between the two things, more complex organization by and large gives a greateɪ autonomy of the organism from the environment. As pointed out especially by Schmalhausen (1949), evolution has tended to improve the homeostatic adjustments, so that the processes of life can go on despite environmental variations. The transition from the "cold-blooded" reptiles to the "warm-blooded"

mammals constituted progress. So did the development of sense organs in animals which permit the organism to receive more varied
and more exact information about the state of the environment, and

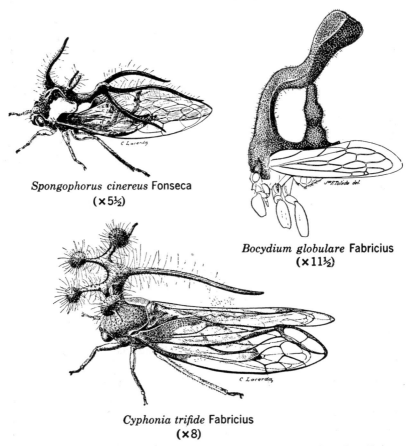

Spongophorus cinereus Fonseca
(×5½)

Bocydium globulare Fabricius
(×11½)

Cyphonia trifide Fabricius
(×8)

Figure 14.2. Some Brazilian representatives of the family Membracidae (homop-
terous insects), having weird outgrowths on their bodies. The function, if any,
of these outgrowths is unknown. (From Costa Lima.)

to react accordingly. The development of the nerve system in general,
and particularly of the brain as a coordinating organ, has been most
efficient in increasing the ability of life to hold on and to widen its
control of the environment. An interesting definition of evolutionary
fitness and progress suggested by Thoday (1953) is "probability of
leaving descendants after a given long period of time." It is reason-

ably certain that this probability is, in general, improved in the higher, compared to the lower, organisms.

Although progress is not necessarily the same thing as success, it is a fact that those groups of organisms which on other grounds may be considered most progressive are likely to become also abundant, diversified, and "dominant." The succession of the "ages" of amphibians, reptiles, mammals, and man attested by the fossil record (Chapter 12) is a case in point. This succession corresponds to what is regarded as progressive evolution among vertebrate animals. A similar reward for evolutionary progress was the accession to dominance of the "higher" flowering plants at the end of the Mesozoic era. On the other hand, a failure to "progress" does not always result in the organism's becoming rare and extinct. Among the "living fossils" shown in Figure 12.3 at least the horseshoe crab (Limulus) and the opossum, and probably also Lingula, are common and prosperous species, apparently in full possession of their respective adaptive niches.

Man, the Pinnacle of Evolution. One of the cheapest ways to gratify our ego is to consider ourselves superior to others. For this reason, the opinion that man stands on the topmost rung of the ladder of progress must be carefully scrutinized. It happens, however, that by all sensible criteria of progress man is superior to other creatures.

Mere growth in numbers may not be an unmitigated blessing, as man is finding to his discomfiture in the overpopulated countries of southern and eastern Asia, but mankind has increased manyfold since the invention of agriculture, and has occupied most of the habitable surface of the globe (Chapter 13). The case is less clear in complexity of the organization of the body, since there is no way to measure this complexity precisely. We can say, however, that the vertebrates in general, and among them the mammals, possess remarkably elaborate organic systems. Man belongs to the class of mammals. There can be not the slightest doubt that man is now the dominant species; with the development of biological technology all other species will exist only on man's sufferance.

The conclusive evidence of man's superior position is that he, and he alone, has evolved the genotype which enables him to develop and maintain culture. As pointed out in Chapter 13, the transmission of the cultural inheritance is superimposed on biological heredity, but the former is a vastly more efficient process than the latter. Biological heredity is handed down only from parents to children; culture can be transmitted to anybody. Acquisition and transmission of culture have conferred upon man as a species an unprecedented degree of fitness in the sense of Thoday's definition (see above). Unless man-kind chooses to destroy itself by atomic explosions or similar means, it is more likely to endure than any other creature. Man's biological pinnacle is a solitary eminence; no other species can aspire to dispute it.

Biology gives no warrant for the belief that man was preformed in the primordial life, or that the evolution of life as a whole had as its purpose the production of man. Evolution does not strive to accomplish any particular purpose or to reach any specific goal except the preservation of life itself. Evolution did not happen according to a predetermined plan. Nevertheless, when man contemplates the whole perspective of the evolution of the Cosmos, he can see that the origin of mankind was one of the outstanding events in the history of creation by evolution. This event is represented symbolically in Michelangelo's beautiful fresco reproduced as the frontispiece of this book.

Considered biologically, man arose because of the action of the very same forces which bring about the evolution of all other organisms. Natural selection responded to the challenge of environmental opportunity, and compounded an adaptively highly successful genotype from genetic elements contributed ultimately by mutation. In a sense, the origin of man was a lucky accident. Evolution is not repeatable, because slight differences either in the environment or in the genetic materials might have resulted in something different from man. But in another sense man was not accidental. Natural selection is, in Fisher's words, "a mechanism for generating an exceedingly high degree of improbability." In other words, selection creates gene combinations which would be almost infinitely unlikely without it. Laplace was right, but only in part. Perhaps a "vast intelligence" could discern in primordial matter the distant coming of man; but this intelligence had to be divine, not human.

Genetically Determined Educability. It has been pointed out in Chapter 13 that man, like other biological species, became genetically differentiated into races. This differentiation occurred in response to the differences in the physical environments of the different countries which man inhabits. But as time went on, man's physical environments became more uniform or more easily controllable. The reverse was true of cultural environments. Here the diversity is steadily increasing. Man is inseparable from his culture, and cultural environments can be dealt with only by learning to choose among many possible courses of action the one appropriate under the circumstances. Biological evolution has produced the genetic endowment which has made culture and freedom of choice possible. But from then on, human evolution has become in part a new and unprecedented kind of evolution—evolution of culture and of freedom. This certainly does not mean that the biological evolution of man has come to a halt, as some writers like to suppose. The two kinds of evolution, biological and cultural, are combined in a new and unique process which is human evolution.

Human behavior is conditioned by education in a wide sense of this word, which is the sum of a person's experiences. The conditioning occurs from infancy on—coming from parents, playmates, neighbors, teachers, companions, friends, enemies, and also from books, newspapers, and all other means of communication. Of course the outcome of the conditioning depends upon the person conditioned. Education is useless without a brain to absorb it, and an educable brain presupposes a human genetic endowment. The biological uniqueness of the human genotype lies in the fact that it permits a greater degree of educability than the genes of any other biological species.

Equality of Men. The problem of the equality of men is a topic of discussion which often generates more heat than light. Evolutionary biology should help at least to state the problem correctly. Equality and inequality of men are religious, ethical, and legal, not biological concepts. Men may be equal before God and before the law without being biologically alike. Indeed, men are not biologically alike; no two men, identical twins excepted, have the same genotype. To some people this fact is emotionally repugnant, a repugnance which can be due only to misunderstanding of the meaning of heredity. Heredity of mental, emotional, and personality development is mostly conditioning, not destiny. Excepting genetically controlled mental diseases, "normal" human genotypes permit a great latitude of intellectual and emotional developments.

Whether the genetic endowment makes some people superior and others inferior is another story. This question has no meaning unless the basis of the value judgment is made explicit. Superior or inferior for what? Most people will agree that a congenital idiot who is incapable of performing ordinary work and unable to take care of himself is not a useful member of any society. But is a football player superior or inferior to a chess player? How could we compare the values of a scientist and an artist? Of a thinker and a man of action? Of a farmer and an industrial worker? Clearly, mankind needs all of these and many other kinds of people. And, fortunately, most human individuals can be trained to perform competently many of the functions that are needed in human society, although some individuals may be more successful in some functions than in others.

Here one must beware of a specious argument which is the more misleading because it is so plausible. The argument runs about as follows. Since we know that races and breeds of wild and domestic animals often differ in genetically conditioned behavior, how can it be that human races are an exception? The answer is simple. The race horse and the draft horse, or the fox terrier, the dachshund, and Great Dane, differ in their temperaments, and these differences are, to a large extent, genetic. But these differences are there because they have been built into these breeds by the artificial selection which fashioned them to serve different needs or whims of their owners. Certainly a race horse with a temperament of a draft horse would be a failure, just as a draft horse with a temperament of a race horse would be. Now human races, no less than human individuals, suffer frequent and often drastic changes of fortune. The adaptive advantage of educability is the one constant in human evolution since the beginning of its cultural, or truly human, phase. Genetic differences between races are, then, secondary to those differences rooted in cultural heredity.

Evolutionary Ethics. Biological evolution has contrived human genotypes which make man, in the words of Thomas Jefferson, "formed for society, and endowed by nature with those dispositions which fit him for society." Among these "dispositions," surely one of the most important is the ability to distinguish between right and wrong. It is man's moral sense which makes him truly human. Where does this moral sense come from? All religions claim either that ethics are based on supernatural revelation or that the ability to discriminate between good and evil has been implanted in the human soul by God. On the other hand, according to Chauncey Leake: "The probability of survival of a relationship between individual humans or groups of humans increases with the extent to which that relationship is mutually satisfying." May, then, man's ethical sense be a product of biological evolution by natural selection? Or, perhaps, the religious and the evolutionary explanations are the two sides of the same coin?

Flushed by the tremendous successes of natural science in their time, some nineteenth century scientists felt that no problem could be insoluble in mechanistic terms. In his *Principles of Ethics* (1892), Herbert Spencer (1820–1903) attempted to show that ethics are "part and parcel" of biological evolution. Good conduct makes for pleasurable life in society; wrong actions are socially disruptive. Natural selection has encouraged the spread in human populations of those moral qualities which were useful for the preservation of the life of individual members of society, and hence for the maintenance of society as a whole. Thomas H. Huxley (1825–1895) entertained, for a time, ideas like Spencer's; however, in his celebrated lecture given in 1893 he pointed out quite clearly the weaknesses of these ideas. According to him, "Cosmic evolution may teach us how the good and the evil tendencies of man may have come about; but, in itself, it is incompetent to furnish any better reason why what we call good is preferable to what we call evil than we had before." And further: "The practice of that which is ethically best—what we call goodness or virtue—involves a course of conduct which, in all respects, is opposed to that which leads to success in the cosmic struggle for existence."

Julian Huxley, a grandson of T. H. Huxley, is the most active modern exponent of "evolutionary ethics." Although philosophers and theologians usually believe that the validity of an ethical code must rest on divine sanction, J. Huxley proposes "a morality of evolutionary direction." Although not a believer in orthogenesis, J. Huxley thinks that he can discern a direction in biological and in human evolution, and that this direction "consists basically of three factors—increase in control over the environment, increase in independence of the environment, and the capacity to continue further evolution in the same progressive direction." If so, then "anything which permits or promotes open development is right, anything which restricts or frustrates development is wrong."

This is certainly an interesting idea, but it may be questioned whether it meets adequately the above-quoted objection of T. H. Huxley against evolutionary ethics. Suppose that the evolutionary direction which our life has followed until now can be known beyond reasonable doubt. Would this necessarily mean that this direction is good and that we ought to help its continuance? Evolution has produced a mind capable of knowing that it has evolved and that it can evolve farther. Can't this mind also scrutinize the wisdom of the process which gave birth to it? But such a scrutiny can be based only on criteria of wisdom derived from sources other than the evolutionary process itself. Man knows not only that he has evolved and continues to evolve, but that he is also in the process of learning how he may promote his own evolution in the direction of his choice. But what should be the basis of the choice? As G. G. Simpson rightly wrote: "It is futile to search for an absolute ethical criterion retroactively in what occurred before ethics themselves evolved. The best human ethical standard must be relative and particular to man and is to be sought rather in the new evolution, peculiar to man, than in the old, universal to all organisms." Evolutionary ethics have not been formulated yet, and one may reasonably doubt that they can be made scientifically convincing or aesthetically satisfying.

Epilogue. The evolution of the Cosmos has not been everlastingly uniform. Some important "dates" can be discerned which mark periods of titanic stress and crisis, leading to events of transcendental significance. The first date is, of course, the beginning of the universe itself. According to the estimates which physicists and geologists are able to make, this beginning occurred some 5 billion years ago. Some 2 billion years ago life appeared there, and biological evolution was inaugurated. As far as anybody knows for sure, this happened, in the whole wide universe, only on a tiny speck of dust which is our earth. Biological evolution created some millions of species of organisms, which explored various possibilities of living. Most of these species eventually became stranded in the blind alleys of opportunistic conformity to the favorable situations in the environment which proved only fleeting and temporary. But some organisms made evolutionary "inventions," which permitted them to spread, multiply, and, some of them, to become dominant. Half a million to a million years ago, one species made an evolutionary "discovery" of unparalleled significance; it became capable of extra-biological transmission of acquired and learned experience. This species became human, and opened up a new, cultural or human, evolution. About two thousand years ago this species had advanced far enough to be able to receive the Sermon on the Mount. The development of science, at first slow and hesitant, but during the last two centuries rapidly accelerating, is enabling man gradually to acquire a better understanding of himself and of his environment on earth and in the Cosmos. Julian Huxley thinks that man "finds himself in the unexpected position of business manager for the cosmic process of evolution." This judgment may be a premature one, but man does struggle against the bounds of his nature, and this struggle makes his existence worth while, and contains a hope of a noble future.

Suggestions for Further Reading

Berg, L. S. 1926. *Nomogenesis or Evolution Determined by Law.* Constable, London.

This is perhaps the most thoughtful book ever written by a believer in evolution by autogenesis.

Noüy, Lecomte du. 1947. *Human Destiny.* Longmans, Green, London. (Also available in a paper-bound edition of The New American Library.)

This is a popular presentation of the finalist point of view. The book contains numerous and important factual errors in its presentation of biological and geological information. A point of view related to finalism is presented also in the following article:

Osborn, H. F. 1934. *Aristogenesis, the creative principle in the origin of species.* American Naturalist, Volume 68, pages 193–235.

For a critique of the autogenetic and finalist theories of evolution, see particularly G. G. Simpson's books, quoted among the suggested readings in Chapter 12. Concerning the evolution of man and of man's unique abilities, see the suggested readings in Chapter 13.

The problem of the so-called scientific ethics is discussed particularly in the following books:

Huxley, T. H., and Huxley, J. 1947. *Touchstone for Ethics.* Harper, New York and London.

Huxley, J. 1941. *Man Stands Alone.* Harper, New York.

Huxley, J. 1953. *Evolution in Action.* Harper, New York.

Leake, Chauncey D., and Romanell, P. 1950. *Can We Agree?* University of Texas Press, Austin.

Waddington, C. H. 1942. *Science and Ethics.* Allen & Unwin, London.

Index